For:

Mary —

Thank you

Anthony Herrera

April 2004

Preface

In the summer of 1939, six months after the discovery of uranium fission, American newspapers and magazines openly discussed the prospect of atomic energy. However, most American physicists doubted that atomic energy or atomic bombs were realistic possibilities.

October 11, 1939, President Roosevelt reads a letter from Albert Einstein warning him of the dangers of Nazi research into uranium fission.

For the next two years, official skepticism continued to stall U.S. research efforts. A large-scale U.S. atomic project did not begin until December 6, 1941, one day before the bombing of Pearl Harbor. It became the "Manhattan" Project in August 1942.

In 1943 the Manhattan Project, built Los Alamos in the Sangria de Cristo Mountains, a U.S. crash program to develop an atomic bomb.

August 6, 1945 - "Little Boy" a uranium bomb was dropped over Hiroshima Japan. August 9, 1945 - "Fat Man" was detonated over Nagasaki Japan ending World War II.

August 1999 – At MD Anderson Cancer Center Dr. Martin Korbling said to me, **"This country – with a dynamic leader – within three to five years – we could have the cure for cancer."**

The Cancer War

Bell Mare of Mississippi, Inc
217 East 86th St # 265
New York, NY 10028

ISBN 0-9619800-6-0

Cover design: Basha Plewinska
Technical: Steve McGraw
Assistant: Ellen Gorman
Photograph: Trevor Brown

Publisher Bell Mare of Mississippi, Inc.
www.thecancerwar.com

The Cancer War
(My Story)

By

Anthony Herrera

This book is dedicated to the memory of:

Cleavon Little
Peter Hammer
Linda Aronowitz
Mary Ellis Bunim
Earl Strickler
Ken Raper
Sallie Burdine
Larry Pace
Lary Gabbard
Ray Armagost
Francis Hamer
Peter Laqueur
Hank Worsham
Evans Harrington

and
to
everyone
whose lives have
been hurt by disease

There was a lump. A lump was sticking out on the left side of my neck. It looked as if a large snail had crawled under my skin. The lump protruded about half an inch from just under my ear lobe running down to my Adam's apple. I felt it. It was solid. Still dripping from the shower, in the locker room of my squash club with a towel around my waist, I was standing in front of a large mirror. I moved closer and turned my head all the way to the right to try to conceal the lump. What if I had to do a close-up? Would it show? I am an actor.

I was in great shape for a fellow ten days away from turning fifty-three years of age. Professionally things were beginning to work again; four commercials, a college lecture, several guest shots on the CBS soap opera, **As The World Turns** and serious "talk" with Proctor & Gamble Productions and the new executive producer about the return of the character I had originated in 1980, James Stenbeck. If I had to do a close-up, I'd just turn my head, make it a profile shot and conceal the lump. No problem.

I had left New York City in the summer 1992 and toured theatre in my home state of Mississippi and in South Africa. I returned in August of '95 very low on money and depressed. The next twelve months were tough. I lived in a series of sublets, had a twenty-dollar a day budget for food and transportation. I went back to therapy with Dr. MacCavoy, a clinical psychologist who had earned her Ph.D. in Vienna. I cut down on hard alcohol, played squash five to seven times a week and got back on my feet emotionally.

If going back on **As The World Turns** didn't work out I could finish putting together a new show of poetry and jazz with my friends "B" Spears and Mickey Raphael of the Willie Nelson band. I had our first show booked in Jackson, Tennessee for mid-March. I had a great agent for commercials, Cunningham - Escott - Dipene.   They kept sending me out on auditions with meager results for over a year until July of '96 when we had a string of winners: a voice over account in Canada, Toyota, Mita Copiers, and The New York Times.

So be it, back on "the show" or a mix of commercials and touring, either way I'd be working. January 2nd, there was a call from London. It was from Gaye Brown, long time friend and veteran of the English stage. She had just worked with a young director and had given him a copy of **Smoke & Mirrors**, a murder mystery/comedy I had co-authored in 1991. I produced three old-fashioned bus and truck tours of the play with New York actors in Mississippi and Louisiana. I took the play to Johannesburg for a five-month run. The laughs came at all the right places on both continents. The "young genius" had read it and found it was clever and very funny. He thought he could get it produced in London, the West End – our play in the big time.

No matter what . . . 1997 was going to be my year!

* * * * *

Thursday, January 9th I took Basha, my ex-wife, to a fundraiser hosted by Linda Dano of **Another World,** also a Proctor & Gamble Soap. I liked these functions and to chat with fans. Basha, an exotic Polish beauty, always enjoyed dressing up in one of her originally composed, antique outfits. We had a good time.

It was cold that night. I got a cab to drop her off at her apartment before heading uptown to my latest sublet on 89th Street. I took her hand and put it on my neck. Her immediate response was, "Oh, Anthonee you need to see about that. Don't let that go."

When I returned to my sublet I phoned Patsy in Nashville, Tennessee. We had been dating, seeing each other, involved, on and off since 1993. I told her about the lump in my neck. She reminded me that I had some emergency dental work done when I returned from Africa in 1995. A full frontal x-ray, showed a spot in my left jawbone. My dentist couldn't determine what it was. Since there was no pain, and no obvious complications, we decided to wait to see if it caused any problems, and it never did. Patsy speculated that the mysterious space had become infected and that poison was oozing out and causing the swelling in my throat. Made sense to me. Normally, I would have had an extra shot of bourbon and forgotten about the whole situation.

For some reason I didn't. At 8:30 the next morning I was in my dentist's office on the fifty-second floor of the Empire State Building. A needle, a little pinch, some Novocain, and he drilled out a filling in my back left molar, checked-out the tooth. No infection. He replaced the filling. He wrote out a name and address on Central Park South and handed it to me. Before I could question him, he said, "Dr. Beller is an oral surgeon we work with. I want him to find out if there is an infection in your jaw. Take a cab. I'll call him and tell him you are on your way."

Dr. Beller's office was on the ground floor. As I walked into the waiting area of his office a very pretty girl who appeared to be in her twenties came in and said, "Mr. Herrera, I'm Yolanda, this way please. He'll be right in." I took off my coat and sweaters. Dr. Beller came in and introduced himself. I climbed into the chair. He immediately shot some more Novocain into my left jaw. Then he cut the gum, drilled a hole in the bone, took out some of whatever the hell was in there, stitched up my gum and asked me to wait.

I was getting a bit groggy from the drugs and was slow getting into my sweaters. Yolanda was asking me questions about **As The World Turns**; she and her mother had watched for years. Even with a numb face and difficulty focusing I enjoyed talking to her. Within ten minutes Dr. Beller came back in.

"There is no infection in your jaw."

"What do you think it is?"

"I don't know."

He handed me a piece of paper with a name and an address.

"Dr. Gilbert is the Chief of Head and Neck Surgery at University Hospital. He doesn't usually see patients on Fridays, but I just called him and he's waiting for you."

Dr. Beller helped me with my coat and walked me to the door.

"Please go now. He's waiting for you."

The wind was blowing a light snow through the streets of Manhattan. Taxi drivers drive fast in New York. Even in heavy traffic I arrived at the University Medical Center in minutes and found Dr. Seller's office. He had a crew cut and was impeccably dressed. He asked me about my medical history. There was not much to it. Other than the flu, I'd never had any problems physically.

Fortunately, the left side of my face was still numb when Dr. Gilbert stuck a needle into the protrusion on the side of my neck and extracted some fluid. He sprayed my throat with something I couldn't taste and with what looked like a crooked pair of pliers, clipped out two chunks of flesh. He put these tiny parts of my body into little glass containers, handed them to an attendant who had magically appeared at the door, and they were on their way to a lab.

Next, he made several phone calls. No CAT scan machines were available. He called a private imaging clinic, and handed me a piece of paper with another address.

"Go now!"

"What do you think is wrong with me?"

"I don't know. I will have a better idea after I get the pathology reports and the CT results."

Another cab -- minutes later -- another doctor. Dr. Louis, was Cuban and had a warm demeanor. The goop you have to drink to fill your gut with barium was not pleasant, but by now I was like an animal stunned by a blow to the head. I moved wherever I was led.

Everything was strange; the locker in the changing room wasn't big enough to hold my coat, sweaters, pants, etc. I left my coat on a chair and put on a thin robe-like garment and couldn't get it tied right but it didn't matter. The room with the CAT scan machine was cold. An attendant helped me onto the narrow table that slides into the machine and then stuck a butterfly needle in the vein in my arm. My butt and shoulders hung over the side.

A second doctor came in and introduced himself. I didn't remember his name. He was young.

"Have you ever had a CAT scan before?"
"No."

I have claustrophobia. I was afraid of sliding into that tube. I had seen a television special some years before on this new technology. I closed my eyes. This was really happening.

I heard the doctor drop something. He mumbled and then dropped it again. I was scared. I could be up, dressed and out the door in a couple of minutes. I shut my eyes and said to myself, ***"Herrera, you stay on this table."***

I heard the young doctor knock over something else. Dr. Louis came in and took charge. I looked up for a second as he hooked up a small bag of fluid to the line in my arm.

"Are you allergic to iodine?"
"No."

"You may feel a slight burning sensation in your arm when we start the IV; it will be just a second. Relax." Easy for him to say.

* * * * *

My closest friend in show business, Cleavon Little, the black sheriff in **Blazing Saddles** and Tony Award winner for the Broadway musical **Purlie**, was a kind, gentle man. He was born in Chickasha, Oklahoma but his parents were from Mississippi. I was from Mississippi. Our Southern history enhanced our friendship. Cleavon died of stomach cancer in 1992. I was with him the day before he died.

* * * * *

I kept my eyes shut as the table began to move. A voice came through a speaker on the big machine. Everything was very crisp and clear.

"Take a deep breath. Hold it."

I shut my eyes and held my arms tight to my side and said silently, ***"Cleavon, don't let me panic. Keep me on this damn thing."***

Then the speaker: "Okay you can breathe."
I did. Then, "Take a deep breath. Hold it."

This went on for what felt like four days. I never could relax. Cleavon helped me stay on that table.

I got dressed. Dr. Louis showed me the CT of my head and neck on the computer. The images looked like a fancy coloring book. He pointed out a foreign shape in the left side of my neck. It was **25mm** by **45mm** in mass, about the size of a walnut.

As I left his clinic Dr. Louis tried to comfort me. He shook my hand and looked me in the eye.

"I hope you don't have to come back. It is my opinion that the mass in your neck is benign."

2

It was dark out and funnels of snow were whirling along 1st Avenue. I found a pharmacy within a couple of blocks. All the drugs from earlier that day seemed to wear-off as soon as I hit the night air. The pain from the oral surgery and the biopsy took over. I had a prescription for painkillers and asked the pharmacist to fill it right away, but he had trouble with his computer and my Screen Actors Guild insurance number. I walked up and down the aisles attempting to read the labels on various products. The pain in my jaw and throat was getting worse, fast. The pharmacist couldn't get his system to work. After twenty minutes I finally asked,

"How much is it?"

"Thirty-two dollars and fifty cents." I paid in cash. He gave me a cup of water.

The Dumpling King was right across the street from my sublet apartment. For some reason Chinese food sounded good. I got jumbo shrimp with lobster sauce to go. Next, the liquor store. I got two bottles of Spanish champagne out of the cooler and three off the shelf and as I put them on the counter, Jack, a friend from the squash club, came through the door.

"Herrera! Hey. What are you doing? Five bottles of Champagne? Five? Must be party time!"

"Right."

"Better cool it. Ha! There goes your squash game."

No one had to tell me my situation was serious. I phoned a former girlfriend, Laura Sudarsky, a plastic surgeon and related the events of the day. She told me that a colleague of hers had just been diagnosed with throat cancer and asked, "Are you prepared to live your life in a very different manner?"

"Yes."

I knew what she meant. If I had throat cancer, they would take out my voice box.

* * * * *

I watched the snowstorm, drank champagne and thought about my life. I was going to be fifty-three years old in a few days. I once read that fifty-three is the Bermuda Triangle year for men.

Tom Gries, film director, gave me my first job in show business as Charlton Heston's stand-in on the movie **Number One** in New Orleans in 1968. For ten weeks I worked on the set every day for twelve to fourteen hours with Tom Gries, the cinematographer, Michel Hugo and Moses himself, Mr. Charlton Heston. When we wrapped I made a deal to drive one of the picture cars back to Hollywood. I secured my Lambretta motor scooter on the generator truck and along with three other picture cars and drivers we caravanned West – out of the South.

Seven years later Tom hired me for a good role in **Helter Skelter**. I had kept in touch with Tom over the years. He was pleased that I had found Stella Adler, the legendary acting teacher. "You're doing the right thing; Stella's the best." Tom was a beacon, a hero who became my friend. He died of a heart attack on a tennis court at the age of fifty-three. Peter Hammer, another close friend, had edited my documentary **Mississippi Delta Blues.** We had worked hard, drunk hard and our film won five awards. Peter died of cancer at fifty-three. Cleavon Little died at fifty-three.

* * * * *

The shrimp were good. The Darvon and champagne numbed the physical pain and allowed me to slip into a rather calm mood. I didn't even get tipsy.

On one hand I had had an incredible life for a country boy from Wiggins, Mississippi born in 1944. I had been self-supporting since the age of fourteen. After high school I went to "Ole Miss." In those years if you were poor, came from a little town and didn't have a powerful family, to go to "Ole Miss" was a dream come true.

I graduated with a Bachelor of Arts in Zoology and English Literature, and I became a member of the Sigma Chi fraternity.

When was a child, the Saturday night movie at the Straub Theatre was the event of the week. In the dark theatre the conflict between the good guys and the bad guys seemed to make sense out of life. In the weekly serial, Buster Crabbe would end up hanging on the edge of a cliff, but in the last episode, he too would get out of trouble and save the day.

To be an actor was a childhood fantasy that I did not admit to until I was nearly twenty years old. I moved to New York City when I was twenty-five. I found Stella Adler and studied the craft of acting with her for three years. She had taught Marlon Brando, Warren Beatty and Robert DeNiro, to name a few. I worked as a waiter in Oscar's Salt of the Sea on Third Avenue and did off-off Broadway.

I have made a living as an actor since 1974.

* * * * *

The wind whipped up thick sheets of snow that flooded the night. I sat and watched and thought. I had made a lot of mistakes in my life, failing at marriage the greatest. But at this moment, I didn't feel any regrets or sadness. My accomplishments and my failures were just a list of facts about my life.

No matter what Dr. Louis had said about the lump in my neck, I knew something very serious was wrong with me and I had a choice. I could load up my car with champagne and head south, stop and drink with the people I cared about, find my way into the swamps of Louisiana, put the barrel of my .38 Smith & Wesson revolver to my temple and pull the trigger. A plan? Maybe.

I got a bit tipsy, but not maudlin or depressed. Instead, I started to panic. Mentally I caught the fear before it filled my chest and fought to hold it at bay. Then slowly I was able to calm down and began to see myself at the bottom of a dark canyon with a horse, wearing a revolver and carrying a .30-.30 Winchester rifle, getting ready for a dangerous journey.

* * * * *

Monday morning Dr. Gilbert took my call right away.

"Mr. Herrera, the lab report is positive for lymphoma. We aren't sure of the exact diagnosis but it is lymphoma."

I was surprised that my voice broke as I repeated the word *"lymphoma."*

"Yes. I've made an appointment for you for tomorrow with an oncologist, Dr. Levine. However, it will be another week to determine the exact diagnosis."

Lymphoma is cancer. Cancer sounds mean, dangerous and deadly. *Lymphoma* -- I repeated it over in my mind, and in a soft whisper, as I would wake-up in the mornings. It is not a harsh sounding word. No matter how the word sounds, *lymphoma* is mean, dangerous and deadly.

* * * * *

At University Hospital, Dr. Levine's waiting room was packed with patients. I just stood there holding my coat. He came through, young, hurried and reading a large file. I stepped in his path.

"Dr. Levine, I am Anthony Herrera. Dr. Gilbert sent me to you."

"Oh yes. You'll have to wait."

He did not look at me when he shook my hand or when he spoke to me. As he moved toward his office an elderly man looked up at him and smiled,

"Good morning, Dr. Levine."

The doctor passed by him and didn't acknowledge the patient's greeting. I looked at this tall man sitting. He was neatly groomed, gray-haired in his late seventies. He had a kind face. He was frightened. He reminded me of Bop, my grandfather. I didn't like the way this doctor didn't look at me or the way he rushed by this old man.

I studied other people in the room, the fat woman trying to read a magazine, the black man speaking softly with his wife, a Puerto Rican child with her parents and others. We appeared to be handling it fairly well, but we were all scared.

I waited. I tried to formulate questions to ask this doctor, but about what? I had heard the word cancer all of my life. People got cancer and died. I had heard the word lymphoma but really didn't pay much attention to how it was used or what it meant. Now it meant a cancer that was in my body.

Finally, I was called in to see Dr. Levine. He nodded at a chair in front of his desk. I sat. Again he didn't make eye contact.

"There are three general types of lymphoma cells; the small grade can be maintained with periodic and relatively mild chemotherapy. The middle grade cell can be killed with a stronger regimen of chemo. With large grade cell lymphoma, you can basically forget about survival. Call next Wednesday. We should have the final diagnosis from the pathology by then."

I found a pay phone. This was all really real. I called Basha.

"I have cancer."

"Oh, Anthonee, are you sure?"

"Yes, I just met with an oncologist."

"You must start eating asparagus."

Basha got very upset and out of nervousness, she went on about asparagus. I had to eat lots of asparagus.

That night I woke up in the middle of the king size bed in the new sublet and softly said, "*Lymphoma*."

Chemotherapy, large grade, middle grade lymphoma cells, diagnosis, pathology report, these were no longer just words. They were now my reality. What the hell had happened to me?

I heard one of the patients in the waiting room mention The Cure For Lymphoma Society. The next morning I called and went to see them at 215 Lexington Avenue. They were supportive and gave me some pamphlets. I read some of them but did not learn that much about the new world I had been hurled into, except that a lot of people suffered from this disease.

* * * * *

I met Dr. Bobbie MacGuffie in 1980. I had just moved back to New York after five years in Malibu and Beverly Hills and had just begun the role of James on **As The World**

Turns. I met her daughter, Martha, in a sushi bar. I was studying my script for the next day and she was reading a play. She was an opera student and needed part time work and I needed someone to prompt me on the twenty-five to forty pages of dialogue that I had to learn daily for work. We became friends and after a few months I was invited to her mother's house in Rockland County. One Sunday, Cleavon and I drove up for lunch. I followed the directions up the Palisades and off exit ten to South Mountain Road. Martha had given me no warning as to what we were about to encounter. As I drove into the driveway some one hundred yards up on a hill was a castle. Not a huge castle, but a castle.

Over the next few years I found the matriarch Dr. MacGuffie, one of the most remarkable people I had ever met. She was the first female plastic surgeon in New York State, operated at Nyack Hospital five days a week, had a menagerie of raccoons, ferrets, rabbits and two golden retrievers. She had a special cage for wounded animals that she would find on the road or people would leave for her to heal.

I too was adopted and was given the Unicorn room on the second floor of "the castle" whenever I needed to spend the night. The room was decorated with some twenty unicorn figurines and carvings. The sheets on the bed had unicorns in the pattern. The Unicorn protected the castle.

Another daughter, Janey Hudson was an oncologist at the Veterans Hospital in Syracuse, New York. I phoned Janey and told her the news and that I did not like Dr. Levine. She assured me that lymphoma was treatable and that there were lots of oncologists to choose from in New York City. She emphasized how important it was for me, or any patient, to feel like they had a team effort going with their oncologist. She assured me that she would help set up appointments with several doctors until we found the right team but I still had to wait for the final diagnosis.

I had to wait five more days before for the final pathology report. I didn't know how to fill the time. Talking to friends helped a little, but I still had to wait. Going to the gym, walking the streets of Manhattan, getting drunk, nothing helped, and for some reason I didn't want to drink that much.

I no longer felt like the iron man that could party late and then be in the studio at 7:00 a.m. for a twelve-hour workday.

* * * *

Dr. Levine put a folder on his desk and took out the pathology report. He didn't look at me. He started drawing circles on a blank sheet of paper with lines coming out of them. They looked like a child's bad drawings of a bug. His voice was too loud as he described:

Malignant Lymphoma: Mantle Cell Type.

"It is very rare and it will kill you."

"You are going to die."

"This disease will kill you."

I remember distinctly these three sentences in the first twelve minutes in his office.

The phone rang behind him; he pushed his chair back, picked up the receiver, leaned back and talked. I stared at his drawings of the circles and their funny looking legs.

"YOU ARE GOING TO DIE."

Reading the papers upside down, I noticed the name Kathrine Chatham, M. D.

Dr. Levine finished his phone call and rushed out. A young woman, a little overweight, who looked to be no more than eighteen came in and sat in a chair by the door. She smiled, adjusted her skirt and in a cute little voice said, "I'm a junior in medical school and this is my first day to observe, if you don't mind."

"This is my first day to have Mantle Cell Lymphoma and I do mind."

She got up and left. A nurse came in and put a big stack of manila folders on his desk.

"Sorry to interrupt, but these are for doctors." As if that meant something to me. Dr. Levine came back in.

"I need to take some bone marrow out of your hip bone to see if there is lymphoma there also." He motioned with a movement of his head for me to come with him. We went into a room across the hall.

"Pull your pants down mid-butt and get on the table. Face the wall. Count to fifteen. This is going to hurt."

He wiped the top of my right buttock with something cold and proceeded to drill through my skin into my bone. It was a very long fifteen count and he was correct. It hurt. It hurt like hell. It was excruciating pain. It hurt more than any pain I had ever felt in my life. If it had lasted another two seconds, I would have passed out.

I couldn't believe he didn't use an anesthetic.

"Could I see what caused so much pain?"

I zipped up my pants. He showed me a little piece of what looked like some dark rose-colored pencil lead. He headed for his office. I stood in the hallway.

"Doctor, I have a show booked in Tennessee in March. Will I be able to do it?"

"Yeah, why not."

"Can I continue to play squash?"

"Sure, just try not to get hit in the spleen. Your CAT scan shows your spleen is massively enlarged."

"Why is my spleen enlarged?"

"Lymphoma is systemic. It's already in your spleen. We're going to try a bone marrow transplant. You need to get your heart and lungs checked out. Check with my nurse tomorrow. We're going to put you through Hell."

* * * * *

I left the hospital and went to Tandy Cronyn's apartment. Tandy and I had been friends since I first came to New York in 1969. In 1993, we toured A. R. Gurney's two-character play **Love Letters** in Mississippi and played eighteen communities, nineteen performances in twenty-one days, and still remained friends. Her mother had been diagnosed with ovarian cancer in 1990 and she died in 1994.

I was greeted with a hug. Then, as was her nature, Tandy started dealing with the practical matters of what I was facing. She would take care of making sure I had food and the necessary supplies in my apartment.

"After your second chemo you won't feel like shopping."

Later that evening I went to Basha's apartment on 44th Street. She was very upset. We called her cousin Magda, an internist in Miami. Magda's husband, Roberto, was an oncologist. He had "heard" of Mantle Cell Lymphoma, but that was about it. He commented that New York City had hundreds of highly qualified doctors and that I was in the best city possible to find treatment. He would try to learn more about this disease and get back to us. Basha fought to be optimistic and her attempts were a bit comforting.

I went back to my sublet on 89th street and went on the Internet until the wee hours. I found a lot of material on many kinds of lymphoma but nothing about this killer, Mantle Cell.

* * * * *

One has to qualify physically for a bone marrow transplant. The hospital has to check your heart, lungs, kidneys and liver to see if your organs can survive high dose chemotherapy, the toxins that they have to pour into you to kill the cancer. A weak organ with a suppressed immune system is more susceptible to disease, and organ failure due to high dose chemotherapy is usually fatal.

The next morning I had a series of tests lined up and I was late. I took a cab, got caught in traffic so I got out and ran the last few blocks to University Hospital. At the entrance, I hurried up to the guard.

"Which way is nuclear medicine?"

"You go to the end of this walkway through the double doors and then at the end of the hall take the elevator to the 3rd floor."

I took off running. Then suddenly I could see myself in slow motion. Running through the cold to *nuclear medicine . . . nuclear* meant death, dead, when I was a kid. I hadn't given *nuclear* any thought except when I worried about the Russians and *nuclear* war. And now I am running toward something *nuclear*, something *nuclear* to do with my body. Why am I running toward something *nuclear*?

3

Over the next couple of days the various tests were all strange and uncomfortable. They injected the vein in the crook of my arm with a nuclear substance called Gallium for one scan. I was still numb mentally, and didn't ask what they were trying to determine about my body with the various machines that were pressed against me or rolled over me. I just wanted to make it through each test, and I did.

One technician gave me his theory.

"Charcoal, Bar-B-Q's, the fat from the meat, steaks, hamburgers and hotdogs, especially the hotdogs, drips down and burns and raises back into the meat and the chemicals in the vapor from the hot coals causes cancer."

All of my life I had eaten meat cooked over wood.

They sent me to the cashier's office. I pulled out my union cards from the Screen Actors Guild and American Federation of Television and Radio Artists. I'd never had to use them before but they seemed to do the trick.

I went back to my apartment and called Dr. Braxter Irby in Mississippi. Braxter and I had been roommates at the Sigma Chi house at Ole Miss. After losing touch for over twenty years, we were reunited when I toured **Smoke & Mirrors** in 1992. One night in Brookhaven, Mississippi, he appeared after a performance. I learned he had become an Internist. Even after all the years of not being in touch we were still fraternity brothers and I just blurted out, "Damn Braxter, I didn't know you were that smart -- enough to be a doctor."

He grinned. "Neither did I Anthony; neither did I."

During the next few years I often stayed at his home and made it my headquarters while setting-up theatrical tours in the South. It was great to renew an old friendship and to get to know Jake, the Irish setter that graciously ran the home and welcomed my visits. Braxter also inspired me because of how hard he worked, the hours he put in every day and his dedication to being a good doctor.

Braxter became frustrated because he searched the Internet and couldn't find anything on Mantle Cell

Lymphoma. There was only the one Xeroxed paragraph from the British Journal of Hematology about Mantle Cell Lymphoma that I had taken from Dr. Levine's office.

1994: "Mantle Cell Lymphoma (MCL) is now accepted as a distinct form of Non-Hodgkin's Lymphoma."
1996: "MCL prognosis poor, life expectancy 18 to 52 months."

It was January 20, 1997. I was now fifty-three years old. I had searched the Internet as had Braxter and nothing else had been published about this cancer. Dr. Levine had reinforced what was stated in the journal by his "you will die" prognosis.

I phoned Janey Hudson in Syracuse and told her the final diagnosis. She had "heard" of Mantle Cell Lymphoma. Basha's cousin, Roberto and now Janey, two practicing oncologists and they had only "heard" of this disease. I told her I had an appointment with Dr. Chatham at Sloan-Kettering. Janey said she would go the medical library at the Veteran's Hospital and talk to the Head of her department. She gave me another number and said to call her there at 10:30 a.m. She reassured me that we could find an oncologist whose expertise and personality would be suitable.

* * * * *

I made the bed, ate some oatmeal then pushed ten numbers on the phone exactly at 10:30; Janey answered on the first ring.

"Doctor Hudson?"

"Yes . . . Hi. I went to the library and I've just come from a meeting with our chairman. He informed me as best he could about Mantle Cell Lymphoma."

"At least he's heard of it."

"Yes. Anthony, this is a severe situation. When are you seeing Dr. Chatham?"

"At 10:00 in the morning."

"Good. She's known as the guru of lymphoma. See if she will treat you. If she will take you as a patient, get to work as fast as you can. This is a very severe situation."

"I get it Janey. This is bad, very bad."

"Yes it is."

I was sitting on the edge of the bed. I looked down at my sock feet and then at my watch, it was 10:32 a.m.

"A severe situation."

I wrote a letter about myself. I wanted this Dr. Chatham to know that I was used to difficulty, struggle and work. I wanted her to know more about me than the fact that I had a rare cancer.

Tuesday morning was cold and gray. I was early, over thirty minutes early, unusual for me. I'm usually right on time or barely right on time. One gets in the habit of cutting it close after years of 7:00 a.m. calls at the studio. I walked around and looked at the bricks on the outside of Sloan-Kettering. They were just bricks, blonde in color, lots of bricks. It's a big building. *'I bet she has short hair.'*

I went inside Memorial Sloan-Kettering, a cancer hospital, a famous cancer hospital at 9:54 am and was directed to the fourth floor. A polite young woman led me into a sparsely furnished conference room with a table and a couple of chairs. I sat with my back to the wall and waited. An attractive, tall woman came in wearing a white coat. She extended her hand and looked me right in the eye.

"I'm Dr. Chatham."

"I'm Anthony Herrera. I knew you were going to have short hair." She smiled.

We sat at the table across from each other and she proceeded to tell me as much as I could absorb about Mantle Cell Lymphoma. She spoke slowly and clearly and kept eye contact with me. This was very important. Dr. Chatham explained to me that Mantle Cell Lymphoma was a systemic disease and a second cousin to leukemia; both are literally cancers of the blood. She reiterated the information about the bone marrow transplant or the stem cell transplant that Dr. Levine had mentioned two weeks earlier, but with more details and added that a transplant could possibly put me into remission.   When she finished, we both stood up.   I kept eye contact with her, "Will you treat me?"

"Yes, I will."

I took my letter out of my coat pocket and handed it to her.

"I want my doctor to want to treat me and not just the disease.   I would like for you to read this, before we get started."

"Please wait for me in the examining room across the hall.   I will read this and be with you in a moment."

"Doctor, as we say down South, 'If you can't ride with the big boys, don't saddle up.'"

She reached out and shook my hand once again and looked right into my eyes.

"We are going to work hard and hope for the best."

* * * * *

I took off my sweater and sat on the examining table. ***"We are going to work hard and hope for the best."***

That's a hell of a long way from, ***"This will kill you." "We're going to put you through Hell." "You're going to die."***

Thank you very much Doctor Harold Levine, I thought to myself, ***"what a jackass of a doctor."***

Dr. Chatham came in and handed me back my letter. "I'm glad to have read that." As she examined me she said she needed to review all my tests, scans and lab results.   She told me about a new protocol for Mantle Cell that Sloan-Kettering doctors had developed with a hospital in Paris.   She said that if all of the reports were clear to her and the diagnosis was correct, we would start chemotherapy either Tuesday or Thursday of next week.

"I will hand deliver everything to you in the morning."

"Good.   I'll be in clinic.   You can meet with the lymphoma nurse and we'll get started."

"Can I continue to play squash and go to the gym?"

Without hesitation Dr. Chatham replied in a direct and calm manner. "No.   I don't want you to get a hematoma – a bruise if you were hit. Your white blood cell count is going to drop with chemo and it will be harder for you to heal. I don't want to take the chance of infection. You can swim and walk as long as you feel up to it; in fact, I recommend it."

The next morning there were patches of snow on the streets and sidewalks. I started walking to the University Hospital but it was cold, about 32 degrees, so I caught a cab. At first I asked politely and then I had to demand my lab reports, scan film, and stained and unstained slides of the cells found in the tumor. I simply said over and over, "These materials belong to me. I have paid for them and I am going to stay here until you hand them to me."

An hour and a half later I was in a taxi weaving through traffic. I felt disconnected from the world, as if I were in a silent bubble floating up First Avenue.

The clinic at Sloan-Kettering was crowded when I found Dr. Chatham and handed over the large brown envelope with all of my deadly data. She nodded, "Good. Now go meet with your nurse practitioner."

Nancy Cody-Lyons was an intense person with black hair and dark brown eyes and an all-business demeanor. Her number of questions seemed endless; age, profession, marital status, medical history, alcohol abuse, drug abuse, smoker, HIV, and psychiatric history? I told her I had been a heavy drinker at one time but felt that it was under control. Her comment was that the lab results from NYU showed that my liver was fine. I told her that NYU had done an HIV test; it was standard procedure.

"Have you ever used IV drugs?"

"Never."

She said that the HIV results were not included in my lab reports and that I could either sign a release form or they could repeat the test. I explained that it had been less than two weeks since all of these tests were done and I would get those results to her in the next two days.

"Fine. Mr. Herrera, do you smoke?"

"Not really."

"What does that mean?"

"I used to be what I would call a social smoker, four or five cigarettes a day over the last twenty years."

"Okay. We'll do a chest X-ray."

"Pot?"

"Never liked it."

"Cocaine?"

"It was never a habit; never a problem. Too expensive."

"Okay. You'll need to meet with the business office. You have insurance?"

"Yes, fortunately. SAG & AFTRA."

"Good. Right. You are an actor. Let's get your calendar."

"Can I go to England before we start? I need to go to London."

"Why now?"

"I co-authored a play some years ago. There is interest in a production there."

Nancy gave me a curious look.

"It won't happen right away but if I can lay the ground work -- maybe next year. I have to have something to think about besides cancer."

"Why don't you call Dr. Chatham right now."

I did and she agreed to the trip. I had to be back Monday morning for an endoscopy. She didn't want me on an airplane after we started chemo because my immune system would be compromised.

Nancy Cody-Lyons gave a look of approval when I told her Dr. Chatham had okayed my trip.

"See you next week."

I stepped out of her office and turned back to watch her as she made more notes. We had discussed very personal issues; drugs, sex and disease. Even as a Southerner brought up in a puritanical era, at this moment her questions did not disturb or upset me. This was New York City and we were discussing life and death. My life. My death.

4

After several calls to England, I was set. Gaye arranged a meeting with Joe Harmston and I would stay with Ann and Demitre Comnas. They lived in Knightsbridge. They are dear friends from years back in Manhattan and I trusted them emotionally.

Ann and Demitre, always the great host and hostess, were extraordinarily supportive. We had some drinks, told stories, jokes. I needed to talk about having cancer and did. They listened and I didn't feel so alone.

On Sunday, I had lunch with Gaye and her son Charlie. She was jolly, strong and encouraging. Early that evening I met with Joe Harmston at his flat in Holland Park. He was a perfect English gentleman. He introduced me to his new bride, Polly, and after a pleasant "hello" she left us. Joe poured us vodka, got out a ledger, a fountain pen and sat poised ready to take notes about the play. I talked. He wrote and continued to pour polite vodkas. I talked on for three and a half hours about **Smoke & Mirrors.**

I enjoyed Joe's company. I didn't mention my condition. I rode back to Knightsbridge through the foggy streets of London in the back seat of a big, black clickedy-click British Leyland taxi. I imagined the eras of Oliver Twist, Sherlock Holmes, right up to the glamorous times of James Bond. A lovely romantic escape for a moment but after a couple hours of sleep I would be on a jet plane flying across the Atlantic Ocean back to New York City and Sloan-Kettering.

* * * * *

Dr. Chatham listened to my lungs, heart and checked out my throat. I developed a sore throat on the plane.

"I'm concerned about a thickened spot in the wall of your stomach. That's the reason I want an endoscopy."

A nurse escorted me to a little room with a video monitor. I was in another one of those blue robes I couldn't get tied. I watched a video on the endoscopy procedure. It was simple and straightforward.

1. They inserted a flexible metal tube down your throat and into your stomach.
2. The doctor would need your help by swallowing to get the tube down the esophagus.
3. The patient would receive "conscious sedation." This will make you groggy and relaxed but still able to hear and follow instructions.
4. You would be able to get the doctors' or nurses' attention during the procedure in case you gagged or had trouble breathing.
5. Once the end of the instrument is in your stomach the doctor would be able to photograph the interior wall and get little bites of tissue, if needed for a biopsy.
6. The procedure is uncomfortable and the patient may have a sore throat and feel sleepy afterwards.
7. Serious complications were rare, but there was a one percent chance the procedure *could be fatal*.

This whole shooting match could end with an endoscopy. There was such a small chance that it would happen. It probably doesn't happen to someone in good physical shape. I'm in good shape, well, except for having lymphoma, cancer. But my body is strong. If it never happened they wouldn't put it on the damn video, and it was right there as the final statement.

There was a soft knock and the door opened. A pleasant looking nurse said, "Mr. Herrera, would you come with me please?"

"Yes, of course."

I held the robe shut. She led me to a waiting room just down the hall and pointed to some empty chairs.

"Please wait here. Someone will be with you in a moment." She disappeared.

What was this going to be like? I didn't like the prospects of this at all. Help them get the tube down my throat by swallowing. My throat was hurting. One percent chance the procedure could be fatal.

A door opened across the hall. The nurse stepped out.

"Mr. Herrera, would you come in please?."

Just as I got to the door and started in another nurse came from down the hall. "Mr. Herrera, wait. Dr. Chatham has changed her mind. No endoscopy. She needs you to go to the third floor as soon as possible and see Dr. Williams. She wants you to hurry. You'll need to change back into your clothes. See me on your way out and I'll give you directions."

Dr. Williams saw me right away. He was gracious. "Dr. Chatham is concerned that your throat is swollen and she didn't want you to choke during the procedure. I'm going to take a look."

He pulled over a stainless steel instrument attached to a larger stainless steel gizmo and showed me a small flexible tube with a little clear bulb on the end, no bigger than the lead of a number two pencil.

"I'm going to slide this right up through your nostril and into your throat and take a look."

It was not painful but it felt a bit strange. As the doctor manipulated the tube in my throat he watched his progress on a TV monitor and then there was his "Uh huh, Uh huh."

He then gently pulled the thing out of my nose.

"Well, Mr. Herrera, this is your lucky day. I have some good news for you."

Immediately I thought that this has all been a mistake: the lump, the biopsies, the CAT scans have all been wrong! I don't have cancer!

"The swelling is due to a sinus infection, not growth of the tumor. I'll call Dr. Chatham and report what I've found. She's waiting to see you."

Minutes later Dr. Chatham said, "Your tumor hasn't enlarged very much since your last scan. And our pathology reports show that there is no lymphoma in your bone marrow. This is some good news."

Dr. Chatham referred to a calendar of 1997 on her desk, "Six treatments of CHOP every two weeks followed by three treatments of ICE, one a week. You'll have to stay in the hospital for twenty-four hours when we administer the ICE, then a harvest of your stem cells and radiation to your neck on an outpatient basis. Dr. Yahalom will determine that schedule. Then somewhere in here, late May or early June, you'll go into the hospital for the transplant and stay for seven or eight weeks. That will be the dangerous period."

"Dangerous, in that I could die?"

"Yes. Your immune system will be taken to zero with the chemotherapy and radiation, and you will be in isolation for most of the time. It'll be a rough time."

"By taken to zero, you mean . . .?

"We'll burn out your immune system with chemo. You won't have an immune system at all. You'll be quarantined. Before anyone comes into your room they'll have to put on gloves, a special gown and a mask. We'll have to keep your environment sterile. In the state you'll be in, any minor infection could be fatal."

"Are you saying I'll be quarantined for two months?"

"No. Once we re-infuse your stem cells we're hoping your immune system will re-establish itself right away."

"What if you don't kill every last lymphoma cell?"

"We'll be counting on your immune system to handle any cancer cells that might be left. You have your first chemotherapy at 1:00 tomorrow."

* * * * *

On the streets of Manhattan people were still out there; walking fast, hailing cabs, jumping on buses. Street after street the same . . . What would it be like? Death? I would stop and suddenly close my eyes and put my hands over my ears to shut out the sound. Perhaps that would be it, darkness, silence.

5

I had a message from my youngest brother. "Anthony, this is your little brother John in Texas. Mother heard from some people in Wiggins that you had cancer and it was bad. Since then she and the old man have been bugging the hell out of me. They keep asking **me** what should **we** do? I'll be in later tonight."

I had told my closest friend in Wiggins, Lucas Wilson. Even though I had left over thirty years ago, cancer is big news in a little town.

I went to Basha's apartment. We had soup. Basha makes very good soup. As Basha prepared dinner she would just stop and stare for a moment and then recover. It wasn't like her to stop moving or talking. She was very upset but tried not to let me see. I wasn't that hungry but I ate anyway. We watched a PBS documentary about lions. I missed the Karroo Desert, Capetown and the beauty of South Africa. After a big hug, I left. The weather was mild and I decided to walk the fifty blocks to my apartment.

Basha lives between Sixth and Seventh Avenues on 44th Street. I walked over to Fifth and started uptown. I stopped in front of the Plaza Hotel and sat by the fountain and thought about the call from my brother. I hadn't heard from any of my family in years.

My parent's marriage was one of the lesser-known tragedies of the Second World War.

In Wiggins our place was named Palm Hill. I remember that on Christmas mornings I would get up and see what Santa Claus had left on that magic eve. We had some money. I got lots of presents.

Then my mother and I would drive across town to the house where she grew up, to her parents home, John and Lucille Blackburn, Bop and Gam to me. Santa had left lots of presents for me there too.

The first five years of my life were pretty much like that of any kid in a small southern town. There were two exceptions: my last name, Herrera, was unheard of in Mississippi, and my father was a bootlegger.

Crip was the black man who lived on our place. He and my father made illegal whiskey in the little house in the back of our five-acre yard. They sold it in another part of the state where Crip grew up.

I helped them and would carry cans of syrup on my tricycle to "Sammy's" house. That's where the still was. My father had a statue of Uncle Sam watching over the still as a mock tribute to the government and the IRS. Work was fun, but it was scary when he would send me into the field at night with a flashlight to look for lawmen that might be coming to raid us and take him away to prison. Once we did find some big holes dug in the cornfield; could have been the sheriff looking for our moonshine. The law never came.

As a child I followed Crip around our place like a little puppy. He was very strong and he could lift a one hundred pound sack of feed and walk with it on his shoulders. I helped him with his cotton patch and when he sold the cotton he bought me a double-barreled pirate cap pistol and a box of caps. Crip was kind to me. Crip was my hero.

Once Dr. MacGuffie's daughter Martha saw a photograph of Crip and me taken when I was about four years old, she remarked, "Anthony I always thought you got your stance from watching John Wayne, but look!" In the photo, Crip and I holding shovels and were both leaning to one side, long before I'd ever seen the Duke.

As an adult I learned the reasons the Stone County Sheriff never busted my father: Daddy never sold any moonshine locally and out of consideration for my maternal grandparents, the Blackburns, merchants, upstanding citizens in this town of 1,500 for over forty years and members of the First Baptist Church.

Several years later my father did get busted. He had financed a bootleg operation run by some real backwoods types in the county to the north, Forest County. I had gone with him that Sunday afternoon but he had sent me home with a man in a blue Ford. My father and four other men had gone way into the woods to inspect some four hundred gallons of moonshine ready for shipment, when ten Federal Revenue men came out of the surrounding woods with pistols and shotguns.

I was in the third grade and the next day at school everyone knew but no one said a word, except for Olan Ray Bond. His family was so crude, country and poor that he only had shoes to wear in the winter months. The rest of the year he came to school barefooted. Right before the first bell rang he blurted out, "Your daddy was arrested last night." The shame was unbearable. I didn't cry. I just wanted to run away.

My father spent one night in jail, and except for a fine, that was it. Even with the Yankee attitude and the strange last name, he was white, had a substantial sum of cash for a lawyer and, in turn, for the judge.

As a little boy my life at home did not seem bad until after he was arrested. Then the fights started. Daddy drank and yelled. My mother cried. It seemed as if the fights never stopped. One time they fought for seventy-two hours straight. I would go to bed and they would be fighting through the night. I could hear them, but I went to school, and when I came home they were still fighting.

One day I came home and found my mother in the back yard by the clothesline. She was crying and turned away when she saw me, but I saw that she had a black eye and her lip was swollen. I ran to her. She started pinning up sheets on the line.

"Your Daddy just got mad. It won't happen again, honey, I promise."

Daddy was now out of the moonshine business and had a used car business forty miles south in Biloxi on the Gulf Coast.

One summer night when I was eight years old, I had been left to watch his used car lot in Biloxi. He'd driven back to Wiggins to get my mother and to continue the fight they'd started the night before. When they drove up she was in the back seat. Her hair was messed up, and I could see her crying and her face swollen. The car was a four-door Chevrolet and Mother had on a red and white striped dress. I got in the front seat. Mother was holding a Bible, splattered with blood. As my father drove the side roads to Wiggins, he would stop and continue to beat my Mother with his fist. She kept quoting from the Bible. He tore pieces off of her dress and threw them out the window. I remember the muscle in my left arm getting tired as I held my hand up on the top of the front seat in a gesture to keep my mother quiet. As long as she didn't talk he wouldn't hit her. When I would put my hand down, she would start quoting from the Bible or talking through her sobbing. This would aggravate his rage and he would stop, lean over into the back seat and beat her. We had a big yard with a circular driveway in the front and another driveway that led to the back of our big white house. He parked the car under a cedar tree in the back and dragged her into the house. He took off her wedding ring and put it on a little nail in the wall where he'd knocked off a picture the night before. It stayed there for the next three days. Just before dawn, when the beating became too horrid to bear, my mother ran a quarter of a mile to our nearest neighbors.

The next morning the entire town knew, and my grandparents, Bob and Gam, drove up in their gray Buick. My father ran down the hill into the woods. I found him and he asked me to bring him two of his homemade beers. I went back to the house and brought them back to him. Some of the men in Wiggins who'd grown up with my mother were threatening to beat up Johnny Herrera. My father came back to the house. Somehow in the chaos, his .32 automatic pistol had disappeared. Gam claimed that she didn't know what had happened, so my father went to the little shed were the water tanks were and came out holding his German Luger. He stood in the living room and said, "I'll shoot the first two . . . and let the third one talk."

My grandmother slipped into my parents' bedroom, called the sheriff and begged him to stop the men. "These children have to grow up in this town."

Bop was a very gentle and quiet person by nature. He was sitting at the steering wheel of the Buick with a nine shot .22 pistol on the front seat. Gam came out of the house and badgered him again and again, "John, if you are a man you will go in and confront Johnny."

Bop left his pistol in the Buick and went in the house. In the kitchen he yelled, "You kicked my daughter!" Then he attacked my father who ducked down. As Bop hit him on the back of his neck and head, Johnny said, "Take it easy, Mr. Blackburn."

Bop hit Daddy about six times, then turned and walked out of our house. It was over.

My father attempted to excuse his brutality by saying, "I was wearing sneakers with rubber soles when I kicked her. It wasn't that bad."

Over the years that followed, Rafael "Johnny" Herrera ridiculed my Grandmother. He forgot that Gam prevented a lot of very angry men from coming out to Palm Hill, tying him to a tree and beating him. They probably would have killed him. And if they had, in those days the law would not have interfered. Justice would have been done.

* * * * *

The next year they had another child, my brother Ralph. There were now four of us. I was the oldest by five years; then Gloria, Carmen and Ralph.

As far as I knew he never hit her again but after a few months, the fighting continued. Yelling and crying. Finally my mother divorced him. He left the state and Mother went back to work at Keesler Air Force Base in Biloxi, where she had been a secretary during the war. That's where she had met the dashing, Johnny Herrera.

After two years of financial chaos, he came back to Mississippi and they remarried and moved to Texas. My father was physically very powerful and had incredible energy. Most of that energy went into anger and persecution. It was my fault, a twelve-year-old kid, my mother's fault and my Grandmother's fault that we were broke and we had lost our place in Wiggins. He was constantly raising hell.

After three months of our new life in Schertz, Texas, I hitchhiked back to Wiggins. Bop and Gam were building a house to rent. I worked as a carpenter's helper. At the end of the summer after lunch on the back porch, I asked if I could stay. I didn't want to go back to Texas and I had already lined up a job at a Yeager's grocery store and I would make all my school money. Gam said that they would make a home for me but I had to follow their rules. I had to be in every night by 9:30 during the week and at a reasonable hour on weekends. I had to go to church every Sunday.

Bop didn't talk much. Gam went on about everything excitable but she drilled manners into me, made me help wash the dishes every night after supper, but she was positive and always urged me to do my best. She loved music and played the piano. Boogie-woogie was her favorite. When there was a project such as building another rental property, Gam and I would get carried away making plans and talk on and on. Then as we calmed down I would turn to Bop, who would always sit and just listen.

"What do you think, Bop?"

He would take a moment and say with a smile.

"Son, it is leg over leg to Dover."

* * * * *

Without realizing it I had walked all the way back to 89th Street and was unlocking my door. I poured myself a shot of vodka and called my youngest brother. My sister Carla and John were born after I left.

"Hello, John."

"Is it true?"

"Yes."

"What the hell do I tell them?"

"Tell them to do what they have done for the past forty years – nothing! And then tell them that if I die, they'll get one hundred thousand dollars and if they don't come to my funeral, they'll get two hundred thousand. Tell them that."

"Okay. Must be pretty rough?"

"Yes. Pretty rough."

I filled him in on the diagnosis and the treatment plan.

My reaction and response was perhaps caustic but I was dealing with cancer and life and death. In 1836 at the battle of the Alamo, Colonel Travis took his sword and drew a line in the sand and gave his men a choice to stay, fight and probably die, or leave.

If either my mother or my father wanted to come through for me now and help me fight cancer, my words would not stop them.

It was midnight. In thirteen hours someone would stick a needle in my arm and toxic chemicals would invade my blood stream attempting to kill lymphoma cells. I couldn't give any more energy to ancient memories. I finished my drink and luckily went right to sleep.

6

At 3:15 a.m. a noise started in the steam pipes, a loud clang, clang, clang in the radiator. Usually in older apartments, this stops as soon as the pipes heat up. It didn't stop, so at 4:00 I took a blanket and went upstairs and got some sleep.

As Hamlet said, *"How all occasions inform against me."*

I didn't know if I would be able to get up and down the stairs once I started chemo. In the living room I had a television and a bathroom very handy. As I understood it, I would throw-up a lot and be very sick and now I had clanging pipes. I had to sleep upstairs. I tried to get the king-sized mattress up the winding stairs by myself but couldn't.

Evan Bergman, an actor and a friend from the squash club, had said to call if I needed anything. I was lucky, no answering machine. He picked up the phone. He'd be right over.

We couldn't get the mattress up the winding staircase. I needed it in the living room. Then we figured it out. Open the basement door; take the mattress out onto the street, up the outside stairs, through the front door and into the apartment. No problem.

We set up the makeshift bedroom and I thanked Evan. There were just a few words about the upcoming battle with cancer. As Evan left he turned in the doorway, "Herrera, this is the toughest part you'll ever play. It's the role of a lifetime."

I paced back and forth, and then I went to my laptop and printed out a copy of a poem that I had loved for years and had always promised myself to commit to memory. The character of Nano, a very old man in the play **The Night of the Iguana** by Tennessee Williams, recites it just before he dies. It is about an orange tree and how the positive force of nature perpetuates life. The last verse reads:

> *Oh courage could you not as well*
> *Select a second place to dwell*
> *Not Only in that golden tree*
> *But in the frightened heart of me?*

* * * * *

Dr. Chatham was surrounded with nurses, interns and several "fellows." A "fellow" has completed his internship and works under senior staff doctors. She directed me to the chemo clinic on the 17th floor.

"Dr. Chatham, you said that we were going to do something new? I take it by new, you mean a new type of treatment, not that I'm the first."

"No. You are not the first. Uh . . . you are the 4th or maybe the 5th in this country."

On the surface I was very composed.

"Oh, the 4th or 5th, I see."

But inside my brain I was screaming, "4th or 5th in this country . . . Screw me Jack. Forth or fifth!" Well, it's a chance and a chance is better than dying.

The young woman at reception found my name and told me it would be about another twenty minutes before they were ready for me and to just have a seat. In the hall by the waiting area there was a long oak bench, like a church pew. It was empty. I sat there. There were two pay phones by the elevators. I didn't feel like calling anyone. I sat. This is it, chemotherapy. What would it feel like? Would it hurt going in? The needle will hurt. How much? Probably not that much. I could just get up and walk out and go to Mississippi and get drunk with my friends and then what? No, I would sit here and wait the twenty minutes.

I am an actor. It now seems as if since I felt the lump on the side of my neck; the test, the scans, the consultations have all been only a rehearsal. Now this will all become very real. I have the opportunity to find out a lot about myself in the few minutes. The first verse of the Tennessee William's poem:

> *How calmly does the orange branch*
> *Observe the sky began to blanch*
> *Without a cry without a prayer*
> *With no betrayal of despair.*

During these days some insights into words that I had read for years became much clearer. Such as, *"no betrayal of despair."*

Growing up in a home filled with emotional and physical abuse, a child dreads most of his waking hours and lives in constant fear of the pain inflicted by selfish and desperate parents. Despair becomes as routine and commonplace as getting dressed or going outside to play. This feeling of dread is with you all of the time, a little gray cloud that you carry in your insides.

Children must find a way to survive, to deal with the chaos and despair imposed on their growth. As a child I found a place where I could make sense of the world: my imagination. In my fantasies, after a big fight with fists or guns the good guys always beat up the bad guys, and the hero usually got the pretty girl. That's the way it was in most movies too. If on Saturday night I could get to the Straub Theatre on Pine Street to see the serial and the cartoon and the cowboy picture, I went into a world that helped me survive the week to come.

When I was a student at Ole Miss I had read that John Wayne was sailing across the Atlantic to Spain to make a film. During the voyage he was caught in a storm. He said to himself that he played tough guys in the movies and now he was going to see how tough he really was. He tied himself to the mast and fought the storm through the night. He survived.

In my thirties I learned more about John Wayne from James Poe. When I moved to California in 1975, I became friends with Jim. He had won the Oscar for the screenplay of **Around The World In Eighty Days** in 1956. I had found a place in Malibu at 18964 Pacific Coast Highway. The little two-bedroom shack was so close to the beach that with high winds the waves would splash up on the deck. Frank Sacks, a young writer/producer, was my roommate. Cleavon Little lived about two hundred yards away, on the other point of "Dog Beach." I was playing Jack Curtis on **The Young And The Restless**, and performing Shakespeare on the weekends at the Will Geer Shakespeare Theatre in Topanga Canyon.

Later Cleavon would refer to that era *"our period of innocent decadence."*

I became involved with Barbara Steele. Barbara had starred in twenty-two horror movies when she lived in Rome in the 60's. Three years later I came to realize that this was particularly good casting on the part of the Italians. Barbara isn't necessarily an evil person but she did abuse the goodness in the men who loved her.

She had a son from her failed marriage to Jim Poe; I got to know Jim when I'd bring him to Jim's house for weekends.

We rarely talked about Barbara but we did talk a lot about the movies. I could listen to Jim for hours. He told me that he once saw David Niven's hands trembling before a "take."

"But David Niven and Cary Grant were the coolest guys to ever come out of England."

Jim smiled. "You're young. You think they were just movie stars. They were great actors. I want you to start watching Henry Fonda, Robert Mitchum, John Wayne, Burt Lancaster and Jimmy Stewart. You think they are just movie stars and they are, but they were also great actors who take their craft very seriously."

I began to study Henry Fonda. There is a big difference in the spine of the characters he portrays in **Fort Apache, The Grapes of Wrath** and **Mister Roberts.** Over the years I studied the astounding work of the rest of the great actors Jim recommended, especially the work of John Wayne. The characters he portrayed in **The Quiet Man, The Man Who Shot Liberty Valence** and **The Searchers** gave his audience a powerful sense of dignity and courage.

Stella Adler would say, "When working on a scene in a script, your choice is your talent. Make your choice big!" The universe had now cast me in the lead role in a real life adventure -- *"The role of a lifetime."* There is no room in me now for despair. I must see this as the lead role in a real adventure. I have to be clear and determined. For the past year in psychotherapy I had been working on the difference between being mean and being tough. My father was mean. Most bullies are. Burt Lancaster and John Wayne were tough.

I have made the choice to climb into the saddle and ride into the dark canyon.

In minutes I would begin to learn what being tough is all about.

When a movie ends there are usually a few moments of darkness before the lights come back on. In minutes there will be toxic chemicals in my body, and within weeks this role I have to play and my life could be over -- endless darkness.

* * * * *

"Mr. Herrera, I'm Karen Klem, your chemo nurse. Would you come with me please?" She was trim and upbeat. She led me to a room with six big chairs in a semi-circle and showed me to the empty one. In each of the other five chairs was a patient with a needle in their arm, connected by tubes to bags of mysterious fluids hanging from metal poles. The man next to me smiled as I settled in and I noticed the fluid in one of his bags was a bright orange. Others were reading, one sleeping and an older lady staring into space. No one was screaming or writhing in pain.

I sat and rolled-up my sleeve and she tied a rubber tourniquet around my bicep. Karen called over another chemo nurse and held up a large clear bag of fluid. It was what they called CHOP. This was chemotherapy. They both read the list of chemical names. As Karen checked labels on the bags of chemo against Dr. Chatham's written orders, she asked me my name and date of birth. The other nurse double-checked. Then they hung the bag on a stainless steel pole with a spindle device at the top, forming little metal arms with curved ends so the bags of fluid wouldn't slip off. There were eight of these arms that held hydration fluids, chemicals to kill cancer cells and who knows what else.

The needle went in with no problem and almost didn't hurt.

"Will I throw-up?"

"No, the first drug we use prevents nausea."

"Will I lose my hair?"

"Yes, with CHOP probably after the second round, definitely after the third. But it will grow back after treatment, sometimes lighter, sometimes darker, sometimes a different color and texture altogether."

"Oh."

"This will take about three hours. Would you like some water or juice?"

"Yes, juice, please."

Karen had taped the needle to my arm and once in, it did not hurt. My arm was resting on a pillow and it wasn't uncomfortable. The other nurse brought me a magazine. So far this wasn't that bad.

About forty-five minutes later Karen returned with a tray holding three huge hypodermic needles filled with red liquid.

"Don't worry, I'm going to inject this into your line."

"This is the tough stuff, isn't it?"

"Yes."

"This is the stuff that kills the cancer cells?"

"Yes. You may feel a little burning sensation."

She finished with the big first hypo and carefully started with the second hypo filled with red liquid.

"You okay?"

"Yeah, I guess."

There was no burning sensation. It was the morning of February the 6th, 1997. The morning of January 9th was when I first saw the lump in the side of my neck. Now that moment seemed like fifteen foggy years ago.

7

After the chemotherapy, nothing astonishing or physically ultra-dramatic happened to me for the rest of that day. I had a voice-over audition at 3:45 that afternoon and an invitation to see Vic Damone at the Rainbow Room that evening.

I wore my best Italian suit. I told my date about my friend Lucas from my hometown. In 1986 I had written and directed a film for PBS based on the Eudora Welty's **The Wide Net.** The story took place in the 1930's. As it turned out Wiggins and Black Creek swamp just a few miles away was the perfect location. Lucas was a great help through out the production. That time together renewed our childhood friendship.

He said he was coming to see me before I went into the hospital. He had never been out of the Deep South. I was excited to be able to show him the city where I had lived most of my life over the past twenty-seven years.

Manhattan was exceptionally beautiful on that very clear night, way up in the sky, at the top of Rockefeller Center. I first came here in 1969 with sixty-eight dollars in my pocket. What wonderful adventures I had had in this most magnificent metropolis. Now I faced the beginning of a new journey, but tonight I would enjoy every note, every smell, every moment.

* * * * *

Patsy came up that weekend and in one of her favorite restaurants we were having a glass of red wine at the bar while waiting for our table. My wine tasted a little bitter. Patsy said, "I'm going to get a good bottle at the table."

The more expensive wine tasted bitter to me too. The chemo had already started to change my body chemistry. I just hoped it was killing the cancer cells.

The second chemo treatment was about the same: a tourniquet, a butterfly needle in the vein, Karen and another nurse reading out the contents of the bags and the three big hypos with the tough red drugs. Karen remarked, "You have large, good veins."

I had large veins from hard labor. As teenagers in that small town in the 1950's we all worked. We unloaded boxcars full of burlap sacks of flour, sugar and potatoes for Ernest Yeager's stores. I pumped gas at Earl Danzey's Gulf Station. I was the janitor at the grammar school during my junior and senior years, which I could do at night and have the afternoons free after school for football practice.

David Redfield worked in the Wilson's Drug Store and Jessie Thomas in the butcher section of Yeager's. I wanted to get strong for football so I loaded pulpwood. The pine trees were cut down with chain saws and then into five-foot, three lengths. You picked up the log, hoisted it on your shoulder, heaved it on the truck and then did it again, all day long. I was the only white in the crew and the black guys I worked with taught me to lift without hurting my back and how to pace myself so I wouldn't burn out. We worked very hard, long hours; we talked and laughed.

When we worked in the woods that were too wet for trucks to maneuver, we loaded the wood on steel pallets and pulled them up to the road with an International Caterpillar. One day we found a beehive in an oak tree down in one of the bogs. The straw boss was white and wouldn't go near it. But one of the black men climbed on the Caterpillar, another jumped on the side and they drove into the swamp. They cut down the tree and chained it on the back of the caterpillar.

As they dragged it out, the cloud of bees swarming around the caterpillar was loud and thick. You could barely see the machine or the men. We all gathered around as Mitchell, the strongest man I have ever worked with, took a big chain saw and cut the log length-wise into two halves. The hive was over four feet long. As the honey poured out we caught it in tin cups, Coke bottles and in our hands. The hive was broken up into big chucks and put into the water barrel. Bees were swarming everywhere. It was unbelievable but nobody got stung and when I asked why, Mitchell just looked at me, "Bees don't bite at dis time."

These men were open and free talking about their lives and sex. Even today, that subject is taboo in most of white society. There were all kinds of stories and laughter about sex.

"You ain't a man till you had the clap. But you don't want to get dat bull head clap. No suh, not dat bull head clap."

* * * * *

I knew that soon my hair would start falling out from the chemo. Not a good look for auditions. I had to tell my agents. When I arrived at the CED office, an agent in reception pulled me aside.

"Are you all right? When you called me to cancel your auditions a couple of weeks ago, I heard someone in the background say the word 'biopsy.'"

I began to shake a little.

"No, I'm not all right. I have cancer."

"Oh my God."

"Ask Sharon if I could talk to her for a minute."

Sharon Bierut was the first person that I met at the agency. In an instant, she was right there; we went into a small studio used to record auditions for clients. She looked at me and I just blurted it out.

"I have cancer. I've just started chemo. I didn't want to tell you. I really shouldn't be going on auditions. In a couple of weeks I'll lose my hair . . ."

"Don't worry about 'the business.' I buried my best friend last week. He died from cancer. We'll handle this however you want."

"I'm not sure, I don't know, I haven't thought it through."

She took my hand and looked me right in the eye.

"We won't do anything right now. You're just not available to audition for the next few days."

She squeezed my hand harder.

"You can call me anytime if you just need to talk, and God bless."

* * * * *

Dr. Chatham had started me on an oral drug, Prednizone, and told me it would give me a robust look and lots of energy. Evidently it had kicked in; I felt vigorous and walked a lot. Every doctor said this cancer had nothing to do with the way I had lived my life. They didn't know why the immune system allows a certain T cell to go berserk and grow in an abnormal way. I had never been a heavy smoker. I didn't even smoke cigarettes until after Ole Miss. I bought my first pack when I was working as a juvenile probation officer in New Orleans before I was Heston's stand-in.

I thought I needed to learn to inhale so I could smoke pot. I had heard how wonderful pot was and intended to try it. The first night I got high I found myself on my back, on the floor of a fancy French Quarter apartment with my forehead burning, and my brain very woozy. I couldn't form a sentence and everyone around me kept saying, "Are you high? I'm so high, is this good shit or what." I just wanted to get out of there but I couldn't move for hours.

The next time I saw Dr. Chatham I told her pot was not my kind of drug but that I'd heard it could help during chemo. Without a second's hesitation she said, "No. No way. You've shown a significant response to the first cycle of chemo. We can continue the CHOP at full dose but this means the chemo is already compromising your lungs. We cannot risk the possibility of spores from marijuana getting in there to complicate things further."

Her judgment wasn't legal or moral. It was purely scientific.

* * * * *

I got in about 8:15 that night and checked my messages;

"Anthony, this is Felicia Behr. Please give me a call in the morning."

Executive Producers don't call you at end of the day to chat. I first met Felicia Behr when she took the helm at **As The World Turns** in October of '96. We talked then about the return of my character: James Stenbeck. I didn't hear anything for weeks, so after Thanksgiving I phoned her and she said that bringing back James Stenbeck was "still on the table." Now they had a story line for me.

"Hello, this is Anthony Herrera and I'm returning Felicia's call."

"Good morning, Anthony, this is Felicia."

"Good morning."

"We've got a great storyline and we're ready to put you to work."

"Felicia, I am very pleased to get this call and would like very much to come back to work. That's not the problem, but I do need to talk to you."

"This story will start in six to eight weeks so why don't you come in next Thursday morning."

"No, this can't wait until next week. I need to talk to you tomorrow."

"Can you be here at 9:30 in the morning?"

"Yes, thank you. I'll see you then."

I phoned Sharon Bierut. I felt I needed an agent to go to this meeting with me. We talked it over and agreed on Carey Morgan. She was very bright and personable. I phoned back and told Felicia's assistant that I would be bringing an agent with me, but not for the usual reasons.

The next morning at 9:30 we were shown into Felicia's office and after we exchanged the standard greetings I told her.

"I have cancer. It is very serious and very rare. I'm being treated at Sloan-Kettering, chemotherapy. I'd love to come back to work but this is something you should know."

We chatted for another few minutes. I can't remember what we talked about. Carey was poised and professional. I said I would talk to my oncologist and see when she estimated chemo would affect my ability to work full production days.

Felicia was also very professional and said she would talk to the head writer and to Procter & Gamble.

Carey and I left CBS and jumped in a cab. It began to rain. It rained very hard and we got stuck in traffic. Cary said that Felicia was shaken about my having cancer.

"She was upset. I bet she's lost someone to cancer, someone very close to her."

I saw Dr. Chatham at two that afternoon. She said it would probably be mid-May before fatigue from chemo would prevent me from working, but that my energy level would drop gradually; also, that I could expect to start losing my hair in three or four weeks.

After I left the hospital I phoned Mickey Dyer-Dobbin, the executive in charge of P&G Productions. She took my call immediately.

"Hello Anthony. I have already had a conversation with Felicia and the writers. We are going to try to make this work."

"I wanted to tell you myself but it seems you ladies are way ahead of me."

I phoned Felicia, I wasn't on hold but a split second. These folks were serious. I gave her an account of what Dr. Chatham had said about my energy decline and not being able to work beyond mid-May.

"I need to talk to your doctor, if you don't mind."

"Don't mind at all, I wouldn't trust an actor either."

Ms. Behr chuckled. She got my humor. I had read years before that a man in his mid-forties was told he was going to die. He bought videos of his favorite Marx Brothers movies, watched them over and over, and laughed a lot and didn't die. I knew that Groucho and Harpo couldn't defeat Mantle Cell Lymphoma, but some humor from time to time could help me get through the day, or the hour, or even the next minute.

The head writers, producers, and other powers at Proctor & Gamble worked it all out.   They started the character in the story line three weeks earlier than originally planned to accommodate my treatment schedule. This was a wonderful and ironic turn of events.

Later that night I found a cable documentary about the "History of the Transplant."   In the early 1900's the Rockefeller Institute imported and sponsored a French doctor unable to continue his work in France where they thought it too radical.

He operated completely shrouded in black robes with only a small opening for the eyes, and required the same garb for his surgical team. He experimented with grafting the limbs of one animal onto another. His approach was primitive and eccentric by today's standards, but a bold beginning. It was the 1930's before the medical community even understood the concept of rejection. The first bone marrow extractions were very atrocious. One scene from the 40's showed two brothers in the process of donating marrow for their sister's transplant. The doctors had to drill into the brothers' thighbones; and their screams seemed more like a horror movie than medicine.

There was a race in the medical world to perform the first heart transplant. A team of young doctors in Boston was working with an infant with a very weak heart and only a few weeks to live. Other than the heart, the baby was in good health. Another child was born in California without a brain. There was literally a vacuum in his cranium, and the infant only had days to live.

The California baby was flown to Boston and they prepared both infants for the transplant; the healthy heart was to be removed from the baby born without an upper cranium and put into the baby with a failing heart.

Because of the power of Catholicism there, the hospital's administration did not lend much support to this pioneer team of doctors. Current thinking deemed any heartbeat as evidence of human life. The anesthesiologist assigned to the surgery, described later as a "grandfatherly type." He would not administer drugs to the first infant until his heart stopped beating because he felt he would be ending a life, so he waited until the infant's heart stopped. The transplant was performed, but because of the delay both babies died.

One week later Dr. Christian Bernard performed the world's first successful heart transplant in South Africa.

Years later in an interview one of the surgeons was asked why the senior establishment of the hospital did not give them the support they needed to perform the procedure successfully. His answer was clear and strong.

"They didn't have the guts. They didn't have the vision."

The filmmaker also interviewed the mother in California. She was sitting in a lawn chair in her backyard in a working class neighborhood.

8

I was now in a world that required all of my strength and focus if I was to survive. I have assets. One of the most important emotional building blocks in my life came at the end of my freshman year at Ole Miss. It was a Wednesday night and I was in the university library trying to study.

I had been to several dances and dinners at the Sigma Chi house and had met most of the members. This night was the fraternity's last chapter meeting of the year. I had been brought up for a bid the week before and one member had black balled me because we had never met. Not only did all of the insecurities of being a teenager rise up in me, but a deeper, darker dread from constant negative reinforcement implanted in me by my parents.

The fraternity meeting ended about 9:30 and it took fifteen minutes to walk to the library. It was 10:30, the library closed at 11:00. My anxiety was such that I could barely breathe. Then at five minutes to eleven two Sigma Chi's, Wyn Howard from Vicksburg and Dynamite Ed Perry from Oxford, appeared and motioned me over.

"Can you come outside with us?"

I grabbed my books. They both looked glum and I thought, 'I didn't make it.'

We went through the big glass doors. The second we were out side Wyn jumped up and grabbed me, "You made it. You made it on the first round. You are a Sigma Chi pledge."

For me it was a marvel just to go to Ole Miss, to make decent grades, but now to return my sophomore year as a Sigma Chi pledge was fantastic for me. I had been accepted by the best of the best in my university and that gave me a level of self-confidence that I had never known before in my life.

* * * * *

Stem cell transplants are performed to create new blood and a new immune system in the hopes that the cancer will not grow back.

Cancer cells grow faster than any other cell in the body, and chemotherapy ***kills all rapidly growing cells:*** the "good guy" cells and the "bad guy" cells. The gastrointestinal tract is made of rapidly growing cells. That's why one's appetite and taste buds are affected relatively quickly. This is also why you lose your hair with certain chemos, like the one they were giving me: CHOP. CHOP kills a lot of stuff in the body including hair follicles.

A patient gets chemo to kill as many cancer cells as possible -- the bad guys. But at the same time chemo kills a lot of the good guys, like the white cells necessary to fight infection. So, before Dr. Janice Gabrilove and her team at Sloan-Kettering developed Neupogen, the patient and the doctors would have to wait for the good guys to grow back before beginning another round of chemo to kill cancer cells.

Once the cancer cells are being attacked and the stronghold of the disease is weakened, the chemo needs to be administered on a consistent basis to kill cancer cells as fast as possible. But if the good guy cells continue to be killed-off at the same rate, the body, the blood, and the organs become weakened. It becomes very easy for infections to develop in the heart, lungs, kidneys, liver, and gastrointestinal tract.

Neupogen stimulates the bone marrow to over-compensate and produce more white blood cells as the normal supply is being killed-off by chemo. White blood cells are regularly re-supplied to the bloodstream in amounts high enough to fight infection, while the chemo continues to bombard the cancer cells. Because of this drug, chemotherapy can be administered regularly, with fewer worries about the chance of infection due to a low white blood cell count.

Neupogen revolutionized cancer treatment.

I needed to have shots of Neupogen daily because the CHOP chemo was causing my white cell count to drop dramatically. If I didn't learn to give myself the shots, I would have to go to the hospital every day for a nurse to stick me. This would have been an unnecessary cost. James Stenbeck was just about to reappear. I did not want to take the time to get through mid-town Manhattan traffic, running from CBS on West 57th and the Hudson River across town to Sloan-Kettering, one block from the East River, just to get a shot.

On television it looks easy. They just stick the needle through the rubber bottom of the vial of liquid, look serious, pull the plunger down, and fill the cylinder of the hypodermic needle with the drug.

But it was not so easy; I had to take a class on:

How to give oneself a shot with a hypodermic needle:

The class was in a small room on the 17th floor where we got our chemo treatments. There were six of us in the class. Five of us ranged from age thirty-five to sixty-five, and there was one teenaged girl from the Dominican Republic. She didn't speak English and neither did her father. The nurse took us very carefully through the procedure. First, wash your hands. Dry your hands with a sterile paper towel.

The best places to stick the needle through the skin are the thighs and the stomach. The diameter of the needle was very small and it was about half an inch long. This was a subcutaneous shot, which means "under the skin." It was not an intra-muscular shot, which required a longer and thicker needle.

The nurse gave us each a new box of hypodermic needles containing twenty-five to start with. An important rule was not to let the needle touch **anything** and if it did touch anything, throw it away and start over. To eliminate bubbles in the cylinder, hold the hypo up and thump the side. This usually worked. Then take an alcohol pad out of its sealed packet, rub the spot where you are going to stick and then stick the needle through your skin. When we got to that part the Dominican girl started crying and whispering to herself in Spanish. The nurse tried to comfort her but couldn't. She tried to communicate with the father who was getting upset. My Spanish is elementary. All I was able to learn was that this girl was only seventeen years old.

This young girl has cancer, she has to undergo chemotherapy in a foreign country, and now she has to stick holes in her skin; no wonder she was crying. It was finally determined that she should be given her shots in the hospital. I never saw the girl or her father again.

* * * * *

That night I had to give myself my first shot. I got everything ready just like I had learned. Before I stuck the needle in my thigh, I thought, this is part of this damn disease -- just do it!

The thought of it hurt more than the little needle. I put the used needle in an empty plastic bottle and sealed it. I had been instructed to save all my medical trash and take it to the hospital for disposal. I felt a slight sense of accomplishment at being able to stick a needle in my leg, push the plunger and send the Neupogen flowing into my body.

I woke up in the middle of the night with a bizarre pain in my legs. It felt as if my bones were going to explode. Gradually the pain subsided and I thought, **"What the hell is this?"** and tried to get back to sleep. Then the pain started again. It was radiating up and down inside my bones. There was no going back to sleep with this level of pain. I had no idea what was happening.

I called the twenty-four hour lymphoma hot line and the resident on duty explained that the Neupogen was stimulating the marrow in my bones to over-produce and that the new cells could not get out of the bones fast enough, and were creating pressure inside the bone. He recommended Tylenol. I turned the apartment upside down. No Tylenol, no painkillers of any kind. I had left my backpack at the studio and thought there might be some left in there, but it was 3:45 in the morning and I doubted if the dressing rooms would be open.

For a few minutes the pain would go away and I would think, 'Ahh, good' and would almost be back to sleep and like a devil, it would sneak back. Mild pain at first, and then it would build like a crescendo to a peak that was almost unbearable. Then it would slowly subside. This went on until dawn.

I checked when I got to the studio, no Tylenol with Codeine in my bag. By the time I finished the morning of taping, the pain was gone.

When I beeped-in there was a message from Dr. Chatham to call her.

"I heard I kept you up last night."

"No, but you woke me up at 3:30 and didn't let me get back to sleep."

"Try of the dose tonight and see if that helps."

Fortunately there was almost no pain the second night and from that point on, Dr. Chatham allowed me to give myself or of a dose as long as the white blood cell counts stayed at a level necessary to fight infection.

The third morning I woke up with hair on my pillow; I reached back and felt my hair. I had always had very thick hair. Gradually patches of my hair felt different. With a slight touch, a bunch of hair came out in my hand. My hair follicles were dying. Over the next couple of days more clumps of hair appeared on my sheets.

"Basha, I'm starting to look like a mangy dog."

"What kind of dog is that Anthonee?"

English is Basha's fourth language after Polish, Russian and French. I explained that mange is a skin disease that causes the loss of hair. We both laughed.

I looked into the bathroom mirror and reached back and felt another lock of my hair. It came out in my hand. I went out and bought a new can of shaving cream, a pack of disposable razors and put on a Dean Martin CD. Music of the 50's -- an era of hope. As a kid in Mississippi I had never seen or heard of pizzas. I thought the lyrics went, *"When the moon hits your eye like a big piece of pie."*

It takes longer to shave one's head than I would have imagined, three hours. That included being very careful. I knew I didn't need any extra cuts and bleeding. I didn't want to lose any white blood cells and chance an infection. I only had one little cut but it didn't bleed much. I looked bizarre and was very self-conscious even though I was in the apartment by myself.

Gaye Brown had called from London and wanted some blue jeans for her son Charlie, so I delivered a pair to a friend who was going to England. It was a nice evening so I walked. I knew **everyone** would be looking at my shaved head. As I passed people, street after street, no one took any notice of me. I realized this was New York City and I would have to have a boa constrictor wrapped around me before anyone would give me a second glance. I did wish I had thought to get a hat, though.

When I delivered the jeans to David, who had been one of the producers on the soap, he handled the news about my having cancer well. He was kind. I still had some energy so I decided to walk back home. The night air felt very strange and cool on my baldhead. As I got near the Broadway area there was an opening of what looked like a new disco but in fact was a glitzy computer show. I was dressed fairly well so was whisked right in past the line at the door. Bingo! I got a free beer and a cap with a Microsoft logo to cover my shiny head.

I walked on along the great White Way. I enjoyed the lights of Broadway. When I first arrived in New York there was a huge sign with a man blowing smoke rings, advertising cigarettes, right up there in Times Square. I had been in this city a long time. I had never acted on a Broadway stage. On 47th Street I shut my eyes and put my hands over my ears trying to shut out all stimuli. It nearly worked. Was this what death would be like? I would never even see this street again, let alone act in one of these theatres.

As I crossed 50th street --I couldn't believe it -- there was a short fellow standing at the corner with a boa constrictor wrapped around his back and shoulders. This reptile was at least seven inches thick at the fattest part of his body and over five feet long. I stood a polite distance away and watched. The man wanted someone to notice him in the worst way and as the pedestrians scurried by, I realized that I was the only one in all of New York City paying any attention to this small man and his very large snake.

* * * * *

My wig was made at Bob Kelly's on West 46th Street. The wall in the entranceway was covered with 8 x 10 glossies of some of the greatest actors ever. I thought I am right here getting ready to sit in a chair and be fitted for a wig, just like Fredrick March, Elizabeth Taylor, Meryl Streep, John Randolf and Hume Cronyn. I had worked with John Randolf when I was Heston's stand-in. I had admired some of these familiar faces for years; there was Tony Randall in a Shakespearean costume. As I looked at the photos, I got over my uneasy feelings about being there with cancer, for a hairpiece. Then I thought how fortunate I was, to be part of the acting profession. If you haven't been raised in show business, just sitting in the same room where all these great actors had been was exciting.

The wig-maker said I looked familiar and that we had worked together before. I told him I didn't think we had. I sat in a barber's chair in front of a mirror. He took several Polaroid's from different angles and then he brushed my hair, flattening it down tightly on my head, and began to methodically apply strips of long white tape in all directions on my head. He explained that he was making a skullcap. He had worked with several actors being treated with chemo over the years, and found this was the best way to get an accurate shape of one's head.

"It was a beard," he said. "I made you a beard for a soap, **As The World Turns**."

"You're right. That must have been '81 or '82. We were going back in time and I was a 17th century English Lord."

I watched as he carefully added strips of tape and, before long, there was a solid white cap covering my head. Just as he finished he caught my eye in the mirror and said, "I've made wigs for a lot of cancer patients. I wish you luck."

* * * * *

Dr. Chatham explained that I was continuing to respond well to the chemotherapy and that she could tailor my chemo treatments to accommodate my work schedule. I learned later from Nancy Cody-Lyons that Dr. Chatham was very pleased I had gone back to work.

My typical clinic visits with Dr. Chatham were brief; a nurse would come in and take my temperature and check my blood pressure. Dr. Chatham would come in and feel the lymph glands in my neck and under my arms; then I would lie down on the table and she would listen to my heart, lungs and stomach. We would chat briefly and she assured me that the chemo was doing exactly what it was supposed to be doing and that would be about it.

The day I went in for my third treatment I was very down. I didn't know exactly why, but it was like the bottom fell out. I had been doing so well with my "*adventure*" plan. I had been complimented by several of the nurses about my positive attitude. I was determined that Dr. Chatham was not going to see that I was slipping into despair. So I carried on about work at the studio and how much I liked my chemo nurse. I thought I had her fooled.

I sat on the end of the table buttoning up my shirt after she finished. She turned back on her way out. She grasped my right hand and squeezed it very hard and pulled my face close to hers. She locked her steel blue eyes with mine, just held them there and squeezed my hand even harder. This lasted for a good minute. She slowly let go and left the room without a word. My positive energy was back. And I said to myself, *"Damn, she's good."*

Nancy suggested that I attend a seminar for patients who were facing a bone marrow transplant. She would be conducting the program, and the panel would include a psychologist and two previous transplant patients. We would be able to ask questions and voice our concerns.

"You need to come to this and bring someone close to you who will be seeing you while you are in the hospital."

Basha is nearly always late. She wasn't this night. There were about fifteen patients, each accompanied by a spouse, family member or close friend. The two former transplant patients were Bill, a fellow in his early thirties from Pennsylvania, and Janet, an attractive woman in her mid-forties from Brooklyn, New York.

I was headed into the unknown, into pain and a grueling battle with the possibility of dying. I appreciated the generosity of these two people, who had both been in remission for several years.

Nancy opened the evening with information about the bone marrow or stem cell transplant so that the non-patients would have as much of an understanding as possible. I realized that having cancer is like being in a bizarre fraternity, and as with any selective order, there are a lot of new terms, phrases and rituals to learn. It is the dark side of Mother Nature that provides one with this involuntary membership.

The sooner the patient, his family and friends absorb the new vocabulary, the less a patient's condition will seem strange and alien. As they become used to hearing and saying phrases like systemic, blood count, white blood cell, hemoglobin, x-ray, CAT scan, Gallium Scan, etc., the jargon becomes more familiar; but the knowledge and understanding of these terms in no way diminishes the horror of the bone marrow transplant.

The oncologists are after the particular stem cells that create the blood and immune system. There are two ways to obtain these stem cells. Historically they have drilled holes in the bone to extract the marrow. A newer technique, using Neupogen, is to stimulate the bone marrow to over-produce stem cells and then circulate the blood through a centrifugal device. This is the less invasive method used to harvest stem cells.

I was told that I was too old to be considered for a donor transplant. I was fifty-three. Instead I would get an autologous stem cell transplant; they would take out my own stem cells and freeze them. Then they would continue to cook me with chemo and radiation to kill the cancer before re-infusing my cells and hoping for the best.

The most dangerous period of time during treatment is when one's immune system is "taken to zero" or rendered completely non-functional. If any infection enters the defenseless body, there is no immune system to fight it and the patient usually dies.

Janet told us that now she felt healthy and led a normal life. She also tried to prepare us about "**Shake and Bake**". "You'll be given a drug called "ampho" to protect your lungs from pneumonia. This will cause chills, it will make you shake and shake, and it will feel like your muscles will tear away from your bones. They won't. You'll get very cold even if you have a fever and you think that you'll never warm-up or quit shaking, but you will."

I could tell from his dress and speech that the young man from Pennsylvania was a country boy. He said he had resisted taking any kind of dope for pain because he was afraid of becoming addicted.

"I finally did take the 'rescues', and once I did, I realized that I could have saved myself a lot of suffering if I'd done it earlier. I didn't get hooked on anything."

Janet interjected, "I found out the same thing."

If one met either Bill or Janet today, they would never suspect what they had been through. They both said, each in their own ways, that the autologous stem cell transplant combined with total body irradiation is the closest thing to hell that could be devised and conducted by civilized man in a civilized society.

9

The CBS Television studio on West 57th street was the home of **As The World Turns** when I first appeared as Stenbeck in January of 1980. Over the years my character had been thrown out of an airplane, trapped in a burning house, shot in the back by his son and suffered several deadly fates off camera. But someway he always managed to return and stir problems for the citizens of Oakdale. He became known as *"the man you love to hate."*

I felt safe in this environment and after the first day the actors, make-up people, technicians, and wardrobe staff were all too busy with the production day to pay much attention to my baldhead. Larry Briggman, who plays John Dixon, called me Q-ball a couple of times and then quit. It was just Briggman's attempt at humor. We had worked together in 1974-75 and I knew he meant no malice.

Work was the best therapy possible. The story line for James was never dull. He was always very busy seducing ladies while bolstering his financial empire. In this story line I was selling some stinger missiles on the black market. How James acquired stinger missiles was never discussed but he had some and decided to pick up some extra cash.

The physical and mental demands of the show distracted me from the battle raging in my body between my cancer and the chemotherapy. But just as Dr. Chatham predicted, my energy level decreased steadily as the number of CHOP treatments progressed.

Basha had found a special soft-foam mattress cover developed for NASA in a health catalogue. It cost three hundred dollars but I ordered it for my dressing room. This was something new in my life, spending money for my comfort and care. By the beginning of April I would have a twenty-minute lunchtime nap in my dressing room, and one a bit longer at the end of the day. The three hundred dollar mattress cover was worth every penny.

When I saw Kathryn Hayes, who plays Kim Hughes, she asked in her character's blue-blood style, "How long do you think you'll be with us?"

"I don't know, Kathryn. I mean I **really** don't know." She suddenly realized that her question had a double meaning, under my present circumstances, and her hand went quickly to her chin.

"Oh, Anthony, I didn't mean. I wasn't implying . . ."

"That's all right Kathryn. It's a damn good question."

* * * * *

Karen Klem had left and I was assigned a new chemo nurse. During my fourth infusion of chemo, I was sitting in the same room on the 17th floor with several other patients, working on my dialogue for the next day. My new nurse, Elizabeth introduced herself. She was different from Karen Klem, somewhat voluptuous.

"Where's Karen?"

She had gone to another floor to work with post-transplant patients. I don't like change. I trusted Karen. Who was this Elizabeth? Before long she won me over with her sweet smile and warm personality. She arranged a pillow and tray so I could study my script with a minimum of discomfort while the needle in my arm fed chemicals into my bloodstream.

One way I learn dialogue is to write out each line or speech. I was busy scribbling away when I noticed Elizabeth bring in a tall, distinguished-looking man in his late sixties accompanied by an elegant, refined-looking woman, obviously his wife. He sat in the corner chair and I could overhear Elizabeth explaining the procedure. This man rolled up his sleeve, and I thought if I had to cast someone as CEO of General Motors or the Secretary of State for a big Hollywood film, he would be perfect; distinguished, confident and a commanding presence.

His wife nodded courteously, and I asked if this was his first treatment. It was. I related that not much in the way of side effects had really happened to me the first time, except my taste buds changed. He smiled politely and I went back to work on the script.

A couple of minutes later all hell broke loose. As soon as Elizabeth put the needle in his arm the man completely fell apart. He started moaning, sobbing aloud and writhing in his chair. Then another nurse ran in, closed the curtain around his chair and helped Elizabeth calm him down, which took a good ten minutes.

There were five other patients in the room and our compassion for this man could be felt among us without looking at each other. The emotions fueling his outburst were what we all had felt our first day and continued to feel every time we had that needle stuck in our arms.

* * * * *

To escape the stressful atmosphere of the room, I went away to a wonderful memory. I had met Gene Hackman when he was filming **The French Connection.** It was January; he was standing in the middle of Madison Avenue at midnight, in the snow, playing a scene where his character watched the bad guys from France dine in a fancy restaurant. I introduced myself during one of the breaks and told him I was studying with Stella Adler; that must have meant something to him and we started talking. I told him how much I admired the way he played the "Don't sell that cow" scene in **Bonnie And Clyde.** When the assistant director came over to tell him they were ready to do a take, I would get out of the way, but Mr. Hackman would say, "Don't go away -- this will just take a minute."

We talked for two hours in the middle of the street while the temperature dropped and the snow kept falling, just Gene Hackman and me. He reminisced about his first years when an off-Broadway play could be produced for seven or eight thousand dollars and how he performed in one play after another for years. I now realize that he was probably bored and I was giving him a chance to tell stories, which is something most actors love to do. But he was kind enough at the end of the shoot, about 5:00 a.m. to introduce me to the casting director and suggest that maybe he could find some work for me on the film.

I was chosen to be an extra for the big chase scene on the subway, where a young French actor brandished his character's .45 automatic and said, "You stop this train and I blow you in half" to the conductor. Just before the take, the Frenchman would jump up, grab the hanging bar on the subway car, and do fifteen chin-ups to get his adrenaline pumping. I noticed him do this repeatedly that day, thought how clever he was, and how people watching this film would never imagine that playing that scene involved chin-ups.

Good memories helped me through the chemo sessions.

* * * * *

In my early years as Stenbeck on the show, remembering the French actor, I would jump up and down when the stage manager began the count down. Even though I may not have been sure of the first line of dialogue, at least when the little red light on the top of the camera came on, my face would be filled with energy.

The next morning was a hard day in the studio. The story line was reaching its peak and my character was in a lot of trouble, as usual. This particular day one of the daytime magazines was holding a photo-shoot on the set. Lillian, the hairdresser, always took great care of me and made sure the wig fit right, so I never had to think about it while taping scenes. She double-checked that it looked all right for the photo shoot. I also had an interview. What if the journalist noticed? Would he ask why I was wearing a wig? I didn't want the press to know. The producers and I hadn't worked out exactly what would be said to the public.

We were all working under pressure to accommodate the photographer, and to get actors back for the afternoon's rehearsal and taping.

The minuscule patch of lace that held the front of the wig on my head was glued down and covered with makeup, but it protruded a little. If any of the cast or crew saw it, they never commented. The fellow who interviewed me was young, his attention was focused on his note pad and his list of questions about James and the story line. Minutes later I was back to the studio floor, going over the blocking and taking a last look at my lines. This work was intense and there was no time to think about cancer but the chemo had begun to wear me down and I wasn't jumping up and down before the camera rolled.

* * * * *

Dr. Chatham explained that Dr. Janice Gabrilove would be in charge of the transplant. Somehow I managed to miss my first consultation with Dr. Gabrilove. It was right there in my daily reminder for February 7th at 4:30 p.m. in my own handwriting. When I called to reschedule, Dr. Gabrilove responded with a smile in her voice.

"Mr. Herrera, you stood me up."

"Doctor, I promise I'll show up this time."

"See you on the 23rd at three o'clock."

Dr. Gabrilove was a native New Yorker. However, if she had been raised in a small town in the South or the Midwest, in high school she would have been head cheerleader, most popular and valedictorian. She was petite, and I thought it a bit bold for a patient to think of one of the great pioneers of Hematology and Oncology as "cute" but I thought she was cute. Our discussion about Mantle Cell Lymphoma was not cute.

"In your opinion, why did I get cancer?"

"I don't know. At this time we, the medical community, have no idea why."

She began to go over the transplant procedure. Their objective was to eradicate the Lymphoma with CHOP and ICE chemotherapy.

"Then we will do a stem cell harvest. We will stimulate your bone marrow to over-produce stem cells with a regimen of Neupogen shots, so there will be an over-population of young "baby" stem cells in your blood stream. Your blood will be centrifuged through a machine, which will remove the newly developed stem cells. These cells, destined to create your new blood and immune system will be tagged with your name and then frozen."

"Have you ever lost anyone's cells?

"No."

"Has that clinic ever lost anyone's cells?

"No."

"I thought you could take the stem cells out of my bones."

"We used to and sometimes we still do, but I prefer this method."

"Why?"

"It is not as difficult for the patient and we get 'cleaner' cells to work with."

"You'll be in charge of the transplant?"

"Yes. Dr. Chatham will still have a role in your care. But as far as the transplant, from beginning to end, you are under my care."

"What will happen? I mean I've been told it will be a very rough time, that I could die."

"Yes."

"Will it work?"

"We hope so. But I don't know for certain."

"Oh. How do they do it? I mean the transplant itself."

"After the total body irradiation and chemotherapy protocol, your immune system will no longer exist. We'll give your body a full day of rest. Then we will bring your cells to your room, while they're still frozen. We will put them in a warm bath, thaw them out in your hospital room, and once they are up to normal body temperature, we'll re-infuse them back into your blood stream."

"Oh."

"Then they should scoot right back into your bones and start back to work. Since they are your own cells, they will feel right at home. There will be no graft versus host problems. The cells came out of your body. That's why we call it an autologous transplant."

"Auto, like in automatic transmission?"

"Not bad. Autologous means cells derived from the same individual, you are both donor and the recipient."

I came up with a southern country boy analogy. "If a barn is my body and we have rats in the barn and they will keep multiplying until they squeeze out or strangle or devour every form of life, we either kill them or they kill me. So we take some babies from every animal, and hide them away from the barn, and then stand outside and fire .22 rifles and .30-.30 rifles through the side of the barn, hoping to kill rats. Then we move to the other side of the barn and fire with shotguns, hoping to kill from a different angle. But to make sure we've got all of the rats, we douse the inside with kerosene and set it on fire, but then put out the fire just before the beams and supports are burnt, so the barn won't fall down. We then put the baby animals back in, so they will grow and multiply and live happily ever after, we hope."

"That's pretty good; I'll use that metaphor, if you don't mind."

"Please do. Will the radiation and chemo kill every last one of the lymphoma cells?"

"Again we hope so, but I don't know for sure. If not, we hope that your new immune system will take care of any that are left."

"I think I understand."

"Mr. Herrera, I have said 'I don't know' three times since we have been talking. Does that upset you?"

"No, doctor. You can't know everything. But if you bullshit me, I'll see through it and that would upset me."

She smiled. "And I can learn from you."

Her words stuck in my mind: ***"Does that upset you?"***

"Dr. Gabrilove was concerned about my emotional state as well as the disease. She knew that patients wake up before dawn and review everything their doctor had said to them. They weigh every word, every pause in their speech, trying to make some sense out of why they have cancer, why has this happened to them and wonder if they are going die. I was more than a big white rat to this doctor.

* * * * *

I asked for a psychiatric consultation, and was referred to Dr. Holland. She was originally from Texas and still had a trace of a Southern accent, which was a comforting touch for me. I explained that I'd had years of psychotherapy and had recently been working with a Dr. MacCavoy here in the city. I told her I didn't think I would slip into a depression during the difficult times ahead. We went over my psychiatric and family history, including what was a bi-polar episode at twenty, but in those days it was called a "nervous breakdown."

She pointed out that my mood was cheerful overall, and that I was grounded, but not euphoric. She agreed that leaving my abusive parents and living with my grandparents had made a significant, positive difference in my life.

She asked about my relationship with women and whether I had any emotional support. I explained that my ex-wife and I were now close friends, but that now I was romantically involved with a woman who had a drinking problem, and I didn't think she would have the wherewithal to be there for me consistently through the upcoming ordeal. Dr. Holland thought I should continue to see Dr. MacCavoy while in the hospital, and said she'd also be available if I needed her.

My next meeting started on an upbeat note. Laura Sudarsky said that I should have lunch with her friend Christopher Horan at Sloan-Kettering. He worked in the Medical Physics Department and was in charge of Radiation Safety. He made sure that the use of radiation didn't get out of control and spill over into other rooms and nuke people. He was a big cheerful Englishman, and his diction was so British and humorously delivered that it sounded slightly incongruous to hear him addressing such a serious subject. His manner was more like what one would expect to see on Monty Python. We gossiped some about our mutual friend, who had been somewhat wild and adventurous in her youth. She'd spent one summer working on a rescue helicopter in the Bahamas, and once jumped thirty feet to get to the victims of a speedboat crash.

After a chuckle, Christopher asked about my family. I told him since my grandparents died; I hadn't had very much contact with my parents or siblings.

"You are going to need a strong support system."

"I have a few close friends. They mean a lot to me, and I know I can depend on them. But, I'm doing okay. I've had tons of psychotherapy and I feel ready."

His mood changed. He picked-up his coffee cup but didn't drink. His voice was suddenly serious.

"Keep these friends close, because there will come a time when you will lose control."

"You will lose control." Those words dominated the rest of the day and that night. From his tone of voice, I knew he meant that I wouldn't lose control of my bladder and bowels. He meant that I would lose control of my ability to reason, to hope, to dream about getting well. I would be in such a state of agony that I wouldn't know what was happening to me and I wouldn't be able to do anything about it. I would have to depend totally on others.

* * * * *

My mood lifted the next morning when Charles Durning called. He was in town, opening on Broadway with Julie Harris in **The Gin Game** and had two tickets for me that Friday night. I would take Basha.

In the early seventies there were three popular bars frequented by actors: Jimmy Reys, where almost everybody was out of work, Joe Allen's, where about one third of the patrons were working on television or off-Broadway and half the staff were working off-off-Broadway. Charley-O's on 46th Street was the watering hole for the Broadway crowd. After my waiter's shift when I felt up and confident, that's where I went. One night Jason Robards and Colleen Dewhurst were at the next table.

That's where I got to know Charles Durning. After several decades of acting and over a hundred plays to his credit, he landed in a Broadway hit, **That Championship Season.** I lived on 50th Street and 1st Avenue and Charlie lived on 50th and 2nd Avenue, so we would often walk across town together. I was intrigued by the wealth of stories he had to tell about his years in the acting profession. He had also just been reunited with the love of his youth, Mary Ann. Their story was in many ways like a fairy tale. When first in love, they were forced apart by cultural tradition; her parents, both from Italy, had arranged a marriage to the boy of their own choice. Now, twenty years later, Charles and Mary Ann had been reunited because her daughter had come into Charlie's dressing room and introduced herself. Charles and Mary Ann had both been married, divorced and were falling in love all over again. For me, in my mid twenties, both his acting and real-life stories were mesmerizing.

One night in the drizzling rain, I made a remark about my struggle to become a working actor, I'm going to give it two more years and if I'm not working on a regular basis by then, I'm going to quit."

I was stunned at Durning's reply.

"Then quit tonight."

"What?"

"If you're only going to give it two more years, then quit tonight. You have to commit for a lifetime to be an actor."

I knew in my gut he was right. That conversation changed my life.

I had seen Charlie and Julie Harris some twenty years before in **The Aupair Man** at Lincoln Center. They were wonderful in that production. As **The Gin Game** began to unfold, a glow seemed to appear around the two actors as they talked and listened to each other. What a joy it was for me to watch the richness and depth of their performance that only comes after a lifetime of work and dedication to one's craft.

Mary Ann had just discovered that she had a serious health problem. After the show Charlie invited Basha and me to his hotel to see her. Charles and Basha discussed World War II; Basha's father had been a prisoner of war in Germany, as had Charlie. Charlie had landed at Normandy on D-Day and fought in the Battle of the Bulge. Mary Ann and I got involved in a discussion of life-threatening illnesses and the trials we each faced, going into private wars of our own.

When we said goodnight, Charles and Mary Ann both leaned out the door and waved goodbye as Basha and I got on the elevator. That picture of the two of them stayed in my mind. We were all smiling, but I thought to myself *"this might be our last visit."*

* * * * *

10

In the studio, my time in the hair and make-up chair was always upbeat. Lillian the hairdresser was great. The wig only took some three minutes to get right. I had less hair on my face and we had to fill in my eyebrows with make-up. But after a couple of weeks that was routine too, and I took more time to lie down in my dressing room on my expensive mattress cover. My energy had diminished each week just as Dr. Chatham said it would.

I had to move and found a short term sublet on West 72nd Street one-half block from Central Park. It was only one room but there was an elevator and it was in the rear of a big building, away from all the street noise so it was very quiet and peaceful.

One night I had watched a program on ethics and morality. The next morning I was up very early and walked to work. A fine mist hung in the spring air and the grass and trees in Central Park looked like a page in a fairytale book. I was in a meditative state; enjoying nature's beauty, pondering morality and ethics as I unconsciously drifted into the street at Columbus Circle. I was jolted out of my reverie by screeching tires and a cab driver cursing me in a foreign language as he sped around me. I jumped backwards and yelled, "Yeah. Screw you too . . ." And within a couple of seconds was back to contemplating the beauty and complexities of the universe. I laughed to myself and thought, ***"That's life in Manhattan."***

* * * * *

ICE chemotherapy takes twenty-four hours to infuse and requires an overnight stay in the hospital.

An Argentine doctor in her sixties, whom I'd never met before, examined the veins in my arms. She asked how I got such superb, big pipes. I told her about some of the physical labor I had done in my teens, and she remarked, "See, it is still paying off; you won't need a catheter to get ICE." That was good news. Even though I'd been told it was a relatively simple procedure, I dreaded having the catheter, or port, put in my chest.

It was May 28, 1997. It had been thirty-three years since I had to spend a night in a hospital. There was a curtain between my bed and the other patient in the room. He was a jet airplane mechanic from New Jersey, and six months earlier, a local oncologist had said there was nothing more they could do for him; that he was going to die. A friend had convinced him to at least just drive into Manhattan and take a look at Sloan-Kettering. At 6:30 that night, after circling the block three times, they parked and walked into the Emergency Room.

"They started working on me right away. Dr. Moskowitz came in and took over, and he worked on me until 1:00 the next morning. That was four months ago, and tomorrow, I'm going home."

I felt less alone as we talked way into the night. Even though nurses and doctors were coming and going all through our conversation, the curtain was never pulled aside. I never shook his hand or saw his face, but I remember his name was Bill.

* * * * *

I had finally gotten a lease on an apartment on 84th and Third. After the ICE infusion I wanted to find out if I had the strength to walk the fifteen blocks home. I did it.

The writers on **As The World Turns** added two extra days' work after the week I was supposed to have finished. I usually took a nap in my dressing room at lunchtime and then slept for about an hour after taping.

Luckily these scenes took place in a jail cell. I would put on my prison jumpsuit as soon as I was through with make-up and into my wig, go to the studio floor and lie down in my cell. Days on the set of a soap are long, hard and tiring under normal circumstances. I was very low on energy and hugging hell to put my scenes on tape. I finished at 7:30 that night.

I said goodbye to the crew and they all wished me luck. I went to my dressing room, changed out of my costume and needed to lie down for a moment. I didn't wake-up until 2:00 the next morning.

* * * * *

I had thought that my second meeting with Dr. Gabrilove was to go over more details about the transplant. Instead she wanted to check me over physically, check my hemoglobin and white blood counts, and see if they were strong enough to do another bone marrow aspiration. Nancy Cody-Lyons was in on this visit and had another long list of questions. Dr. Gabrilove examined me and then stepped out to get the lab results for my counts.

Dr. Levine and his drill immediately sprang to mind; I said to Nancy, "I have some Tylenol with Codeine in my bag; I'm going to take a couple just in case we drill into my bone."

"She's not going to hurt you."

I had grown fond of Nancy and thought I could trust her. She was tough and direct, but I had trouble believing they could remove any bone marrow without causing incredible pain. Even though it lasted only fifteen seconds, nothing I had ever gone through had come close to the shock or amount of agony I had experienced at the hand of Dr. Levine. I didn't know that the human body was capable of feeling, much less enduring that kind of torment.

Dr. Gabrilove returned and announced, "Your counts are fine."

She patted the table as a signal for me to climb up on it and started taking out instruments from the cabinets. I lay face down, unbuckled my belt, and gripped the end of the table with both hands. I could hear the clink of the metal instruments.

"Would you please lower your pants just a little?"

I did and grabbed the top of the table again.

"Mr. Herrera, you can let go of the table, you will feel something cold on your skin. We are going to go slowly and I will need you to tell me if you are feeling pain or pressure."

She wiped the top of my buttock with a swab that numbed my skin. I gradually eased my grip.

"Now I am puncturing the skin and adding some anesthetic. Okay? Now I am moving through the muscle, do you feel pain or pressure?"

"Pressure."

"Okay. Good."

"Now, a little further, getting closer to the bone. Pain or pressure?"

"Pressure."

"Fine, now I am touching the periosteum, which is the layer of connective tissue covering your bone. Pain or pressure?"

"Uh, pressure."

"Mr. Herrera, you may have to be a hero over at CBS but not here. Pain or pressure?"

"Pain."

"All right. We just add a little more anesthetic. Let me know if there is pain."

"I will. Yes that's better."

I could hear the tiny tink tink, as what I assumed was a needle adding anesthetic into the drill, which had penetrated layers of my skin and muscle, was now through the periosteum and into the bone itself.

"Pain or pressure."

"Pressure."

I heard the tiny tink again. Silence, then all I heard was the soft sound of what I realized was the turning of a manual drill. A couple of other little sounds and that was it. There was a bit of an uncomfortable, dull sensation in my bone and muscle, but it was over.

Nancy applied a bandage I remained perfectly still and said, "I don't want to offend either of you ladies but in my opinion, that Dr. Harold Levine is a sadistic son of a bitch."

No one said a word. Dr. Gabrilove sat down to label the vials of fluid and marrow she had aspirated. I took a quick breath to hold back the tears welling-up in my eyes. My emotion was not the result of physical pain, but relief and gratitude for Dr. Gabrilove's kindness.

"Why did that doctor do that to me? Why the hell did he put me through so much agony?"

Dr. Gabrilove looked right at me and simply answered, "Some doctors think that the patient can take it. That's not my philosophy. I'll be right back."

Nancy was writing in my chart.

"You were right Nancy, she didn't hurt me."

Nancy's look went right into my brain. "I'll never lie to you."

I knew what she meant. If I was going to die, and she knew it, and I asked, she would tell me.

When Dr. Gabrilove returned my spirit was stronger, "Doctor, medical science is moving fast, you developed Neupogen, in Scotland they just cloned Dolly, why can't you just give me a couple of pills for this lymphoma and let me go back to work?"

There was a quick smile in her eye as she replied, "Maybe in a couple of years, Mister Herrera. Not quite yet. But keep that positive attitude. We know that a positive attitude helps the immune system."

* * * * *

My next consultation was with the Chief of Radiation Oncology, Dr. Yahalom. It is the practice in teaching hospitals that the patient meet with one of the Fellows or Residents before seeing a senior staff member. Dr. Hoffe was a tall, blond and very well presented young lady who looked like she came from old money.

She looked at my eyes, throat and ears, then listened to my lungs, heart and belly. We went through the litany of questions I had been asked a thousand times since January 10th: birth date, profession, prior medical history, etc. I told her that I drank heavily in my late thirties and early forties, and that it could be said that I had abused alcohol. With charm and perfect manners she looked at me and asked, "And how long have you been in recovery?"

"'Recovery? I don't believe in recovery any more than I believe in 'closure.' I loathe euphemistic clichés. In my late forties I decided that I was going to control my drinking rather than have my drinking control me, and if I live through all of this, the first thing I'm going to do is open a bottle of Champagne."

"Oh" she said. After our interview, every time I passed her in halls of the hospital, she always greeted me with a smile and a warm, "Hello, Mr. Herrera, nice to see you."

Dr. Yahalom came in with my chart. He was in his mid-forties and had a take-charge personality. As he examined me, "You look younger than fifty-three."

"I look like crap now compared to before the chemo. I played a lot of squash before I was hit with cancer."

"You still don't look fifty-three years old."

Then we went over the list, the same list they all went over. When we got to alcohol, I started to explain again, "In my late . . ."

He glanced at my chart and cut me off. "Your liver's fine."

He went right on down the list and then explained in general terms why they were choosing to use radiation and what a "local boost" meant in oncological radiation. A local boost was required because MCL is a particularly insidious lymphoma; it is especially hard to kill because it hides in the body. It is a mean and sneaky lymphoma.

They would radiate the tonsil area of my neck first, because that is where the disease originated. I interjected with my analogy of the "rats in the barn" Dr. Gabrilove had liked, and Dr. Yahalom proceeded to give me his more succinct version.

"I was an Israeli Army Officer. Terrorists occupy the village. We are going to attack with machine-gun fire, but first we are going to hit their headquarters with a few rocket grenades."

Then he went over potential acute and chronic side effects of the treatment: in terms of the neck and left tonsil region, I could develop dental problems and xerostomia. Risks associated with Total Body Irradiation included fatigue, change in taste sensation, cataract formation, pharyngitis, esophagitis, pneumonitis, sterility, hypothyroidism, and induction of a secondary malignancy. He spent a good deal of time going over all of this, then he gave me a booklet on the TBI process.

When we finished, Dr. Yahalom told me I would have to get tattoos for the local boost of radiation. The path of the radiation beam had to be exact.

That night I realized he had made no moral judgments or even cared if I drank too much during a certain period of my life. "Your liver is fine." Likewise, Nancy Cody-Lyons didn't blink when she asked if I'd had an AIDS test. These doctors and nurses were fighting cancer with science not with society's values. If I had been a heavy smoker and had damaged my lungs I would not have been able to tolerate chemotherapy and they couldn't proceed with the transplant. Without the stem cell transplant, their best effort would have been to prolong my life for a few months with chemotherapy.

Dr. Yahalom had looked at me like a side of beef as he determined how to cook me with radiation in order to kill the Lymphoma, without killing the rest of me in the process.

* * * * *

I was not comfortable with the fact that I would have tattoos, tiny spots, put on my face and neck. I met a tall, black man with a great smile and a very deep voice. He made James Earl Jones sound like a tenor. He explained that the tattoos would be invisible to the naked eye.

"How can the technician who is going to zap me with radiation see them?"

"Laser."

Even though he spoke softly, "laser" seemed to resound throughout the room. Laser -- there was another word that sounded futuristic, like **Star Wars** and nuclear medicine. This was the cold reality of cancer; lasers and radiation aimed at my own jaw and neck.

"Will the radiation beams hit my vocal cords?"

"I don't think so."

"Can you find out for me?"

"Yes."

This man's voice was like listening to music. I ask him what was the most difficult part of his job.

"Little children, they are usually very frightened."

"I guess they are.   I'm not little, and I'm very frightened."

"Sometimes it is hard to get them to stay still."

"How do you manage?"

"I tell them stories."

"You have the voice for it."

He smiled. "Thank you."

"My voice is important for my work."

"I know, 'Mr. James Stenbeck', I watched you on the show in the eighties. Don't worry, no one will bother you, we've had lots of celebrities here."

"I read that Bishop Tutu was suffering from cancer and was in New York. He was treated here, wasn't he?"

"Yes."

"I lived in South Africa. He is a great man."

"So you see Mr. Herrera, you are in good hands, I tattooed Tutu too."

* * * * *

How could a kid deal with cancer?   I thought back to that first weekend, the snowstorm, the painkillers and the champagne. I had lived fifty-three years, but the idea of this ordeal for a little kid to face left me shattered.

I imagined a frightened child, getting poked with a needle, not really understanding, and having to get radiation shot through their body because of something called cancer. A friend's daughter, whom I'd known since she was seven, was on the 11th floor of this hospital with terminal brain cancer. Peter Hammer was my friend. Cleavon was like a brother. Cancer took them away from me.   These two men were emotional guideposts and stabilizing forces in my life. And two years ago Evans Harrington, my major professor at Ole Miss was diagnosed with cancer. Now this damn disease might kill me in the next couple of months.

I was slipping out of the saddle.

Stella Adler had said many times to her students, "Darlings, don't ever forget, it is the duty of drama to uplift the human spirit."

Back at my sublet I put on a video of my favorite film, John Ford's **The Searchers.** John Wayne portrays the protagonist, Ethan Edwards. In one of the first scenes, Ward Bond, who plays the Captain of the Rangers, says to Ethan:

"I haven't seen you since the surrender. Come to think of it I didn't see you at the surrender."

As Ethan straps on his revolver he retorts, *"I don't believe in surrenders."*

As the story unfolds Comanche warriors slaughter his brother's family and capture his niece. There are moments in the film between Ethan and his brother's wife that strongly suggest that the little girl is his daughter. He spends the next seven years searching for her. Ethan is an angry man. Despite all odds and difficulties he doesn't give up. The French filmmaker Godard remarked about the ending, "Every time I see John Wayne pick up Natalie Wood, I weep." Martin Scorcese simply says it is my favorite film. Spielberg watches it before every project. When asked why, "**The Searchers** inspires me."

After fighting the evil of the world and the evil within him, Ethan's humanity prevails. I watched all one hundred and nineteen minutes of the film and at the end I felt stronger.

11

The next day, I had to be zapped with the first local boost of radiation. The waiting took a lot longer than the procedure. I got on the table and shut my eyes. I didn't want to witness what they had to do to me. Then I heard, "Mr. Herrera, this is Dr. Yahalom, the radiation will not hit your vocal cords."

There were nine more days of local radiation. I also had to prepare for the "harvest" of my stem cells, by regular injections of Neupogen.

The collection of my stem cells was much more civilized than the horrific scenes in the PBS documentary on The History of the Transplant.

During the five-day regimen of Neupogen, I could not waver from the prescribed amount even if there was the radiating bone pain. If that occurred, I could take Tylenol with Codeine. The objective here was for my bone marrow to over-produce. Then they would centrifuge my blood through a machine and harvest the baby stem cells for an autologous transplant. If they didn't get enough cells the first time, we would wait forty-eight hours and try to collect more. This would give the bones two days to produce more young stem cells. The timing was very important.

Nancy Cody-Lyons scheduled me for June 20th and June 22nd. As she hung up the phone with the doctor in charge of the procedure she muttered, "jerk" under her breath. She wasn't aware that I'd heard her.

After the second shot of Neupogen I had to take Tylenol with Codeine for the pain.

On the 20th, I was due in the blood department at 8 a.m. for the six-hour procedure. They made me comfortable in a bed raised almost to a sitting position. A slender, frazzled doctor came over with a stack of patient records. He didn't look at me.

"Herrera, Mantle Cell Lymphoma, Dr. Moskowitz patient?"

"No."

"You're not Herrera, patient number 388308?"

"Yes. I am."

"You're not Dr. Moskowitz' patient."

"No."

"Who's your transplant doctor?"

"Dr. Gabrilove."

"Really?"

He looked through his stack of orders again, "Oh. Oh. Yes. Dr. Gabrilove. It's right here. It doesn't make any difference."

"It will make a difference if someone labels my cells with Mr. Brown's name rather than Mr. Herrera. I want to watch my cells from the time they are taken out of this contraption, put in one of those little baggies, to when they're labeled with Anthony Herrera date of birth 1/19/44 patient number 388308." Nancy was right. This doctor is a jerk.

The night before I had been on the phone with Patsy. As a joke I said, "Hope they don't lose them." She didn't get it and replied, "You'd just have to do it again."

"No. They burn my immune system down to zero. If they lose my cells, that's it. I'm gone."

The doctor came over a few minutes later. "I was a bit rushed. I spoke to the nurse."

"I appreciate you telling me."

Again my big veins were an advantage. Because of the nature of the procedure, the gauge of the needles was larger than normal. I watched as my blood flowed out of my left arm into a clear tube, through the centrifugal device, and into another clear tube, before circulating back into my right arm. The engine gently hummed away and I asked my nurse, "How much does this machine cost?"

"About thirty-five thousand dollars."

"What? That's it. Where is it made."

"Chicago or Detroit, I'm not sure. Why, something wrong?"

"Yes. I don't want a Briggs-Stratton lawn mower motor gathering my stem cells. I want a machine made in Switzerland or Germany that costs at least a quarter of a million dollars."

She gave me a blank look and then giggled. "If this one messes up we'll order you one from Europe."

"Thank you."

"You're more than welcome. I know you're particular, so I'll label your bag of cells right here in front of you."

I liked this nurse.

* * * * *

The next week I had my second round of ICE. After I'd checked-in and was all hooked-up for the twenty-four hour chemo infusion, Dr. Moskowitz came in to see me. Mantle Cell Lymphoma was rare and he followed my case with particular interest.

This time the fatigue got to me; I slept most of the night and the following day. When we finished, I didn't even consider walking home. Fortunately I found a taxi right outside the hospital. This course of the ICE chemo made me feel like I had a mild case of the flu. I just wanted to sleep. I let the answering machine pick up my messages and I listened to them when I had the energy. One was from United States Senator Thad Cockran, "Hello Anthony, this is Thad calling from Washington. I've heard you were having some serious health problems and I wanted to wish you the best."

Thad was the dorm manager my freshman year at Ole Miss and lived across the hall. We had been in touch occasionally over the years and he was actively supportive of my PBS production of **The Wide Net**. I listened to his voice every day until I went into the hospital. It made me feel that I was still part of my home state. I looked up to Thad as a freshman in 1961 and ever since have admired him as a gentleman and as a United States Senator.

The lab report came back from Dr. Gabrilove's aspiration. No lymphoma found in my bone. We would proceed with the transplant.

I hadn't heard from Lucas in Wiggins so I called him.

"I go into the hospital in a couple of days. Are you coming up?"

"Anthony, you see, I've never been on one of those big planes. Kinda scares me."

I was stunned and didn't hear much of what he said after that. He went on to make more excuses and ended with, "Let me know when you feel better."

Basha and I once spent the 4th of July with Lucas and his family. A few years later I went to Wiggins and spent Christmas with them. I felt very close to his wife and daughter. I was hurt but couldn't emotionally afford to dwell on it. I even had a bit of a sad silent chuckle at the irony. Lucas is a hunter. A fellow who takes great pride in killing a deer with a 30.06 rifle but he is afraid to get on an airplane.

* * * * *

Two days before I was to check into Sloan-Kettering I received a call from a lady in admissions. She had a long list of questions. We went through the usual; address, date of birth, insurance information. She sounded young and was polite. However, when it came to my family she seemed to want to force the issue that they should be notified in case of an emergency. She couldn't understand why someone with five siblings and with living parents wouldn't want them contacted in case of an emergency -- a nice way of saying -- *if you die.* I finally had to say, "Miss, this is the way I want it. Please contact Barbara Plewinska if there is an urgent situation." I gave her Basha's number and address.

Later that night I tossed in the darkness and thought of the young lady in admission -- when she went over the spelling of my last name and religion, she assumed I was Catholic. I said no. Protestant? No. Jewish? No. Then I ask her if she had seen the film **Breaker Morant**. She hadn't. Then I went off on a monologue about during the Boar War in South Africa that Morant was about to be unjustly executed by the British and asked if he wanted a verse read from the Bible and he responded that he was a pagan. His fellow soldier who was also being unjustly executed asked, "What's a pagan?" Morant answered "Someone that doesn't believe that God's in his heaven dispensing justice throughout mankind." At that point the young lady interrupted, "Mr. Herrera can I put down other?" I laughed quietly, "Yes, of course. Sorry to ramble on."

Most of my answers must have sounded odd. I had lived so long away from my brothers and sisters and my parents that it seemed normal. But it is not normal at all.

In the morning doctors will put a tube in my chest to infuse more chemo into me and they will start spraying my body twice a day with nuclear particles.

I go into the unknown tomorrow and if I am able to deal with each event with dignity so that I approve of my behavior, then I believe that I have a better chance of staying alive. If this treatment kills me? Well . . . Peter Pan said, ***"To die must be an awfully big adventure."***

12

I used the main entrance on York Avenue, went through the Admitting Office quickly, and expected I'd have at least a day to relax before any serious procedures began. I mentally reviewed what we learned at the seminar in March about the six-to eight-week stay. I unpacked my laptop, books, a picture of my first wife, Lane, my second, Basha, and one of John Wayne. I also set up a CD and tape player, and put two VHS copies of my documentary film **Mississippi Delta Blues** on a shelf by my bed.

I could see the ivy-covered walls of Rockefeller University, the Fifty-ninth Street Bridge and a few tugboats making their way down the East River. So far so good.

A nurse appeared with pills in a little plastic cup, and presented me with a printed schedule outlining the rest of my day. I was due for TBI (total body irradiation) on the fifth floor in thirty minutes, and then the seventh floor where they would place a catheter or a "port" in my chest to infuse me with hydration, chemo and other drugs. The next stop was the eighth floor for a chest X-ray to make sure the port had been put in the vein and didn't puncture the lung, and that the line was in my vena cava. I was to go back to my room for lunch and then return to the fifth floor for a second session of TBI.

I took a tape of **The Best of Bob Wills** and went to the Nuclear Treatment Center on the fifth floor. They showed me into a rather large room with a desk and phone. One wall held numerous rows of slots, each containing a lead shield. There was my name: Herrera # 388308 - d.o.b. - 1/19/44.

They placed the lead shields on a thick sheet of plastic and then the technician introduced me to a strange contraption mounted on a small platform with locking wheels so it could either be rolled around or stationary. The platform was about three feet long and a foot and a half wide. It had a bicycle seat, two sturdy metal bars some six and a half feet tall on each end, and two bars running across the top. The bars featured protruding bolts, to which thick, clear plastic sheets were attached by big wing nuts at the front and rear. There were two thick leather cuffs, linked to the top bars by stainless steel chains, which hung down on each side.

There was a heavy, white, long-sleeved canvas jacket with brass buckles on the back hanging in the middle of this rather odd-looking apparatus.

They explained that my body position was very important; and movement had to be kept at an absolute minimum. They would secure me in the jacket, and my arms would be held by the cuffs, so if I fainted, as some patients did, I would not fall and hurt myself.

An inch-thick, full-length plastic plate on adjustable pipes supported the lead shields to protect my lungs from the radiation.

This equipment looked more like it was designed for the clientele of a sophisticated S&M establishment, rather than patients in a hospital.

I never took my watch off. I had bought an Ebel watch in London in the mid-eighties, before they were marketed in the US, and it was the only decent watch I had ever owned. I worked with it on. I slept with it on. I played squash and showered with it on. I never took it off. They insisted. They said it had to come off for the total body irradiation. I objected. They insisted. I took off my damn watch. I was allowed to keep my pajama bottoms and a t-shirt, and that was it.

Stella Adler said many times. "When you are in new or unusual circumstance; watch, observe details and remember how you reacted physically. The emotions are stored in your muscles and sinews. So I thought take mental pictures, listen for different sounds. That'll be better than worrying about the atomic particles flying through me.

I never fooled myself. This wasn't a movie or a play. It was real enough. I tried to deal with each new development, whether it was a peculiar piece of machinery, or an inexplicable procedure, or even pain itself, as a challenge in this adventure. Mother Nature had cast me in this role, without my consent.

This approach seemed strange to some. When I told my friend Doris Ann Benoist from Natchez, Mississippi she was shocked at my analogy, and exclaimed with her fervent aristocratic southern accent, *"adventure, adventure?* How can you possibly use that word? Anthony, my dear, this is a tragedy."

"It may very well end in tragedy. In a real life adventure we cannot predict how it's going to end."

"Well, this just seems all so *awful* to me . . . I just don't understand how you can say an *adventure,* but I'm going to pray for you every day anyway."

* * * * *

I had to straddle, rather than sit on the bicycle seat. They bound me up in the canvas jacket and cuffs and explained again that the seat and the jacket and cuffs were to protect me from injury if I fainted. I didn't ask what percentage of patients faint. I understood and accepted the straightjacket and the bondage cuffs.

The technician was a big fellow from Brooklyn. He and a nurse double-checked that all my buckles were fastened, and my lungs were protected. At the seminar we were told we could bring our own music for the nuclear sessions. I asked them to put on the tape I brought and they were most pleasant about it. The music started and when they heard Bob Wills' **"Take Me Back to Tulsa"** they stopped and looked at me as if I had just come down from the moon. I couldn't let this go by, so I began to explain that this was western music, western swing, and that Hank Williams was country music while Bill Monroe was really mountain music.

They indulged me but did not seem interested. They finalized the preparations and then explained that the procedure would take twenty-four minutes, with four-minute blasts at the beginning and the end, and some longer, six-minute blasts in the middle. They would be in a booth and able to see me, but I would not be able to see them. They pointed out a microphone and speaker on the wall; I could communicate to tell them if I felt dizzy or faint, or if I felt I was going to throw up.

I would face the machine that would blast-out the radiation this morning, and then in the afternoon I would be bolted back in, but turned around and blasted from the back. I skipped any attempt at humor at this point.

The door they hurried out of was a good eight inches thick. I then heard the heavy clang on the outside as they locked me in the Nuclear Medicine Radiation Room.

A voice came through the speaker.

"Okay. We're just about ready. Are you doing all right?"

"Just fine."

I thought to myself, *"Is this guy kidding! Am I doing all right? I've got a deadly cancer in my body, I've been pumped full of enough chemicals to drown a goat, I'm bound up like Houdini in a contraption that I couldn't escape from if I tried, I'm looking at a machine that will in seconds start to spray nuclear particles through my body, I could die from the amount of chemicals and radiation I'll get during the next three weeks, and now this clown wants to know, Am I doing all right?"*

He does this all day long, five days a week. He was not the reason I was in that room. I was the 10 a.m. patient #388308. I should try to cooperate. And I did.

"Here we go."

The machine made a low dim whirring sound and it went just like they said; still for four minutes, then a little rest, then again and again . . . the six minutes sections and so on, for twenty-four minutes. My legs got a little tired, but other than that it was not too bad for being nuked for the first time. When I could shift my attention to the tape player though, Bob Wills never sounded better.

"Take me back to Tulsa,
I'm too young to marry."

* * * * *

My next appointment was to get a port put in my chest, so they could pump-in more chemo and pump it in faster. The port would also be used later to re-infuse my stem cells.

I met a handsome, young doctor who Dr. Gabrilove had told me was Sloan-Kettering's best at this procedure: inserting a "triple lumen catheter". He said it would take four or five minutes. There were two nurses, and one asked me if I wanted a general or local anesthetic. I said "Since I've never been put under and all you're going do is put in a little tube, a local."

They rubbed my skin with something cold and injected a local painkiller.

The doctor assured me, "This will numb the area where I'll be working."

The first probe was a bit uncomfortable. Then the second probe under my collarbone. Then the third and fourth. He was sticking a 21-gauge needle in my chest, trying to locate the vena cava. He was not succeeding. I could sense and hear his frustration. I said, "If I'm ever in a scene where I'm shot by an arrow -- now -- I'll know how to play it." The pain intensified with each attempt until I muttered, **"Son of a bitch."** One of the nurses gave me her hand and said, "Squeeze". I squeezed. She yelled. "Arrrrgggghhhh . . . I forgot to take off my rings."

I had nearly broken her fingers. We all agreed I should get some morphine. They started the morphine drip. A very big camera was positioned over my chest and partially covered my face. Normally something this close makes me very nervous but I was in too much pain to care. The procedure took forty minutes and if the morphine kicked in, I never felt it.

* * * * *

Joel Aronowitz and I had worked together for years at CBS. He was an assistant director and editor. Joel often brought the right dose of humor to the set when things started to deteriorate after working a string of twelve-hour days. His wife, Linda had cancer and was on the eighth floor. Joel came up to my room while I was eating lunch. He was going out to get Chinese food for Linda. I looked at the chicken breast, potatoes and broccoli I had started, and decided to stick with what they had brought me. Joel thought the arrow in the chest line was funny. He made a joke about being a good

Jewish husband and helped take my mind off the pain in my chest.

At 5:30 I had my second blast of TBI for the day. The morphine was starting to feel like a hangover from drinking too much mead. I'd never even had a sip of mead but that's how awful I felt, like there was something sweet, thick and heavy creeping slowly through my system.

I had to take off my watch again. The ritual of getting into the contraption for the machine to spray me was the same, but I forgot to bring my music. The same fellow from the morning was in charge but there was a different nurse, younger, pretty with dark hair tied-back in a ponytail. They strapped me in, facing the back wall so the machine could blast me from the rear. They hurried out and closed the big door.

Before the machine began to whirl, I felt warm, then nauseous. I was bolted in, between two pieces of plastic in a straight jacket with my wrists in leather cuffs. The nausea got worse. I called to the speaker above my head.

"I don't feel too good. I think I'm going to be sick."
Nothing. Then a bit louder,
"I think I'm going to throw up."
"What?"
"I'm going to vomit. Somebody get in here."
"You don't feel well?"
"No. I don't feel well."
"Do you think you're going to be sick?"
"Yes! I'm going to vomit. I can't see the bucket. Please get in here! Get in here!"
"Okay. Okay. Wait a minute!"

The young nurse pushed the big door open. Just as she came into the room, somewhere behind me a phone began to ring.

"The bucket is right there."
The phone kept ringing.
I yelled, "Get me the bucket. It's right there! Get me the bucket!"

The phone kept ringing . . . for some inexplicable reason this nurse crossed behind me, went to the far end of the room and answered the phone. I belched once, and then I belched again and up it came. I vomited all over the plastic shield in front of me. I vomited all over the floor. I vomited all over myself.

The technician and the other nurse came in and immediately started unscrewing the big wing nuts holding the plastic shield in place. The younger nurse crossed over to us and just stood there.

It was a mess. It took a few minutes to get the shields off, the cuffs off and the canvas jacket, which was also covered with vomit.

The young nurse shook her head in disbelief. As I got down off of the little platform, I remarked.

"I guess I shouldn't have had lunch."

The young nurse, "Well, what did you eat?"

I gestured to the quart or so of liquid and lumps all over the contraption and the floor, and answered.

"Take a look!"

They cleaned the floor, the equipment, and me and then helped me into a fresh straight jacket, bolted me back into the contraption and proceeded to spray radiation through me.

There were three more days of TBI that week. They went by without incident. I never vomited or saw the pretty young nurse again.

* * * * *

The surgeon who installed the triple lumen catheter in my chest came by the next day and explained the complications necessitating multiple attempts at the procedure; my clavicle, or collarbone, was considerably larger than most. He assured me that he had eventually been successful, as the x-ray showed the tip of the lumen was resting nicely in the vena cava and had not punctured my lung.

With a triple lumen catheter port in your chest, they can hook-up multiple IV lines attached to the bags of chemo and other fluids they need to infuse into your body. Mid-pole is a stainless steel rack holding a pump, which regulates the infusion of various fluids at designated rates. My pole held two bags of chemo, one of hydration fluid and a smaller bag of some kind of antibody. The pump was blue and needed adjusting each time one bag would empty and they added a replacement.

During my first two days on the eleventh floor, everything was strange and new: the trays of food, this view of the river, the nurses and the 7 a.m. "vital signs" drill to record my temperature in centigrade, weight in kilos and blood pressure. Then breakfast. I lost all taste for food, but for some reason I did like Diet Coke, Gator Aid and Carnation Instant Breakfast. My intake of the Instant Breakfast seemed to keep them happy, as did the Gator Aid because of the electrolytes.

On the third day the novelty of being an inpatient evaporated, and it seemed as if I had lived in Room 1116 for weeks. The total body irradiation was sapping my strength. I had no interest in going on-line or even turning on my computer, but music provided some escape. I listened to Willie Nelson and Louis Armstrong. I had known Willie and Family since 1987 and had heard his repertoire many times back stage.

When I toured theatre I always had selected pre-show music before each performance. One of my favorites by Mr. Louis Armstrong was the last song and as the lights went down I always made my entrance during the second verse of:

"Give me a kiss to build a dream on and
My imagination will thrive upon that kiss."

* * * * *

The mucus in my mouth and throat was changing, becoming thick, so I had to use a flexible straw to drink. I tried to sleep when there was not somebody taking my temperature or checking my blood pressure or adding another bag to my poles. There were now two poles, and four blue pumps, and ten or twelve hanging bags of fluids, depending on the hour of the day. The nurses would always tell me what they were adding but I couldn't, or didn't care to try to keep track of the drug and chemo regimen.

At one point that afternoon, after dozing a few minutes, I looked up and Dr. Chatham was standing at the foot of my bed.

"Doctor, if I make it through this, I want to go to South Africa for Christmas. Do you think that will be possible?"

"I wouldn't think so. Let's concentrate on what you have to deal with now. How are you holding up?"

"It's getting interesting on an emotional level. One's thinking about their life gets a bit serious when mother nature has a 12 gauge double-barrel shot gun, loaded with buck shot, with both hammers cocked back and a very nervous finger on the trigger, pointed right at my forehead. I don't spend much time worrying about what the casting director thought of my last audition."

Dr. Chatham gave me a grin and spelled it out.

"The next six weeks are going to be very intense for you. It's going to be rough. Picture the worst flu you've ever had in your life and multiply by one hundred. That's where you're going. This is going to be rough, very rough."

I was silent for a moment.

"Yes. But one advantage, is that, unlike most people at my age, I'm being given the opportunity to stop and really consider my life, where I am, where I came from, and where I'm going. It's like a mandatory exercise in being honest with yourself and the core of your life."

* * * * *

13

By day five the TBI and the local boost of irradiation had taken its toll. My left jaw was swollen from the soft tissue burns inside of my cheek. I looked like I had a golf ball between my teeth and my cheek. The radiation had obliterated some mucus glands. I had to moisten my mouth and throat by sucking cup after cup of water through a straw. Then a few days later my mucus got so thick that they hooked me up to a suction machine to prevent me from strangling.

Somewhere toward the end of the first week I began slipping into more of a daze. Throughout the day different teams of doctors and nurses would float in and out of my room. Dr. Kapusinski was the resident Fellow on day rounds for the month of July. He had red hair and was always congenial. When I saw his name I remarked that I had been to Poland three times, once in the mid-eighties, before anyone imagined the iron curtain would fall, and twice since the wall came down.

He smiled, "Really, well I'm a Mexican."

"You're kidding."

"No. My grandfather left Poland for his own safety in the thirties. He tried to come to the States but Immigration turned him away so he ended up in Mexico. He was a painter. He fell in love with that country and made a life there. So after med school I came to New York, and I still haven't seen Poland."

"Will you go back to Mexico to practice when you have finished your residency?"

"I will go wherever I get the best offer for my research. Hematology is my thing. I love being in the lab. All of us have to make rounds."

He stayed a half hour. We talked about music, Mexico and cancer. I thanked him for his time as he left. He simply said, "Talk is important."

The "pain team" came in, introduced themselves and explained they would attend to my "Palliative Care." They checked the contents of one particular bag of drugs. I asked, "What is Palliative Care?"

"Pain and symptom management, which in your case will require varied levels of medication including opiates."

Their presence momentarily relieved my misery. They were all doctors and all three of them were tall, beautiful women with long, light, flowing hair, or maybe that's the way they appeared after my first squirt of opium. The painkiller IV line was equipped with a plunger enabling me to self-administer the opiates as needed.

The discomfort became more intense. I developed mucositis, an inflammation of the mucus glands. My tongue was swollen from the radiation. They were always asking, "On a scale of 1-10, how much pain are you in?" I never knew how to respond. So after a few days I asked, "Is thrashing about and screaming a "10"? For communication's sake we agreed that a thrashing and screaming scenario would be a "10." I calculated that my mouth and throat were at "7" and the rest of me at about "5"; she quickly wrote that down. I guess they have to keep asking until they have a number to put write in my chart.

They emphasized. "Mr. Herrera, rather than suffer unnecessarily, use the rescues. That's what the medication is there for, and it is always available."

It became difficult to sit up. The nurses wanted me out of bed twice a day, even if it was just to sit in a chair. Sleep was never possible for long because the staff was constantly checking my vital signs, feeding me pills, removing empty bags, adding full ones and constantly adjusting the pumps.

A collection of plastic jars made urination relatively simple, but getting to the bathroom to defecate was a major undertaking with its own methodical routine: make sure the suction pipe from my mouth was stowed safely on the table and didn't fall on the floor, unplug the electrical cords from both pumps and make sure the cords and plugs were wrapped around the poles' top sprockets so they wouldn't get tangled in their little wheels. Then, grab both poles, with all the bags wagging back and forth, and roll them six feet to the door and over the threshold bump. If I wanted the door closed for privacy, it took more effort to position all of my equipment inside the bathroom and close the door. The most important step was washing my hands, as by now I had little or no immune system.

It had been only five months since I had noticed that lump. I took a long look at myself in the mirror. What I saw bore little resemblance to my last series of 8 X 10 glossies. My skin was an ugly, dull, matte gray. I had no hair on my scalp, face or anywhere else on my body. My face was twisted from the golf ball-sized swelling in my jaw, and my eyes seemed to have sunken back several inches into my emaciated skull. I looked like a corpse. I thought perhaps that all this physical anguish was actually purgatory or hell. I didn't study the ghoulish figure in the mirror again.

* * * * *

Dr. Bobbie MacGuffie came to visit. She brought me a book with lots of pictures of Africa. Every few months Bobbie goes to Africa with "Americares." She has built and maintains several hospitals in Kenya. She flew to Rwanda during the Tutsi and Hutu war and told me how they'd cleaned out a building filled with abandoned infants. She and the other doctors put the dead babies in a trench. They put the live babies outside on the ground, scrubbed down the floor of the one room "hospital" and then set-up makeshift beds for the babies with blankets on the floor. She wore a silver-dipped, fifty-caliber machine gun bullet around her neck, which she'd removed from a little girl's thigh after it had killed the girl's mother. She also specialized in burns and reconstructive surgery at Nyack Hospital in New York. She was that kind of doctor. It meant a great deal to me that she had found time to come into the city to see me.

She knew a lot about pain.

"The body doesn't remember physical pain. If it did a woman would never have more than one baby."

"Bobbie I'm dealing with it better than I would have imagined. But what you just said will help. When extraordinary pain hits, I'll just think that it will end, hopefully, and then that moment will be gone. Bobbie, life seems different. I see life so differently."

"No, Anthony, you just see more."

After she left I realized that I was seeing more. The core of my life had been about work. Work and the adventure of leaving a town of fifteen hundred, going to Ole Miss, New Orleans, Hollywood and New York.

Work, as top priority, had not always resulted in a positive way to live. When Basha and I married, I didn't know how to bond with her but I knew how to work. There were problems in getting the final funding for **The Wide Net** and I put all my energy into getting that film done and I did. I would wake up in the middle of the night in a panic about the project. Now I know that I should have been waking up in the middle of the night to embrace my bride.

* * * * *

Carnation Instant Breakfast in the mornings and a Diet Coke in the afternoons became the only sensations that offered physical relief from the persistent, feverish anguish pervading every cell in my body.

The pain team would always come in when I was dozing and seemed to emerge out of some thick mist.

"Why aren't you taking more 'rescues'? You can, you know. Are you afraid you'll become addicted?"

"As much as I hurt, I don't give a damn if I become addicted or not. It just doesn't seem to help."

"Remember the pump will only allow you a certain amount of Dilauded. Only one dose every fifteen minutes, so don't worry about taking too much."

"Okay, but I feel awful whether I'm loaded on painkillers, or not. I just don't want to go too far."

She gave me a curious look but didn't respond. I think she wrote down my last remark.

Dr. Gabrilove came in at least three times a week. She kept a close watch and *always* made me feel better emotionally. She assured me things were going according to plan. The physical misery was a given.

My favorite music helped a lot. I listened to Willie Nelson's "The Red Headed Stranger" and Louis Armstrong's Greatest Hits over and over. These two artists had their work cut out for them in Room 1116 at Memorial Sloan-Kettering, and they did a great job.

14

Once a week, they administered "Ampho" to protect my lungs against infection. They covered my face with a mask and I inhaled the vapor, which coated my lungs with the drug. After my first blast of Ampho, I realized why Bill and Janet had exchanged such a knowing glance when they mentioned **"Shake and Bake."** I suddenly got very cold and starting shaking. They gave me Demerol. My entire body was trembling, yet my fever shot up at the same time. They brought in a blanket. The rigors continued. Another blanket. Then the jarring motions of my body would shake the blankets onto the floor. It did feel as if the muscles and ligaments were going to be ripped off my bones. They brought in more blankets. I think there were at least seven piled on top of me, before the weight of the blankets kept them from falling off the bed. The first **"Shake and Bake"** lasted twenty-five minutes.

The contrast between my days and nights diminished. There was the morning routine of having to get out of bed, having to stand-up and get on the scales. I no longer thought it was odd to have three tubes dangling out of my chest, or the crooked suction tube hanging out of my mouth. If it slipped out when I was asleep, I would gag and feel around until I found it, without really waking up.

Around ten most mornings the Resident and several other doctors would come in, ask a few questions and discuss among themselves how I was doing as far as blood levels and other things I didn't have the energy to inquire about. I gauged my condition from their initial reaction, and if they didn't run out of the room yelling "code blue" I guessed that I would make it through the rest of the day. As soon as they left, I just wanted to drift back into the semi-conscious state that would help the time to pass until August 1st when I was scheduled to have my stem cells re-infused.

In the early evening I would wake up, check the clock and then drift off again until 10:30 when Seinfeld came on. I was either bored or insulted by most programs, but Seinfeld's cast and writers were clever and consistently funny. For that half-hour each night, I was marginally less aware of the agony.

I perceived time differently; it no longer seemed important to carve it into hours or days or weeks; the room had become my universe. When I would go for an x-ray they would take me in a wheelchair, not for the more common reason of insurance liability, but because I couldn't walk more than a couple of steps.

It was all more and more like a bad dream, lost in the bog of a swamp, light and shadows and darkness mixed, falling and being pulled under by quicksand and seconds before suffocation, being belched back up into the mud. The horror seemed so real, but somewhere in my subconscious I was hoping it was a dream and I could look forward to being relieved when I woke up. In more lucid moments I knew this was not a dream and the only escape from this nightmare would be to die.

* * * * *

I had a dream that tapped into some of my experiences in Hollywood. I had worked with some of the best stunt people in the business like Buddy Van Horn, Kitty O'Neal and Ron Rondell.

I learned firsthand how they make cars flip-over in the movies: they fit the car with a crude cannon on the back floorboard and load it with dynamite and a piece of a telephone pole as the projectile. When the stunt man swerves hard in one direction, the cannon is fired simultaneously, and as the car tilts, the blast propels it into a full flip. The number of times a car rolls-over is controlled by the quantity of dynamite in the cannon.

That month in Room 1116, I had two very powerful dreams. The first one started on a movie set in a stunt car with two bucket seats in the front and a cannon fixed to the floorboard in the back. Dr. Gabrilove was driving in a dramatic action scene, with a shoot-out between a gang of terrorists and the good guys. Then things changed; the flames we were driving through and the explosions in the street were not controlled, but real. The terrorist's guns were not firing blanks, but real bullets and some were hitting our car. We were in real danger of getting killed. The commander of the terrorists jumped in the back of our sedan as Dr. Gabrilove raced through the battleground. He had a automatic pistol. He was going to kill us. He and I fought. I twisted the pistol from his hands, hit him several times in the head with it, and tied him to the cannon in the back. Then I climbed into the front seat next to Dr. Gabrilove as she continued to guide the car through the flames, explosions and the enemy's line of fire.

It was one of those dreams that are very real. The details were crisp, the objects had real textures and I could smell the smoke and burning rubber.

When I came to the reality of my bed. I thought that some where in my subconscious I had a lot of trust in Dr. Gabrilove. She was at the wheel and I was fighting. Working together we had gotten away from the bad guys.

* * * * *

Fever was a constant. It ranged from 101 to 103 degrees. I had burns from the radiation boost covering the inside of my left cheek, so I sprayed and rinsed my mouth with antiseptic solution as often as possible. I had diarrhea and developed an infection at the tip of my "port." With my immune system at zero, they had to pour drugs into me to prevent the slightest infection from spreading.

Dr. Frank was the new Fellow on rounds. His ties were always kept very neat with tab collar shirts. He was very intense and would stand silently by my bed. I could see him suffering from a sense of helplessness, at not being able to ease my suffering. I wanted to tell him it was all right, not to worry. But it was not all right. His empathy made me know that he cared about my condition and that helped.

One day he walked around my room and looked at the pictures on the wall and studied the poster of **Mississippi Delta Blues**.

"How can I find a copy of this film?"

"There's one right here."

I pointed to the shelf under the table by my bed.

"You're welcome to take it and view it at your leisure."

"I'm interested." He smiled. "I play clarinet in a jazz band with a bunch of doctors."

The pain team came back. They seemed to get more beautiful. In my state, just their smiles made me think I was drifting off the planet. Again we discussed the "Rescues"; I had only taken six rescues in the previous twenty-four hours. They thought six was a moderate amount.

That night from out of a deep sleep, a hammer-like thud hit my chest, and the piercing pain jolted me so strongly that it catapulted my upper body into a vertical position. I felt like there was a vise grip on my heart. I couldn't breathe or talk, but fortunately a nurse in the hall heard the sounds I was making from the pain. As she ran into the room, I was clutching my chest and she grabbed an oxygen mask and held it to my face. The excruciating pain intensified but then something in my chest snapped and all my muscles slowly began to relax.

Still gasping, I explained, "I thought I was having a heart attack. I used to treat my grandmother for angina pectoris with nitro, oxygen and bourbon. I helped my grandfather treat her for years."

"Yes . . . Mr. Herrera."

Cold dollops of goo were being swabbed on my skin and they hooked me up to an EKG machine. A couple of other nurses and interns appeared as the needle scratched its jagged lines across the monitor. All watched intently. A voice I had never heard, from a face I'd never seen said, "Mr. Herrera, You didn't have a heart attack. Your heart rate is normal."

Another voice said, "Mucus probably backed-up and blocked your esophagus and caused what seems to have been a violent muscle spasm."

They unhooked the machine.

"We'll check on you in an hour. If you need anything just ring."

* * * * *

One day during this bizarre reality, four teenaged girls came for an unexpected visit. One was my biological daughter. We had seen each other twice the past spring, and before that it had been five years. She had enrolled herself in school in New York and was leaving her mother's home in California to move in with her half-sister's stepmother in Manhattan.

Basha and I had met with my lawyer in February after I was diagnosed. On the way to his office she picked two leaves off a tree in Bryant Park. She carried them with her and explained that the leaves were a symbol of hope.

I'd originally retained Doug to handle the paternity suit my daughter's mother filed sixteen years ago. Over the years I had grown to respect him, because even though we became friends, his primary concern was always what he thought to be best for the child.

I signed my new will. Basha witnessed it and the lawyer made it legal. Basha was visibly nervous; she thanked the lawyer, looked at me with a firm smile and left, still carrying her leaves.

"Doug, as far as my daughter is concerned, I could give a damn about the law. I am not talking to you as a lawyer but as my friend."

"Okay. Fine."

"Doug, as you well know, this child was conceived by deceitful means and for mercenary motives. There has been so much that is morally wrong and emotionally wrong about this child. I want to do what is right."

"Then you have to tell her. If you die, and you might, and you haven't told her you're sick, it will affect her for the rest of her life. Maybe not right away, but years from now when she's grown, a decision not to tell her will cause her major problems."

"We haven't been in touch in four or five years. Her aunt tells me she wants nothing to do with me."

"She may say that to her aunt, her mother, and even to herself but it is not the truth, not when it concerns your possible death. I would suggest a letter."

"She may never get it. The mother is not mentally balanced. You've seen enough for yourself, even in court."

"Oh yeah. My secretary still can't believe her rampage here in the office. When she was yelling that the judge was a lesbian and that the CIA controls the orphanages in this country and all babies should be born in Cuba."

"Oh yes. So, you think a letter is best."

"Yes."

I took a long pause trying to think what to say or ask next. Doug watched me closely and then said, "You'll find a way."

It took three days of staring at a blank computer screen before I could write a word. Then I thought of a scene from the movie, **Donovan's Reef.** The character played by Jack Warden meets his grown daughter for the first time. To break the tension, he poured some rum in their teacups and quoted from **Alice In Wonderland;**

> *"The time has come the walrus said*
> *To talk of many things*
> *Of sailing ships of sealing wax*
> *Of cabbages and kings."*

There was no soft way to word my letter after that. I made it personal and direct.

My daughter's aunt, her mother's sister, was a friend of many years. I phoned her and asked if she would hand-deliver the letter to my daughter. Under the circumstances she agreed without hesitation.

A week went by. I had sent the letter overnight. At the end of the second week I phoned the aunt. She had been busy. She said she would take it in person, that day, to my daughter.

The aunt called that night; "I made the mistake of phoning first and my sister wanted to know why it was necessary for me to hand-deliver your letter. So I told her. Her first words were, 'Is it for sure he's going to die?'"

"Did you hand the letter to her or my daughter?"

"Yes. She read it and was shaken. She is going to call me in a couple of days. Do you think you're going to beat this?"

"I have no idea. Overall I'm in good spirits."

"I am very glad to hear that. Try to stay that way."

The next week I'd met my daughter's twenty-two year old half-sister for lunch. She told me she thought my daughter needed me in her life, and how much she hoped that we would get along. I replied that we had always gotten along and that the age-old problem was really her mother's tirades at what a bastard I was. The young woman sitting across from me burst into tears and sobbed, "I know. I know. I'm not going to raise my children to hate men."

I reached over and offered her my hand. She readily took it. We agreed there was a chance that something good could come out of my having cancer. How we all might be able to grow in a positive way, and be better to one another.

My daughter had called my room earlier and said she was coming to see me. For a fifteen year old she is very independent. She has had a successful career as a feature film actress since the age of five.

She came in with three friends. We exchanged some empty words. She stayed about ten minutes and left. After that I didn't hear from her.

* * * * *

My second survival dream seemed like it lasted for three days. The bedcovers were tangled around my middle and arms and legs. They felt as heavy as a horse blanket. I couldn't get them off and there was something very strong moving and writhing in the covers and all over me. This creature was very powerful, about six feet long and skeletal. It moved constantly. It wrapped itself around me and would crawl up and down my torso. I tried to get the blankets off of it. Somehow I knew if I exposed the creature to light, it would lose its power. I couldn't get my hands on it and I couldn't control the blankets because of its serpentine force. Then there would be a lull in the struggle. I would pull the covers back but it would twist and writhe further underneath, avoiding the light.

It was as though I was trapped in the binding covers, fighting to breathe, feeling suffocated and unable to control the contortions of this force that was trying to consume me. I finally caught the creature's head under the blanket. Its skull was shaped like a cross between a dog's head and a snake's head. I got a tight grip, and with all the strength I had in my

15

I was released from Sloan-Kettering on the 21st of August 1997. With Basha's help I went to my apartment on 84th and Third Avenue.

My diet consisted of chicken broth and fruit that I could peel. The doctors didn't want me eating anything that had been grown close to the ground such as; lettuce, strawberries, tomatoes, etc. Fruits and vegetables with thick rinds, such as bananas, oranges and avocados that had to be peeled were safe.

For the most part, I slept and watched old movies, comedies; I didn't want to see anything but funny stuff. **The In Laws** with Peter Falk and Alan Arkin is my favorite American comedy made in the last forty years. Within a month, without realizing it, I had memorized every line of dialogue in that film.

The Video Room was on the corner of 84th and Third Avenue, about a hundred feet from my front door. After about ten days, I would ease out to rent a movie and talk about film with Howard, the manager. Within a few weeks I had seen every comedy they stocked.

The street smells of food, dogs, exhaust and just the air itself was very intense. Every few feet a new odor was blasted into my nostrils. My olfactory nerves must have just started to kick back in.

I made my own chicken broth, and one night ventured to have a minuscule bite of a short thigh. It was an odd sensation, as if I had put a tasteless, course rubber object in my mouth. I chewed and ate it anyway.

* * * * *

Basha and I would go on short walks. At first she would put her arm around my waist for support. Then one Sunday afternoon we crossed Fifth Avenue and went into Central Park. I made it without assistance, even though a rest or two along the way was necessary.

Basha, as usual, had on a unique outfit: green leather Italian World War II pilot's pants, an antique silk blouse and a vest. She looked particularly radiant and beautiful. I felt so lucky that this special friendship had survived our tumultuous marriage and divorce. It was a perfect autumn afternoon and the leaves were just starting to change color. Lots of squirrels were running and jumping on trees, then checking us out before racing up the trunks; the air was crisp with a gentle breeze. I was very relieved and very thankful to be alive.

* * * * *

As The World Turns put me back on contract in late October. My energy was low so I only worked two days a week with just a few pages a day.

Cindy Hsu, the anchor for the CBS New York noon news called to ask if I could make an appearance that week, and discuss my treatment for lymphoma. I jumped at the chance and phoned Dr. Chatham to ask her what she thought was the most important thing I could say about cancer treatment.

"Make sure you have the right diagnoses."

I thought that a bit simplistic at first, but with a little thought, I realized how right she was.

I was still wearing my character's wig, but decided to do the news without it. My hair was just growing back and no more than meager stubble. My baldhead made more of an impact. They posted my e-mail address on the screen for less than twenty seconds and I was deluged with an amazing amount of e-mail from people with questions about all sorts of cancers.

Felicia Behr and some other producers watched the news broadcast in the booth. Felicia said, "Let's go without the wig from now on."

The lady has guts. It made sense as James had just been released from prison: an inmate hairdo.

She added, "Yes, and you have an Anthony Hopkins look."

I replied, "But I want a Caesar Romero look."

The mature folks in the booth laughed. The younger set was bewildered by the name, Caesar Romero.

* * * * *

The New York Sports Club, where I first discovered the lump, was only three blocks from my apartment. I began to go over and just watch a few squash games. One night I passed a café and it was as if suddenly a part of my brain was re-activated: I wanted fish. I went in and ordered broiled bluefish. It was delicious. Every night for the next three weeks, I ate bluefish.

In October it was time for my three-month check up. I was nervous. They had me scheduled for a CAT scan and a Gallium scan. A CAT scan shows form and shape. In a Gallium scan, the nuclear substance Gallium seeks out, clings to, and dramatically highlights unusual cells like lymphoma cells, so they appear like fireworks exploding in the sky. When a radiologist has noticed an irregular shape or blip on the CAT scan and then sees something glowing in the same spot on the Gallium scan, in my case that meant lymphoma.

It sounds strange, but one gets used to being stuck with needles and drinking strange tasting, thick liquids. They injected me with Gallium. It is "nuclear," so the nurse carries it in a lead container labeled "Nuclear Material." The injection is simple. The nurse ties a tourniquet around your upper arm, takes a hypodermic needle out of the lead container with the nuclear label, sticks the needle in your vein, pushes the plunger and that's it. There are nuclear particles floating around in your body. It takes forty-eight hours for the Gallium to do its seeking and clinging. Then you climb on to a table, the huge camera moves over your body and scans the images into a computer.

In November of 1997 there were no strange shapes, blips or lumps on my CT, nor was there any irregular glowing on my Gallium scan. When I got the results I went by and caught Dr. Gabrilove between patients. She exclaimed,

"Here's my star."

She was almost as excited as I was about my progress. I was in remission, or to use a term I liked even better at the time, "NED": No Evidence of Disease. And there was more good news; if my blood work continued to improve I would be able to go to South Africa for Christmas.

* * * * *

Patsy and I were trying to make plans to go somewhere for Thanksgiving. I just wanted to have the holiday in her home, but her children were going to be with their father, and she wanted to go somewhere. She had been invited to a wedding in Oxford, Mississippi and I wanted to see Evans and Betty Harrington. I flew to Nashville the night before and we drove to Oxford Thanksgiving day. I had called and Betty told me they would be happy to see me, and that Evans had just come home from some tough chemo in Memphis. He wasn't in good shape.

Early Friday night I drove out to Evans' and Betty's home in the country. We ate off of TV trays in the living room since Evans couldn't sit at the dining room table. His face was puffy and legs were swollen from the chemo. He summed up his situation with one swift comment. "The difference is that you went to Sloan-Kettering, and I stayed in Memphis. That's why you're in remission and I'm not going to last much longer."

That was it as far as discussing cancer. Evans loved to tell stories about poets and novelists. Over the years I had heard most of them many times, but it was wonderful to see his smile and hear the glee in his voice and he related one of his favorites:

"When I was in graduate school here, in the early fifties, Doctor Pendergrass was chairman of the Department. He managed to get a published poet from New York City to come all the way down to Ole Miss for a seminar. He stayed drunk the entire time and in one short week he managed to insult most of the faculty and seduce three wives of three different professors in History, English and American Literature. He covered most of the School of Liberal Arts. I went with Pendergrass when we drove him to Batesville and put him on the train. As the Illinois Central pulled out of the station, Doctor Pendergrass waved him good-bye, smiled and genteelly said, 'I prefer my poets dead.'"

We laughed and swapped anecdotes till one in the morning. Betty walked me out. She gave me a big hug.

"I'm so glad you're here."

"So am I. How long?"

"His oncologist says probably six months."

"Is he going back to Memphis?"

"He wants to stay here."

"Will you be able to handle it?"

"Yes, honey, I'll handle it."

It was raining. It seemed right that it was raining. Lights were shining on the courthouse in the square, a poetic sight. It was cold and the rain kept falling as I drove around and around the square. Many of the positive aspects of my life were shaped here in Oxford: Ole Miss, Sigma Chi and Evans Harrington.

Patsy loaned me her car again to go back out the next afternoon. She was generous that way. Evans' daughter was there with two grandchildren and Betty's daughter. The house was full of life. Ole Miss was playing Mississippi State, the rival game of the season. During half time Evans remarked, "Never paid that much attention to our athletics until I retired; now I root for the Rebels every Saturday."

It was a very close game and we were losing. Then, with only twelve seconds left to play, the Ole Miss quarterback threw a spectacular touchdown pass and we won.

By ten o'clock everybody had gone home except Elizabeth. As we capped a near perfect day Betty served up some vodka and tonics, and I seized the moment and was able to let Evans know what he had meant to me and to my life by his favorite medium: stories.

"I was thinking about the time when in Twentieth Century Poetry . . . Once in Stella Adler's script breakdown lecture I remembered you had said . . . When I was writing the script for **The Wide Net**, I remembered your input on D. H. Lawrence . . ."

Just after midnight it was time to leave. Evans was too weak to stand and didn't have the use of his right hand. I didn't know how to say the last goodbye to my major professor, my father figure, but as I stood and put out my left hand, he took it and the words came to me.

"Evans, I sure have enjoyed this."

Our handshake became very firm.

"So have I Anthony. So have I."

Evans died two days later.

16

Reading and answering fan mail was one of those things I always "meant to do". I never threw one letter away and they all usually ended-up somewhere in my dressing room. One day I noticed a letter from Kokomo, Indiana. I liked the sound of the name Kokomo. The letter was neat, hand-written and two full pages long from a Brenda Gabbard. Her husband, Lary, had Mantle Cell Lymphoma and was considering a bone-marrow transplant. She had followed my case through the soap-opera press and was very pleased to know I had survived. I took the letter back to my apartment and put it on my desk.

During the next two weeks it was as if this letter always managed to find its way to the top of the piles, constantly resurfacing on the mess of scripts, notebooks and clutter on my desk. It is lonely enough to get hit with cancer but when the disease is foreign to most oncologists, it is even a more peculiar sort of alienation.

The Gabbard's telephone number was easy to find through information in Kokomo since he spelled it Lary. Brenda answered the phone. I introduced myself and she put Lary on the line. We talked for two hours. He was forty-eight years old. He didn't smoke or drink alcohol. He was a vegetarian. He ran up to eight miles, three times a week. He was very happy in his work. He was very much in love with his wife. They had been happily married for twenty-five years. He adored his family.

Lary's main concern about the transplant was that he would not be able to sleep in the same bed with his wife. I assured him that in his physical condition, he would not want anyone he loved sleeping next to him, both for his sake and theirs. Once initiated into this bizarre fraternity, most of the social decorum and proprieties are gotten out of the way very quickly, and the frankness and openness in our conversation would have astounded most healthy people, especially southern and mid-western folks.

* * * * *

The Christmas Season had not been "jolly" for me since the age of seven. Images of family joy were on television, radio, magazines, and Holiday music was piped in stores everywhere.

In my teens until my late thirties I went to my parents for Christmas. The big event was a tag football game with my brothers and sisters. The first three days were usually upbeat even though we were treading on a thin layer of tension. I always made the mistake of staying too long and then there would be a night in the kitchen when my father with just a few chosen sarcastic remarks would make mother cry.

I went to their house less and less over the years. But kept up the pretext of "being in touch." The decline and death of my Grandfather changed that.

My brother John called in May of 1983, "Bop and Gam are going down hill fast and mother can't handle it. You'd better get down here." I was working on the show long hours and four to five days a week, but I found a flight that left LaGuardia Saturday morning at seven for New Orleans – a rented car and I could be in Wiggins before one o'clock in the afternoon. John would drive over from Austin. Bop just wanted to stay in his house with his wife. Mother would hire a nurse and leave. Gam was losing her grip on reason at times, became difficult and the nurse would quit. I jumped on a plane every other weekend, met John in Wiggins and we would attempt to improve the situation. This went on for a couple of months until my mother stuck them in an old folks home. One lady in Wiggins that we had all known all of our lives said to me, "Why isn't your mother here taking care of the Blackburns instead of staying out there in Texas with that Latin husband?"

Mother would return now and then and was there when Bop died in October. My father arrived two hours before the funeral and as we all were leaving for the church my father turned to me in the front yard and asked, "Why don't you walk your mother to the car? I don't do that stuff anymore."

That snapped the last thread of the tether to my parents.

* * * * *

The powerful memories of South Africa were luring me back. On my first visit in 1993 I was a guest in a private home in Johannesburg. Lilly, their Zulu maid, and I couldn't understand each other's language very well but we made each other laugh. My return trip kept getting delayed.

"Lilly, today I go home." "Not today Lilly. Tomorrow, I go home."

Finally, after five days I was waiting in the driveway for a taxi, Lilly was standing in the kitchen. We could see each other through the window. She was motioning me away and saying, "Go home. Please go home." She was crying.

Cathryn, a Xhosa woman, ran the house where I stayed when in Capetown. She was plump and shy. When I would arrive she would beam with a smile and then look away. I once made the cultural mistake of hugging her; it was clearly awkward for her, so since that time, she would offer her hand and I would take it.

My first night in Johannesburg, Nick Ashby, a young actor, and I were on our way to a dinner party. I had observed that, other than his driving on the left side of the road, so far I didn't feel I was in a foreign country. The landscape was similar to the hill country of Texas, and the architecture I'd seen the first day was modern and resembled the suburbs in the southwestern United States. This all changed two minutes after our host and three other men greeted us at the door.

"Welcome to South Africa, Anthony. But before I take you in and introduce you to the other guests, I want to hear the rest of the news from this chap here about the lion that recently ate the German fellow." -- I immediately realized – I *was in Africa.*

Two nights later I was invited to another home for dinner. It was a small gathering, and just as we were seated for dinner, the last guest arrived. She was tall, beautiful and elegant, and had a regal air. She wore a white cape, and before she moved into the room I saw a flash of metal as she discreetly handed our host a .38 nickel-plated revolver. He subtly slipped the pistol into the drawer of a console table by the door. The lady was Nicki Van Reenen.

At dinner the conversation soon changed to the German fellow's misfortune. He had been on a safari and was told not to leave the campsite. He was a photographer and had sneaked out late at night to get some shots of animals coming to drink at the river below. They heard him scream, but by the time they got to the river all that was found was one shoe and his camera. Nicki spoke for the first time since she had been seated. "Yes. It always seems to be the foreigners, doesn't it? Could I have some more red wine?"

There was an air of mystery about her. She seemed insular and not interested in much of anything. I was intrigued but kept a distance. I learned that she had been very much in love with her husband of sixteen years, had two wonderful sons and what appeared to be a storybook life. He was tall, handsome, a great businessman, tennis player, loving father and dedicated husband. He had died of lymphoma the year before I met her.

Nicki thought that I might like to "come out to the farm in Stellenbosch." To me a farm is a house in the country with a barn and some animals. But this farm was the Meerlust Wine Estate, the oldest and most prestigious wine farm in Africa. The house was built in the 1700's and was huge. There was no electricity in the house except in the kitchen; all the other rooms were lit by candelabra.

That's where I went for Christmas of 1997.

My memories turned into reality when I landed in Capetown. My strength was low so I slept and rested for two days. Cathryn took very good care of me.

At Meerlust I stayed in a two-story apartment attached to the back of the big house. Dogs and workers' children played on the grounds. There was a new pet. A goat named Roscoe. He was a handsome creature with an impressive set of horns.

For the first time Nicki talked about the death of her husband. "He once said, 'People spend so much time complaining about their lives, their problems that are mostly mundane. What a waste. Then there is lymphoma. That's a real problem.'"

We took a very old worker, who had lived on the farm all of his life, into Stellenbach for new glasses. She was very gentle with him as she helped him out of the car onto the sidewalk. When we returned to the farm, somehow Roscoe had gotten in my rented car and was eating a map that I had left on the seat. I thought this was funny until I took him by his horns and began to tussle. This was a strong goat. After I managed to pull him out and let him go, he backed up a few feet and then reared up on his hind legs. I jumped on the other side of the car before he charged. At that moment I quickly realized two things: physically I was still very weak, and Roscoe didn't like me.

Confrontations with Roscoe consisted of him guarding Nicki's BMW and putting up nonviolent resistance to our leaving. But then one afternoon when we returned Roscoe was standing at the top of the outside stairs that led to the second floor of my guest apartment. To be polite and to avoid his possible wrath I went into the door below. There in the sitting area were magazines and books strewn all over the floor. I went up an inside stairway to my bedroom and discovered in the middle of my bed a neat little pile of goat pellets and a pungent yellow circle that had the distinct odor of urine.

The maids were humiliated, Nicki was embarrassed, but I was amused. Roscoe was telling me that this was his domain and that I should go away. After a hug from Nicki, I flew out of Capetown on New Year's Eve.

Over the Atlantic I thought, ***"I have been on the other side of the world being welcomed into homes with friends I loved and who showed that they cared about me. I was far away from the stimuli of my childhood and from chemotherapy, CAT scans and cancer."***

* * * * *

17

My life in New York was nowhere near normal. My energy level was low and I had to rest a lot. I was in the studio three to four days a week but the work was getting tedious. The new writers did not understand the Stenbeck character. They were writing him like he was John Gotti. James Stenbeck, a European aristocrat, has his own style and follows his own code. Wealthy and powerful figures, in all societies often bend or break rules and laws.

After the stress from the transplant, they estimated it would take at least one year for my body to get back to its normal strength and function. My endocrine system was a mess. Doctor Chatham set me up with Dr. Robbins, an Endocrinologist.

Dr. Robbins was calm and knew how to communicate. He thought a testosterone patch would be the way to start. He explained that testosterone levels have much more to do with the body than just the libido: little things, like in ten to fifteen years my heart muscles would weaken and my bones would become fragile and break easily. It was comforting to hear such long-range terms like ten and fifteen years in reference to my future.

"We better get to work on this. My libido won't do me any good if my bones are breaking and my heart blows-up."

"Right, Mr. Herrera," and wrote out a prescription for ANRODDERM. I was to apply a testosterone patch to the skin of my abdomen or lower back every twenty-four hours, so the drug would ease into my system gradually.

I saw Nancy Cody-Lyons and gave her a carved soapstone hippopotamus for her son. She thanked me and announced,

"You are going to be a help to me here with patients. You are not quite strong enough yet. We'll talk in a couple of months. Oh and I want you to be sure to come to the celebration we're going to have in March, for survivors." And she hurried off.

* * * * *

In late January I heard on the studio PA system, "Anthony, could you come to the office."

This was like when I was a kid in grammar school being called to the principal's office.   Fear ran through your whole body and you knew you were in trouble.   Felicia explained they were taking me off of my contract. She assured me that the hiring of new writers was in the works, I would appear from time to time, and that there would be a big story line for Stenbeck in the fall.

Normally this is devastating news for an actor to be out of work but after Mantle Cell Lymphoma, TBI and an autologous bone marrow transplant, being taken off of contract was just not that big of a deal.

I had always wanted a one-man show.   One of the things that I had promised myself in the hospital was to act on ideas rather than just talk about them. During those summers in California at the Will Geer Theatre we did **A Midsummer Night's Dream** every year and I played Theseus. At the end of the play Hippolyta, his bride, asks him to account for the fantastic tales they have heard on their wedding night. Theseus answers by describing the imagination of the lunatic, the lover and the poet.   I named my one-man show: **The Lunatic, The Lover & The Poet.**

I am by no means a scholar. John Ford said, "Mediocre poets borrow, great poets steal."

I'm not a poet, but I did steal some of the best poetry from some of the greatest writers in the English language, starting with William Shakespeare. There were a lot of poems that I had quoted for pleasure over the years. Getting these fine words ready for an audience was a different matter. I began to rehearse poems with strong visuals. I worked daily and structured the show so that the poems' content went from childhood to youth, to middle age, and then reflection, old age. For the end of the show, I chose the poem that I read aloud every day after being hit with cancer, Nano's poem by Tennessee Williams.

* * * * *

Early Sunday morning the phone rang. It was Lary Gabbard's son to tell me his father had died the day before. He didn't make it through the transplant. I had a set of CAT and Gallium scans the next morning. Three days later the results were "No Evidence of Disease". Dr. Chatham was delighted. I was still very shaken that Lary was gone.

Two weeks later I met with Dr. Robbins for the second time. He was not overly concerned that my energy level and libido were still not back to normal. He repeated that it takes about a year for the body to recuperate. That meant another six or seven months, August or September.

"Doctor, my sex drive, is there any way to crank it up on Friday night and turn it off on Monday morning? I'm starting to get some writing done."

He laughed. "It doesn't work that way, Mr. Herrera."

I had booked **Lunatic, Lover & Poet** in twelve towns in Mississippi for April. I handed him one of my show fliers. He was intrigued by the fact that I had a one-man show and had produced it myself.

"Can I keep this?"

"Please do," I was flattered.

* * * * *

My dear old adversary and friend, Emment Chassienoal sponsored the show in Winona, Mississippi. In the mid-sixties we both were in pursuit of Lane Spell -- a southern beauty. I won her, married her, and we were divorced eleven months later.

I wasn't ready for marriage; neither of us was anywhere near ready for marriage, but we discovered passion together. Her mother kept weeping and saying, "Just a three-dollar piece of paper so you can be an honorable woman." After the nuptials, her mother convinced her that if I wanted to be an actor, one day she would surely see me walking down the highway, a broken bum. That was a long time ago.

Emment and his wife had worked hard to bring my productions of **Smoke & Mirrors** and **Love Letters** to Winona. One night while publicizing the show before the tour I stayed in Emment's home. He called Lane, chatted a bit and then said, "Here's somebody who wants to talk to you" handing the phone to me.

Her first reaction was, "My God. Anthony. I thought you two hated each other."

"We still do, darling, but our love for you has been so powerful over the years that it has overwhelmed us to the point of madness."

"Well, I'm just glad you are alive. I prayed for you and Lord knows, you've always needed it."

"That's probably what got me through - that and remembering your beauty."

Emment remarked loud enough for her to hear, "Make any man want to live."

This phone call ended our twenty-six year silence.

* * * * *

Three weeks later I was back for the performance and there were two little girls about eleven years old in the front row. During the reception at Emment's I learned that one of them, Ruthie Gant, had recently had leukemia. I was introduced.

"You all didn't squirm but twice during the whole show."

Ruthie replied, "How could you watch us and say all of those words."

"I always keep an eye on pretty girls, and you both really listened. Did you like the poems?"

Ruthie, "Yes, especially the one about the dog."
The other girl, "And the one about the frozen man."

"Ruthie, I understand you and I are in the same club."

Suddenly it wasn't a little girl meeting someone she had seen on television and on the stage. We were two people who had been through cancer: a beautiful child who had suffered, been close to death and recovered, and a middle-aged man who was very grateful to be working and alive.

Someone wanted to take our picture. I sat on the sofa, with one girl on each side of me.

"Why do I suddenly feel like Maurice Chevalier?"

"I hope you can come to my hospital one day, St. Luke's in Memphis."

"I hope so."

"We could do a fund raiser."

When we said good night, Ruthie and her friend were just little girls again, shyly and politely remembering to say, "It was nice to meet you and we enjoyed your play."

Just a few minutes before, this child was not just a child, but a person with pride in "my hospital" and wanting to "do a fund raiser." She wanted to do something for others with cancer. Some kid.

* * * * *

The next night I played Meridian and stayed in the home of "Bo" Marseilles. We had been initiated into the Sigma Chi fraternity together at Ole Miss. In his library I found a book of photographs and biographies of famous people. By accident I found a quote that made clear a question about religion that I had been pondering since 1995 in Africa.

As a child I went to Sunday school at the First Baptist Church of Wiggins and when I was eleven I "joined the church." It seemed the thing to do. When I lived with Bop and Gam, I went to Church every Sunday. Once I went away to the university, I didn't go that often. As students tend to do I engaged in many discussions till all hours of the night about monotheism, atheism and deism. I decided that I was a deist as was Benjamin Franklin. God was like a watchmaker; he made the universe wound it up and it ran on its own. Deism lasted for a couple of years. After I left the South I didn't think of religion at all.

However, when Basha and I gave an afternoon party to announce and celebrate our marriage in Bop and Gam's back yard in 1986, the festivities in the late afternoon ended up as so many do with the women in one group and the men in another. There in front of me were a bunch of guys that I had known since early childhood. We'd had a lot of crawfish and beer, and I was getting questions about being "out there." New York? Beverly Hills? Questions like,

"Did you ever go to bed with Raquel Welch?"

I had to say "No." There was a look of disappointment on most faces.

Lucas piped up with a very perceptive question:

"Anthony. Why are you still alive?" Meaning how a country boy from this little town didn't end up dead from an overdose out there in the big world.

Without hesitation or contemplation, "Lucas, I'm alive because of the values I was taught by my grandparents who used to live in that house and at the First Baptist just a couple of miles from here."

* * * * *

After his treatment, I saw Bishop Tutu interviewed on television and he said, "I can honestly thank God for my cancer."

One day in 1994 when I was driving across the Great Karroo desert in South Africa, I stopped, walked into the desert, looked up and said aloud, "What? What is it about this land that makes me feel part of the universe?" I felt a certain power in my chest and in the sky. As I gazed into the blue, I again said aloud, "Bop? Cleavon? You up there somewhere. I know you have become friends. You are of the same spirit."

The words that defined that moment were right in front of me in Meridian, Mississippi.

"Everyone who is seriously involved in the pursuit of science becomes convinced that a spirit is manifest in the laws of the universe - a spirit vastly superior to that of man . . . in the face of which we . . . must feel humble"
Albert Einstein

* * * * *

18

Over the summer Basha and I went to the movies about once a week. I started going to the gym and puttering at squash. I was slowly getting my strength back. I had dinner and visits with friends Tandy Cronyn and Anthony Haden-Guest.

On tour I had noticed how much time per day I spent dealing with lodging. At every venue, renting a motel room, unpacking, packing, and getting to the theatre took at least two hours. If I stayed with friends it was usually more than two hours. Southerners visit.

I had mentioned this to Mike Carter, a friend in Jackson who was originally from Wiggins. He called in May and to tell me he had seen a motor home in our hometown for sale. On my next trip to Mississippi, to book shows for the fall, I bought it. It was a thirty-two foot diesel Allegro built in Red Bay, Alabama. I drove it back to New York and kept it at Bobbie MacGuffie's place in Rockland County.

* * * * *

In June I saw Dr. Robbins and he suggested that I step-up the testosterone protocol by having injections, rather than using the patches. I said fine. He wanted me to come in and have his nurse give me the shot once a month. I commented that I could do it myself; after all, I had taken a class on giving myself a shot.

"Mr. Herrera, Neupogen shots are subcutaneous, or injected just under the skin, but testosterone shots are intramuscular and require a much longer and thicker needle."

"If you don't mind, I'd like to try it."

"Okay with me, but if you find that you can't, don't be embarrassed; come in and let my nurse do it."

"That's a deal. But I'm tougher than I used to be. I think sticking an inch and a quarter needle in my thigh will be easier than being bolted into that strange gizmo and being sprayed with radiation."

It took more than I thought but I was able to give myself the shots.

* * * * *

In August and September there was more work on **As The World Turns** than I'd expected and there were also some more shows to do in Mississippi. So I toured with my RV, "my little house that moves." It was great. The set and new lighting system I had purchased for the show all fit neatly underneath, and my costumes were up top. All the stage manager and I had to do was pull-up and park next to the theatre. It saved time and energy.

In Columbus I was welcomed by Jeffery Rupp at the CBS affiliate WCBI. I began touring in '91 and had been a guest on their Midday Live so many times that Jeff and co-host Bill Gamel would welcome me on the show by saying,

"Anthony, take your usual chair. We'll have your office ready for your next visit."

I had also started going back to Nashville every other weekend to be with Patsy and her children. My physical and emotional strength seemed to be back, and I was finally feeling like a complete person again.

* * * * *

On Tuesday, October 20th I had the regular three-month checkup with Dr. Chatham for blood work and to go over the CAT scans from the week before. I arrived early so there would be no problem getting to work for the afternoon session. I was busy chatting with other patients in the waiting area when my name was called.

In the examining room I hopped up on the table and waited. Dr. Chatham came in and announced, "I saw something on the CAT scan that I don't like."

In that split second all hope vanished. "Shit."

"I want you to get an endoscopy."

"Why. This is it."

"No. There are new things out there."

"I thought that if the lymphoma came back, there was nothing that could be done."

"No. There are new breakthroughs all of the time. Now, I want you to have an endoscopy done by Thursday. I want a pathology report."

I made my way to the studio, and into costume and make-up, because the next thing I knew, I was on the studio floor and we were taping four scenes. The action took place in a wedding chapel. My scenes had more movement than dialogue, so all I had to do was move to my next position and deliver a couple of lines. I held onto the script as long as possible and would stuff it under a pillow or behind a chair when the stage manager's countdown got to three.

I must have heard the other actors because I responded, but Dr. Chatham's "**SOMETHING I DON'T LIKE**" echoed like a whisper and a howl in my brain.

I had to work every day for the rest of the week. I waited for Felicia in her office. I told her my bad news and that I'd be having an endoscopy in the next forty-eight hours.

She was concerned. "I didn't know what it was, but I could tell something was wrong when we were taping." Without hesitation Felicia picked up the phone and asked Vivien to come in with the week's schedule. My scenes on Thursday involved just one other actor and one set.

I suggested, "Maybe I could come in for the morning session and get the endoscopy in the afternoon."

Felicia gave me a quick look. "I'll produce the show. You go call your doctor and tell her to schedule your test."

"Felicia, I want to thank . . ."

"Go call your doctor."

I dreaded the endoscopy. I feared that I would choke. On the video it was clear that the procedure *could be fatal*. For over a year I thought this kind of crap was behind me. It wasn't. The damned lymphoma was probably back. I felt as if I was trembling with panic but my hands and arms and body were still. The fear was inside. My choices were the same as before. I needed some help to saddle up. So I quoted aloud:

> *Oh, courage could you not as well,*
> *Select a second place to dwell,*
> *Not only in that golden tree*
> *But in the frightened heart of me.*

Tennessee Williams may not have suffered from cancer but he suffered. Yet through his suffering he gained the insight and found the positive force in nature. At this moment some of that spirit that Einstein realized and that force that kept the stem on the "golden tree" alive, fused into me and gave me strength to continue to fight.

* * * * *

The endoscopy procedure involved putting a tube down my throat and into my stomach. Then they can look around, take pictures and, most importantly, get little bites of the wall of the duodenum where they had seen the lumps on my CAT scan. Then the Pathologist would determine if the tissue contained lymphoma cells and if so, what kind of lymphoma cells.

It was about noon by the time I got into a gown and was taken into the operating room. To counteract my dread of them shoving a metal tube down my throat, I tried a little comedy. I had an audience.

"I just want everyone here to know that I didn't like the sixties, even though I liked the idea of liberalized sex. I didn't like hippies. I didn't do drugs. So, I want my drugs now! You folks have the good stuff, you're trained in how to give it and it's legal."

Dr. Shike, Chief of Gastroenterology, was in charge. He had a wit of his own. He turned to a young intern, "Mr. Herrera wants to get stoned. Let's get him stoned."

I do remember something in my throat and a voice saying, "That's it, swallow. You can help us. That's good. Swallow."

* * * * *

I heard Basha's voice somewhere in the distance. Her voice moved closer. I heard another voice, one I had heard before. As I managed to get my eyes open, I saw Basha and Dr. Shike in front of my bed, engaged in a lively debate about vitamins.

As I came around, Dr. Shike concluded by explaining that Sloan-Kettering policy was "no vitamins whatsoever." Basha wouldn't be satisfied with that. "Why not?"

"We prefer that patients get their vitamins from food. And some vitamins interfere with chemotherapy. Ah, Mr. Herrera, did you have a nice nap?"

"Yeah, I guess I did. What time is it?"

"Four-fifteen. You got stoned and had a nice three-hour snooze. Just lie there for a few more minutes, and then you can go."

"What did you see in there?"

"There were some lesions in the upper part of your stomach which could cause some problems."

"The blip Dr. Chatham saw under the duodenum. Do you think it is lymphoma?"

"Mr. Herrera, I will not speculate. Dr. Chatham should have news from the lab by Monday."

Basha came with me back to my apartment. We talked. She left. I slept some and suddenly I was wide-awake. Dr. Chatham could have just overreacted. Dr. Shike saw something else in there too. It could be a benign growth left over from all the chemo or an ulcer or who knows what else. It's not necessarily Mantle Cell Lymphoma.

I didn't get much rest and had to be in the studio at 7:15. Being very tired was actually good for me this day. Fatigue helped me cope. I had just enough energy to get through the work, and none left over for worry. Worry wouldn't do a damn thing for me anyway.

* * * * *

Sunday afternoon on my answering machine, "It's Dr. Chatham. Please call me as soon as possible." She'd left her home number. For a second, my heart leaped up in my chest. She has good news and wanted me to know right away. No. She has bad news and wants to be sure to find me.

The lymphoma was back.

19

"Find a doctor you feel in your gut can help you fight the cancer in your body. Get a professional – a psychiatrist or psychologist to help you with your emotions, and get with your preacher, priest, rabbi, your dog or your favorite tree to help you with your spirit. Get these three parts of yourself lined-up and **hit it**." My words of advice that just came tumbling out on a television talk show in Mississippi, on tour in the spring. Now I had to take my own advice. Mother Nature had dealt the hand and I had to play it.

The next day Dr. Chatham laid out my options. The most aggressive was another bone marrow transplant, in the hope of putting me back into remission. The second option was to use chemo alone as maintenance regimen, which would probably keep me alive for 12-18 months, until my body gave out from the chemo, pneumonia or organ failure.

"What happens if we do nothing?"

"The tumor will grow, seal-up your stomach, and you will vomit up everything you eat."

"What do we do?"

Dr. Chatham explained, "In January of '97 we had a plan, a timetable, a set number of CHOP treatments, then ICE chemo, then stem cell harvest, then radiation, etc. We are now in a very different situation with a different set of problems. There are too many variables to lay out a long-term plan. <u>One hurdle at a time.</u> There is no definite route to take, no way to project a timetable. The next step we take, the next phase we enter will depend on the results of the one before it. We have to get over one hurdle at a time."

I tried to take a deep breath. "Okay. So. What do we do next?"

"We will start with Rituxan. Rituxan is a protein antibody, not chemotherapy. It is not as toxic to the body and in **some cases** it kills lymphoma cells."

Kim, a tall, beautiful woman, was now Dr. Chatham's nurse. We sat down and put together a schedule for four weeks of Rituxan, to be administered once a week in the hospital, intravenously. She explained that I could go about my life: work, gym, social life in a normal fashion, but cautioned me to be moderate with alcohol; that was it.

"Can Rituxan put me in remission?"

"Dr. Chatham thinks this is the appropriate treatment at this time."

"How long will it be before we know if it's working?"

"I don't know. We'll finish the four weeks Dr. Chatham has ordered, and then see where we are."

"Kim. What do you think?"

"We. You, just have to keep going."

Kim couldn't give me the answer I wanted. I wanted to hear, ***"This will work. In a month or two you'll be fine."***

I left very frustrated and angry. I calmly panicked. I didn't want to believe the lymphoma was back. With all of the chemo and radiation, I felt I had gone through as much physical suffering as my body could take. That should count for something. But it didn't.

Dr. Gabrilove had said, "You're my star . . ." Dr. Robbins had referred to the condition of my heart over the next fifteen years. What did they mean by all of that crap? On First Avenue, walking to my apartment was more difficult. I believed that I, or we, had won the battle. So did my doctors.

Later that night I wrote Dr. Chatham a letter. The closing sentence read, "I'll go back to Africa and get killed by a lion before I die a gray-skinned bag of bones on the 17th floor."

I was expected to be in the studio at 7:00 a.m. the next morning ready to work. I had forty pages of dialogue and a good story to play; the one Felicia said was in the works when she took me off my contract the previous February. I liked the plot. James was trying to change his ways because he had fallen in love. Love conquers all. Great stuff, I thought, and dove in.

Elizabeth Hubbard plays Lucinda Walsh, the object of James' affection; she didn't like the story line and went so far as to be quoted as saying so, in Soap Opera Digest. Patsy read it and remarked, "It sounds like she doesn't want to work with you." I thought; let Miss Hubbard act silly if she wants. I was very fortunate to be able to use my mental and physical energy on my work. Rather than speculate endlessly on what might or might not happen. Worry would not be productive. All I could do now was to keep going. I pictured Bop every morning, his gentle smile and could hear him say, **"Son, it's leg over leg to Dover."**

* * * * *

Rituxan: It would take four to five hours to infuse, and I would need someone to escort me home. Dr. Chatham checked me out, and I found myself arguing in favor of any alternative to the possibility of undergoing another bone marrow transplant. Dr. Chatham quickly stated, "All decisions on treatment come from me."

Nancy Cody-Lyons came into my room as they were hooking me up for the Rituxan infusion. "It's good to see you but, not back as a patient."

She patted my arm and rushed out. All of a sudden I felt good. This was strange. I had relapsed and I didn't know what the hell was going to happen to me but I felt energetic. It was Nancy's visit. She was in another department now. But she took the time to find me, talk to me and pat my arm.

The next couple of weeks consisted of work, Rituxan and worry. Physically, I felt okay. On Thanksgiving I went to a very posh lunch, took it easy for the rest of the day and skipped dinner. Friday my stomach started to hurt. I didn't feel like eating but tried to convince myself that it was unrelated to whatever Dr. Shike had found in my stomach. Early in the evening I called Sloan-Kettering and the lymphoma resident on-call told me to try some Gas-X. I was relieved he thought that it was just gas, and finally got to sleep. At 4:30 on Saturday morning I started vomiting. Up came my posh Thanksgiving lunch.

Throughout the day the gastric pain got worse. By six o'clock that evening I was in the Emergency Room at Sloan-Kettering.

They were very busy. Finally a nurse appeared with a clipboard and started with questions.

"Mr. Herrera, why did you come in here tonight?"

I explained that I had been a patient since February of 1997; and had an autologous stem cell transplant. I told her about the recent relapse, the endoscopy and the Rituxan, and that I really didn't think this was tumor-related, but instead a symptom of the lesions Dr. Shike mentioned.

She took my temperature, took my blood pressure, weighed me and wrote all of it down very carefully.

I kept saying, "I just want a doctor to check on my stomach."

I kept hearing, "We're very busy. A doctor will be with you soon."

The pain in my gut vacillated between dull aches and sharp pain, but I had to wait. Finally the nurse called my name, put me on a bed and drew a white curtain around me. I waited some more and tried very hard to convince myself that this pain and vomiting was indeed from the ulcer, the lesion, whatever. A tired, young doctor came in reading over my paperwork. "Mr. Herrera. Why did you come in here tonight?"

"Didn't they put that on your clipboard? I've repeated the reason at least five times while I've been waiting on you."

"We're very busy. There were a lot of patients before you."

"Right, doctor, but as my stomach pain increases, my compassion for others tends to decrease."

I repeated all the information for the young doctor, and learned that he was from Virginia, a fellow southerner. He listened, poked, prodded and then told me to drink an entire 8 oz. glass of medicated goop a nurse had brought in. He made me promise to return if the pain did not significantly decrease in a couple of hours.

I went back to my apartment and tried to sleep. Five hours later I was back in the Emergency Room. The young southern doctor was still there. Once I got his attention, we cut through most of the bureaucratic crap.

He sent me downstairs for a chest X-ray. On my way back to the Emergency Room, I got lost in the dimly lit corridors of this monster of a hospital. I was exhausted and couldn't think straight. It was the middle of the night and I couldn't find any people or even a phone. I didn't know where

I was, and kept going down hallways, through doors and finding myself in different hallways. It seemed I stumbled through passageway after passageway for hours. I thought maybe I had died and this was the corridor to hell. Finally, through a double door into a well-lit hallway, I found the Emergency Room.

When we looked over the X-ray, the doctor didn't see anything that concerned him as far as cancer went. I would have to wait until Monday during office hours to see Dr. Shike.

When I got out on the street it was dawn. I took a taxi to my apartment and tried to sleep, but couldn't. The eight ounces of goop wasn't doing any good at all. I began to realize the only explanation was that the tumor had already sealed-up my gut.

* * * * *

20

Monday at noon, I was in the hospital on the eleventh floor. No one had to explain to me how to use the little blue buttons on the side panel of my bed.

Dr. Goy paced back and forth going over the results of the morning's CAT scan and outlining the approach he proposed. Very dashing with a continental accent and wavy hair, his demeanor was more like a French Formula-One racecar driver than an oncologist.

"I want to start with Fludarabine. You've not had this before. There is a chance it may attack these tumor cells."

I was not in a positive mood. "I've never met you before. I'm not agreeing to anything until I hear from Dr. Chatham."

"I'm covering for Dr. Chatham."

"I'll wait."

"Your situation is very serious. Dr. Chatham is not in today."

"Dr. Goy, Dr. Chatham told me, that all directives come from her. That's who I want to hear it from."

"She's not in today."

"Get her to call me."

"I will."

For such a forceful and dynamic man, he handled my obstinate behavior surprisingly well.

Within the hour Dr. Chatham's called.

"Do what Dr. Goy says. He has cleared everything with me. I'll see you tonight."

All of it was back: not just the cancer, the lymphoma, the Mantle Cell Lymphoma, but the needle in my arm, attached to the plastic tubes, hanging down from the plastic bags of saline and chemicals dripping into my body. I had to have a serious think. This wasn't just a lesion in my upper gastric region, and this wasn't a bad dream. The soft sounding but deadly lymphoma was back and had sealed-up my gut. Rituxan didn't work and if the lymphoma kept growing at this rate and the chemo didn't work, I'd be dead within six months.

Dr. Chatham came in about 9:00 p.m. She was wearing a mask, and this precaution shook me. She said we would have to find a new approach to the next hurdle, but that the tumor in my stomach was an emergency.

"I'm increasing the dose of Fludarabine; we'll try that for another forty-eight hours. Then, if there is still no movement, I've already talked to a surgeon. They'll have to open you up."

"This is bad, isn't it, Doctor."

"Yes, this is bad."

"Are you telling me I could be dead by May."

"You could be dead in two to three days if we don't open-up your gut."

* * * * *

Basha came to see me the next afternoon. She looked radiant in her antique outfit, wearing a hat with a veil in the middle of the day. On her it worked. She sat on the side of the bed and as we were in the middle of a conversation, she began to weep. I reached over and took her hand.

"I'm in the best hospital in New York, with the best doctors."

"Oh, Anthonee, I don't want you to die."

"Basha, you are very strong. Right now I need for you to be strong for both of us. Look, you survived being married to me and you're even more beautiful now than you were then."

My attempt at humor and flattery didn't work. She kept crying.

"I'm supposed to be taking care of you, and here you are having to take care of me."

"No, Basha. You've helped me get this far."

She took a deep breath and composed herself. Then in typical Basha fashion, she told me about an article she'd read recently about a cat that had been lost somewhere in the Midwest on a cross-country trip, and then one day, months later walked up to its owners' home in California.

"And dat cat was a dark red cat, can you imagine."

Even with a sealed belly, I chuckled.

Suddenly my room was filled with a team of some eight doctors and nurses headed by Dr. Goy. He gave them a concise history of my case. Basha left.

Mr. Herrera, we have to try and get the fluid out of your stomach.

"I guess if the pressure builds up too much in there – it could burst?"

"Right. And that would be very dangerous."

They left. In a few minutes a young Chinese doctor came in carrying a coil of plastic tubing. She said that the tube had to be inserted through my nose, and then pushed down my esophagus and into my stomach. The tube was clear, just a tiny bit thicker than the diameter of a pencil, and had several holes on the sides of its tip. She proceeded to put some lubricant on the tube, placed it in my right nostril and shoved hard. The tip of the tube hit the back of my sinus and I recoiled. The tube came out of my nose. She put it back in my nostril and shoved again, this time harder. Again I recoiled.

"Wait. That hurts like hell. Why not ease it in slowly?"

"No. I was told to push hard."

"Then get me something for the pain first."

She frowned.

"I'll see what I can get."

I decided to put the tube in myself. When she left the room, I coated the tip with more lubricant, eased it up into my right nostril and slowly pushed it past my sinus, through my esophagus and nearly all the way into my stomach. I started shaking from the discomfort of this long piece of plastic in my body, and began to panic so I slowly pulled it back out through my nose and hit the nurses' buzzer.

"Yes, Mr. Herrera?"

"Ask that doctor to come back in here please. I can get this tube in with some help."

"She's looking for something to help you."

"I don't need a pain killer. Just get her to come back in here."

"All right, Mr. Herrera."

By the time she came back in I had the tube back past my windpipe and managed to say, "Help me push."

"You should have waited . . ."

"Just help me push this damn thing."

She did, and when the tip of the tube got into my stomach, a flood of dull, brown fluid erupted from my mouth and nose. The two-liter container that was supposed to have caught the drainage had not been hooked-up, and as the fluid gushed out of me, the young doctor looked nervous. She scrambled to hook-up the container and it was filled within seconds. I spewed this strange bile all over the bed and all over myself. I looked at the mess and thought of **The Exorcist.**

By the time it was over, the bed was soaked and I was drenched. There must have been at least four liters of liquid locked in my gut. They changed the bed, and I cleaned myself in the bathroom and put on a fresh gown. I suddenly realized why Dr. Chatham and Dr. Goy were so concerned. I was shaken. My stomach could have burst and I would have bled to death.

* * * * *

By the next morning my duodenum had still not opened-up. When Dr. Chatham came in to check on me with her entourage of fellows, nurses and interns, I was not in a particularly good frame of mind.

"I have to be at work on Monday. No matter what, I'm going to be back in the studio Monday."

"With a tube in your nose?"

"I put it in by myself; I can pull it out to shoot a scene, and then stick it back in."

"We'll see."

They left and I called Felicia to assure her I'd be there.

"Anthony, don't be difficult. Do what Dr. Chatham says. She is calling the shots; you understand me?"

"Yes, Felicia. I understand."

Later, one of the young doctors from Dr. Shike's clinic came in and asked about my stomach, listened with her stethoscope and gently but thoroughly felt my abdomen.

"Any improvement?"

"I can't tell just yet; we'll keep a close check."

She left. I didn't mean to be grumpy, but my mood must not have improved very much, because a few minutes later Dr. Shike came in his operating greens.

"Mr. Herrera, Dr. Chatham is a very fine doctor who is very concerned about you and your condition, and she is also concerned about your life, not just your disease. But if you keep arguing with every point she makes, she will lose some of her resolve even if she isn't aware she's losing it. Do you understand what I'm saying?"

"Yes I do, doctor."

"Good."

He turned and went out the door. It took Dr. Shike at least ten minutes to get from his clinic to my room. He works very hard and is very busy. But he took the time to come to my room and kick my butt. Felicia just kicked my butt. I realized I had crossed the line from being tough and full of resolve to being a pain in the ass.

* * * * *

Chemo flowed into my veins and we had another thirty-six to forty-eight hours to see if it was going to kill lymphoma cells, reduce the size of the tumor and unblock the obstruction in my gut.

Dr. Goy came in. "You want your gut to open-up? Get out of bed and walk."

"I'm going to be back in the studio Monday."

"Good. If you get out there and walk around the nurses' station, you'll have a better chance of getting back to your acting than you will if you just lie here."

He left my room; I knew he was right. I unplugged the pump line, hung it on the pole, put on the paper hospital slippers and my mask and went out into the hall. I started walking, but one wheel would stick and pull the pole to the left. The bags of chemo, drugs and hydration lurched back and forth, so I had to pace myself to accommodate the wobbling wheel.

I started to bitch silently about how unfair it was that this damn disease was back. I caught myself, bitching wasn't going to do any good. So I called on my friend Cleavon.

"Come on Mister Little, I need a little help here." In my mind I could see the twinkle in his eye and hear his voice,
"Herrera, do what you gotta do."

I may be headed on expedition through hell but as Hamlet reflected,
"The undiscovered country from whose bourn
no traveler returns puzzles the will
and makes us rather bare those ills we have
than to fly to others we know not of."

I made it around the nurses' station three times and returned to my room fairly proud of myself. Just as I'd managed to get the mask off, and back into bed without pulling one of the lines out of my arm or one of the bags off the pole, Dr. Goy came in.

"I thought you were going to do some walking to help us open-up your stomach."

"I did. I did three laps."

Without missing a beat, he said "Do three more."

I was really beginning to like this vigorous doctor.

It was extremely tedious going around and around in the hall at a snail's pace and to compensate for the wandering wheel. One of nurses helped me change all the bags to a new pole. Now that I was rolling, I could rehearse a poem:
The Shooting of Dangerous Dan McGrew.

"A bunch of boys were whooping it up
in the Malamute Salon,

The kid that handles the music box was
hitting a jag time tune."

Every time I passed the nurses counter they cheered me on as if I was in the Olympics. I caught a glimpse of my reflection in a glass panel. I looked pretty silly. My hair was sticking out in different directions, my hospital robe was flapping in the back and the yellow duck bill mask covering my nose and mouth added to the comic effect. A strange scene being played on a strange set, but as Evan had said, *"Herrera, It's the role of a lifetime."* That night more

fluids, more chemo, more pills and with the aid of sleeping pill
-- I slept.

Thursday after my laps, I got back into bed. Bingo. My
gut was opening up. I've never felt so great in all of my life
about passing gas.

* * * * *

21

I was back in the studio on Monday morning. I had lost sixteen pounds. On the elevator one of the actresses chirped. "Anthony you've lost weight."

"Yes."

"Well, I don't know what you've been doing, but just keep doing it. You look great!"

The previous week had been so surreal that I was amused by her comment. It was a relief to be in the studio, working.

I had cleared the first hurdle; the Fludarabine was killing the lymphoma cells. The next hurdle was to find out if I had a sibling match. Technically it's called an HLA match, and the best possible compatibility rating is a "six out of six". A "five out of six" might work, and would be more difficult for the new immune system to assimilate in my body.

I hoped that with two brothers and three sisters, one would be a match.

I called my brother John. He was the youngest of my siblings. He was an Eagle Scout and had played defensive end at the University of Texas. He was the most emotionally independent of my brothers and sisters who were raised in Texas and it was a conscience effort. He once told me, "As a little kid I looked up and saw how Ralph and my sisters were treated and decided that I was not going to let them do that to me. So I spent as much time as I could away from the house in scouts and sports." He felt the need to try to keep a sense of family. As an adult he once told Mother, "I think of the way you and Daddy treated us as kids and I want to weep."

John had worked with me on both films I made and we had a great time. He and I stayed in touch.

The most distant was the middle brother Ralph. After Bop and Gam died in the mid-eighties, communication with my other siblings gradually dissipated and by now was little or none. Ralph had come to New York to stay with me during the summer break in 1974. Shortly after his arrival we started a little moving company. I was very tired of waiting tables, which I had done for five years while studying with Stella and working for free in Off-Off Broadway productions. Two months after we started "Bread and Butter Movers" -- I had an audition for a role on **As The World Turns** and was hired on to play Mark Galloway.

Ralph stayed until December. He went back to Texas with a new wardrobe and five thousand dollars in cash. Before long he decided that New York was the place for him and returned, "to be an actor".

I was written out of the show after one year and moved to California. He stayed in my apartment, continued moving furniture and began to study acting. Years went by and he rarely worked as an actor. Eventually he made a good living as a grip on commercials and movies.

His resentment toward me grew to such an extent that when I returned from Africa and was bouncing from sublet to sublet he refused to let me stay in his apartment even though he spent most of his time on his farm upstate.

I explained to John that I had no chance of survival with an unrelated donor. But with a sibling match I had a shot. After the hospital had the tubes of blood, it would take four to six weeks to find out whether I had a match. I asked John if he would talk to each of them and he said, "I'll handle it."

Once a month for the next three months, I'd spend five days in a row being infused with Fludarabine. I ran into Karen Klem; she was very concerned that I had relapsed. I asked her if she knew any percentages on the odds of finding a "six out of six" match, in a pool of five siblings.

"I've seen cases with only one sibling who was a perfect match, and others with eight siblings and no match."

Karen gave me a quick hug.

"Good luck."

Her embrace changed my emotions so fast it amazed me. Seconds before I was filled with angst. One second of being held in her arms produced a powerful positive impact.

The holidays were coming up and the studio would be dark. Patsy went to Bogotá, Columbia. Basha went to Poland.

I went to Bobbie MacGuffie's to be with her and family. Dr. Janey Hudson, was there too, and we had some very good talks, but she didn't really want to give me advice and kept saying, "I'm not your doctor." She did say she had a lot of respect for Dr. Chatham, which was comforting.

"Okay, but you're both doctors. What kills most cancer patients?"

Janey answered with one word, "Infection."

I played with the kids. I played with the dogs. These people and this place had been like home for me for the last eighteen years. I rested.

From December 26th through the 30th, I went to Sloan-Kettering's seventh floor each day, sat hooked-up for four hours for my dose of Fludarabine.

I was invited to a very chic party on Beekman Place for New Year's Eve. But it was a rainy and cold night. My energy was low. I decided to stay in bed, watch **Casablanca** and sleep.

* * * * *

I always felt better when I was at work. There was another call on the PA from Felicia to come to the office. "Anthony, you have a heavy storyline to finish. You're working every day. If it starts to get to you, and you need to just get on a plane and go to Jamaica or wherever, just call, and let me know."

"No. I'll be here. I mean, I want to work."

"The offer stands. If you need it."

Fortunately my workload kept my brain occupied most of the time. Then two weeks later Kim called with very good news: I had a sibling match. The results came back on four siblings and my brother John was a "six out of six" HLA match. This was very good news. John and I got along. Our brother Ralph had not sent in blood to be tested; the reason remained unclear. But much more important, the chemo was shrinking the tumor and now with John as my sibling match, I had the best possible scenario for an allogeneic transplant.

Dr. Chatham made an appointment for me to see a bone marrow transplant specialist at Sloan-Kettering named Dr. Roven. I phoned his office and explained that I had to work that afternoon and would prefer to come in early. He started seeing patients at 10:00 a.m., and I was told I would be first. I requested that if they knew he was going to run late for any reason, to please let me know, and I was assured that there would be no problem.

I was in the waiting room early and studied my script for the afternoon. I had a 1:00 p.m. call at the studio. At 10:45, I asked the receptionist if there was a problem.

"No problem. The doctor will be with you in just a few minutes."

Still waiting at 11:30, I suggested that if he couldn't see me that day I could schedule another appointment.

"In just a few minutes Mr. Herrera."

I became more and more anxious. I calculated that it would take half an hour to get across town, and I'd need at least forty-five minutes to an hour to find out what I would be facing with a second bone marrow transplant. But, I also had a responsibility to the studio, where we had to stick to a schedule to get our work done. It seemed that my attempt to be conscientious meant nothing to these people here; all control was left to the whims of others.

Finally at 11:45 I was shown into an examination room. A young Chinese doctor came in and dispensing with an introduction, told me to get on the scale. I tried to explain that I was running out of time, but he wouldn't listen and said he had to record my weight, height, pulse and blood pressure before Dr. Roven could see me.

"I've been a patient here for two years. I just need to consult with the doctor."

"No. I have to get this information. This is the procedure."

"I am running out of time."

"Take off your shirt."

"Why?"

"I need to take your blood pressure."

"You can get a reading with my shirt on."

"It will not be accurate."

"No one else at Sloan-Kettering has ever asked me to take my shirt off."

"For an accurate reading, I need you to take off your shirt."

I took off my shirt. He took my blood pressure twice. This man seemed to be moving as slowly and methodically as possible. I'm sure my frustration level made my blood pressure abnormally high. As I was putting my shirt back on, he left without a word. I paced back and forth in this small room. I tried to read a pamphlet on the counter, but I couldn't concentrate enough to get through a sentence.

After another ten minutes, Dr. Roven came in. He told me his name without looking me in the eye, and gave me a perfunctory handshake as he sat down. As he opened my folder and started turning pages, he didn't say a word. I asked, "How many allogeneic transplants have you or your team done for Mantle Cell Lymphoma patients who've had autologous transplants plus total body irradiation and then relapsed?"

This doctor still didn't look me in the eye. Instead, he crossed his legs and started pulling on his sock.

"I've always thought that the allo was the best approach to consider."

I asked the question again.

He continued to pull on his sock and mumble about the allo.

"Will you be in charge of my transplant from beginning to end?"

"Here at Sloan-Kettering we work as a team. There will be a team of hematologists and other specialists involved in the transplant."

"You won't be in charge?"

"No. That's not how it's done here."

"Dr. Gabrilove was directly in charge of the autologous transplant from my first day on the 17th floor until I was released seven weeks later; she was personally in charge."

"Oh. . . . No one told me that."

His attention went from his sock back to shuffling through papers in my folder.

Our consultation kept going nowhere. I left. The cancer was back. I was getting pumped full of chemo again. In the taxi to the studio, I felt as if my chest had been tightened to the point of exploding in a giant vise grip. As soon as I finished the first rehearsal, I found a phone in an empty dressing room and called Kim.

"Kim, I think Dr. Roven is a jerk. I can't work with him; he wouldn't answer my questions. He wouldn't even look me in the eye. . . "

"All right, Mr. Herrera. I'll tell Dr. Chatham. Call me later."

"I'm in the studio, I'll try."

"If not, first thing in the morning. We'll arrange someone else for you to talk to."

Kim had a kind heart and she tried to be comforting. Still, I couldn't seem to get a real breath. This was one particular instance when having to get to the set, getting caught up in the rush and hurry of the studio and cope with the dialogue were all welcome diversions.

Two days later I met with a very nice lady, Dr. Jakubowski, and she asked me point blank, "Why didn't you want to be treated by Dr. Roven?"

I saw no reason to dodge the issue. "I'm putting my life in the hands of another human being, a doctor. It is important for me, as the patient, to be able to talk with my doctor, for the doctor to listen and for the communication to flow freely, in both directions."

Dr. Jakubowski didn't seem very surprised at my answer. She then explained that Sloan-Kettering doctors had never done an allogeneic transplant with a patient who had already undergone an autologous transplant. I would be their first. The paperwork for a new procedure normally takes six months to process, but she would be willing to make an exception and push it through in six weeks if I agreed to be the first to have the procedure done at Sloan-Kettering.

I thanked her for her candor and told her I'd have to think about it. She said I needed to feel certain about whatever decision I made.

* * * * *

Dr. Gabrilove had assured me when she left to take over the Oncology Department of Mount Sinai Medical Center, that she would always be available to me if I needed her. She urged me to explore my options at other institutions for the second transplant and suggested Dana Farber in Boston, The University of Nebraska in Omaha and MD Anderson in Houston.

A few days later I phoned Dr. Jakubowski and told her I was going to try and find another hospital. She said she understood and wished me luck. Dr. Chatham put me in touch with Dr. Armitage, one of the leading experts in the world on Mantle Cell Lymphoma and his team in Omaha, Nebraska.

I had the next Thursday and Friday off from the studio and lined up the trip. The University of Nebraska Hospital had just completed an apartment/hotel-like complex attached to the hospital. Patients would be housed in an apartment with a family member or a caretaker and be literally an elevator ride away from the Emergency Room. Dr. Chatham was very interested in hearing about these arrangements. I was feeling optimistic about this trip. Before I left, she asked, "Do you want me to contact MD Anderson in Houston? You might want to visit both on the same trip."

"I don't want to go to Houston."

"Why not?"

"I have family there."

"I would think that would be an incentive. You are going to need a lot of support."

"Dr. Chatham, I have the name Herrera and yet I was raised as a Baptist in Mississippi. Everything about my family is bizarre. They are not healthy mentally. Fortunately, I get along best with John, my donor brother, who will come to wherever he's needed. Contemplating a second bone marrow transplant and the distinct possibility of dying is going to be difficult enough without having to deal with siblings who are still emotionally crippled from childhood."

Dr. Chatham gave a slight nod and left. Maybe she didn't listen. Maybe she didn't care. Or maybe what I had said didn't seem that important to her.

When the tumor was found in my gut a few months ago, I had to take one medical hurdle at a time. I realized that I must do the same thing emotionally. I hoped that I was

22

The next morning at CBS as I got off the elevator to go into Studio 42, I ran into Dasha Epstein, a Broadway producer I had known briefly right after **The Wide Net** had aired. I quickly reminded Dasha that we had seen the McGuire Sisters show together and we began to chat. She had produced "**Ain't Misbehavin**" and "**Master Harold & The Boys**" and other hits. I told her about **Smoke & Mirrors**. She asked to read it.

She gave me her address and I dropped off a copy of the play, a great review from the Palm Beach Post and another from The Star in Johannesburg, South Africa.

The next day I jumped on another passenger jet and in a few hours I was in the Midwest – the plains of Nebraska. The patient living quarters at the University of Omaha Cancer Hospital were brand new and constructed very well. The first thing I checked out was the bathroom. There were well-located handrails and ample space to maneuver with a pole, pumps and bags of fluid. No matter how much extra effort it took, I wanted to be able to go the toilet by myself.

My room was on the 24th floor and I was the first patient to stay in this wing of the hospital; there was still packing putty at the bottom of the sink. I looked out over the evening lights of Omaha and reflected; this could be home for three months or even longer. I had seen a documentary on Mexican communities springing-up all over the United States and learned that Omaha had quite a large Mexican population, with its own radio station. I'd been told that I would have a lot of downtime with this transplant, and thought I might hire a Spanish tutor, and maybe even take some guitar lessons. This might be just fine.

The next morning I went to the seminar for new patients facing transplants. There were six of us and Nurse Reilly took us through the process with charts and slides. He referred to Neupogen as "growth factor" and mentioned the fact that the injections themselves could be painful. The other patients cringed at the thought of having to give themselves shots, so he asked me to comment since I'd already been through it. I told them, "It really doesn't hurt that much, just a little pinch," and they all seemed to relax.

Afterwards I was taken to a conference room. Dr. Bierman was right on time, but his opening words threw me.

"Mr. Herrera, I need to know if you are the kind of man who is going to say, 'cure me or kill me.'"

I said something to the effect that I just wanted to stay alive.

"Well, Mr. Herrera, I'm going to spend a few minutes with you, then a resident will come in to answer your questions; and then I'll be back."

"Dr. Bierman, I didn't fly out here from New York to talk to a resident. I came out here to talk to you."

"Okay. Fine."

He went on to talk for an hour and a half about the allo-transplant and the latest findings. One of the most significant studies focused on one hundred sets of identical twins, in which one of each set suffered from leukemia. Fifty had transplants and received their twin's immune system, and fifty had transplants and received another sibling's 6/6 match immune system. The reoccurrence of disease was greater with the fifty who'd received stem cells from their identical twins, and the fifty patients who'd received another sibling's immune system had a much higher rate of survival.

I couldn't quite compute that information and asked Dr. Bierman to go over it again. He did, taking a couple of minutes longer with his explanation, and I thought I understood. I offered a country boy analogy and asked if my comparison would apply:

"We're having a riot in my hometown of Wiggins, Mississippi. Civil order breaks down and they bring our local Stone County National Guard. But the Commander figures out that the local guardsmen are going to have a tough time sticking a bayonet into someone they've grown up with and known all of their lives. But if a guard unit from Montana was transported in to the town, those boys could drive the crowd back, and they would not hesitate to get tough with a bayonet or a bullet."

Dr. Bierman gave me a slight nod of approval and expanded his point. The patient who has an autologous transplant, as I had, was getting the same defense or immune and blood system, which allowed the cancer to grow in the first place. But with an allogeneic transplant, the patient ends up with a stronger, more resilient and sufficiently different immune system to fight the growth of cancer cells.

That was the good news. The bad news was the possibility of not making it through the full allo-transplant procedure. His exact words were, "There is a 70% chance you will never leave your hospital room."

"I have heard about a mini allo-transplant. What would my chances of survival be with one of those?"

"Yes. With the mini allo-transplant, the immune system in your bone marrow would not be burned all the way to zero with chemotherapy, only partially. Therefore, being infused with less toxins, there would be less chance of organ damage."

He went on to say that any oncologist can administer chemo, collect your donor's cells and put them into your body. The complicated period is after the infusion of the donor cells, when they have to maintain a delicate balance using drugs to make sure the new immune system doesn't kill the host, or, that Graft Versus Host Disease doesn't invade and destroy the major organs.

It gets even more complicated. The hematologists and oncologists who've been working on this new approach to the stem cell transplant have learned that a small amount of Graft Versus Host disease (GVH) is beneficial. There are cells within GVH itself that kill lymphoma cells.

"How many of these mini allo-transplants have you done here at Omaha?"

"Seven."

"What time can I call you in the morning?"

"I'll be in my office between 11:00 and 11:30"

It was not possible for me to assimilate any more input at the moment.

* * * * *

My room was very comfortable and I was exhausted, but much too stressed to take a nap. I phoned Laura Surdarsky and gave her an update.

"Go out and have a drink and a steak. You've been hearing about nothing but death all day. Don't sit in that room."

I called the front desk and asked them to get me a taxi. They said I could expect about a fifteen-minute wait. I went down to reception; no taxi. They called again. We waited. They asked a lot of questions about **As The World Turns** but I didn't mind because they were very polite.

It was nearly ten o'clock by the time I got my bourbon and steak. At the next table were two young local couples, who also turned out to be fans, sincerely interested and cordial. A little booze, a great piece of mid-western beef and some conversation were a gift.

* * * * *

Gam used to say, "Honey, no matter how bad something looks at night, it won't look quite that bad in the morning."

As I dialed Dr. Bierman's office I thought she was right even under this peculiar circumstance.

"Good morning, doctor."

"Good morning, Mr. Herrera."

"I want to make sure my thoughts on this are correct. You said that the care after the transplant is the most critical. So the post-transplant phase, getting my new immune system assimilated, functioning and working to kill cancer cells, is the most important factor in my decision on where to be treated."

"Right."

"Then I need to go to MD Anderson because they're way ahead of everybody else with the mini-allo."

"I will be glad to make some contacts for you."

"I'll check with Dr. Chatham. That might be best since I've been under her care. Thank you for your offer and your information. It has helped me plan the next step."

"Good luck, Mr. Herrera."

I hung up the phone and sat on the edge of a bed gazing down at my feet. I didn't think I would stand up. Maybe I could just sit right here for the rest of the day and tomorrow and the next day and the next. Not a good plan.

I went to the window and looked out onto the main street of Omaha. In the late 1800's it was a cattle town. I thought of a scene from **The Searchers** in the early part of the film. The Texas Rangers and John Wayne's character, Ethan, are surrounded by hostile Indians; the same Comanches who had just slaughtered most of Ethan's family. It is night and they are facing attack and possible death at any moment. The captain of the Rangers:

"Do you want to quit, Ethan?"
Wayne looks the Captain right in the eye.
"That'll be the day."
My next trip will be to Houston.

* * * * *

23

The week before I finished work Dasha Epstien called, she was exicted.

"I've read your play. I like it very much and want to move forward. Do you have to play the lead?"

"No, I don't."

"Good. What do you think of Jim Dale?"

"He's great. He won the Tony Award for Barnum."

I phoned Charles Von Nostrand, the president of Samuel French Publishing, and asked him for twenty minutes of his time.

"It is 11:15 can you be here at 2:00?"

I phoned my co-author and he met me at the Samuel French office. I explained my situation and Mr. Von Nostrand was most reassuring that he would take care of my interests. I knew him to be a man of character and I would not have to worry about contracts or my royalties.

He would be the agent if this continued to move forward. This launched a series of meetings between Jim Dale, Dasha Epstien, my co-author and myself. We managed to agree before I left for MD Anderson that Dasha would fly Joe Harmston over from England to meet with her. The conclusion was that we would open off-Broadway in October. This was very exciting because with the track record and financial backing of Dasha and a Tony award winner, we were on our way.

On my last day of working on **As The World Turns,** one of Stenbeck's plots was about to backfire. While James hides in a cabin deep in the woods and waits for his contact to spirit him out of the country, he overhears his son giving the police directions to his hideout. The SWAT team arrives and surrounds the cabin. They burst through the door, and poof: James Stenbeck had disappeared into thin air.

I said good-bye to the crew. Before I got out of the studio the director, Maria Wagner, and Felicia came out of the control booth. Maria and I had worked together since 1980. There were tears in her eyes. I knew Felicia had told her. After some big hugs, I walked out of CBS and stood on the sidewalk at 57th Street and looked at the building. Since August of 1974 -- I'd gone through those doors, frantic about the day's work. As the years passed, I became more confident with my craft. As an actor, I had grown up in this building. I hoped I would one day return to my work and the show that had been such a big part of my life.

* * * * *

Me and Crip-1946

My Grandfather-1961

MAY 26 '43 ATLANTA GA

My Grandmother-1943

Anthony and
Mr. Heston

1968

Tom Gries-
Director of the
film Number One

1968

Malibu

1975

U.S. Senator Thad Cochran
Columbus, Mississippi

John Grisham, Evans Harrington
Oxford, Mississippi

Cleavon Little

Cleavon and Frank Sacks

Sarah and James Brady, Larry Bryggman, Anthony, Kate
McNeil, David Forsyth, Judy Blazer, and Meg Ryan

Don Hastings, Elaine Princi, Eileen Fulton,
Zsa Zsa Gabor, and Anthony

James and Barbara
1980

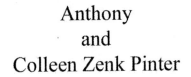

James Stenbeck

Anthony
and
Colleen Zenk Pinter

Basha and alligator - Wiggins

Anthony directing The Wide Net

Willie Nelson, Anthony and Susan Strickler

Basha and "Sister" Bobbie Nelson

Bobby Worsham - Corinth, Mississippi

One Man Show

Paul English
aka
El Diablo

Working with Steve McGraw
on Poetry Theatre

My donor Brother John

Dr. Bobbie MacGuffie

Joyce Neumann
on the Debra Duncan Show

Stella
Adler

24

The MD Anderson Cancer Center in Houston, Texas was where my friend Sally Burdine had been treated for cancer. In the fall of 1983 I would not have been able to make **Mississippi Delta Blues** without the help of Hank Burdine. Hank was from an old Delta plantation family in Greenville, and not only had the family clout, and connections to get permission from local plantation owners to film on their property, but he also had an appreciation of what I was attempting to accomplish: to capture a part of southern culture which would soon be gone forever.

Hank found great locations like Leon's Playhouse and the Salvation Baptist Church on Panther Burn Plantation. Making the film was a creative high for me, because it was my first venture having complete artistic control of a production. It was my film. I overheard a few sarcastic mumbles from the young New York film crew about the "soap opera actor" but I reminded them it was this actor's money financing the project. The following year, with Peter Hammer's brilliant editing – **Mississippi Delta Blues** won five film festival awards. It was a good year for Hank too. He had been courting Sally, a beautiful Florida lady who became Mrs. Burdine a few months later.

In December of 1997 I got a call from Hank. Sally had cancer. He'd kept up with what I had been through at Sloan-Kettering and said Sally needed my input and support. We had long talks and she kept me informed about her research on different cancer treatment centers from California to Florida. She told me that after her first meeting at MD Anderson, she knew that was where she wanted to be treated.

The fact that I had relapsed was distressing to Sally on two accounts. She was upset for me, and it brought up the fear that she too could relapse. But Sally was positive. She reminded me of some of the ideas and encouragement I'd given her the year before. Now she was the strong one giving me support and helping me find the courage to continue to fight.

Hank and Sally had become friends with Desiree and Dick Howe in Houston. They were a dynamic, retired couple and used their time and position to help patients with cancer, and were involved in many volunteer areas at MD Anderson.

Dr. Chatham had written Dr. Medina at MD Anderson and I had scheduled an appointment to see him on March 5th. Sally contacted Desiree and left a phone number with which to contact her on my service. Desiree was in Acapulco. When we connected by phone, she couldn't have been more gracious. She assured me the bone marrow transplant team was great. Desiree and her husband planned to be back in Houston two days before I arrived, and in her soft but firm southern accent, she insisted, "You stay with us on this trip. It'll be our pleasure and we can talk about it." I accepted.

The jet airplane can contribute to life's confusions. In less than five hours, I had gone from the hectic, high-rise lifestyle of New York City, Gotham, to the slower, flat open spaces of Houston, Texas. I received a warm welcome in the Howe's home.

We had dinner and talked about **"IT."** Cancer. I learned that Desiree had lost her first husband of twenty-eight years to cancer and Dick had lost his first wife of thirty years to cancer. We discussed treatments, religion, and courage, but it was not a maudlin evening. It was tough stuff and it was straightforward.

Dick had a splendid collection of music boxes and a German orchestra machine. I told them how much Basha liked music and antiques. Dick was originally from Minnesota and Desiree had been raised in Alabama. She and I told stories about our childhoods in the South. Those first hours in Houston could have been painful alone in a motel, because Desiree and Dick's kindness and compassion, I had a restful night's sleep.

* * * * *

The MD Anderson complex is large and impressive. When I arrived on the eighth floor and sat in the waiting area, I was ten minutes early. I tried reading a tennis magazine, then Time, but I couldn't concentrate. Just like in the waiting rooms at Sloan-Kettering, there were married couples and families, waiting and consoling each other. As I made eye contact with one man, he smiled and nodded. My chest filled with emotion at the simple kindness in the face of the pain and agony we were all dealing with. I smiled and nodded back. I felt a little stronger.

Then a powerful male voice with a military-like command filled the waiting room, "Mister Herrera."

"Yes."

A tall, pleasant looking fellow in top physical condition stepped forward and put out his hand.

"I'm Darnell, Dr. Medina's nurse. Will you come with me please?"

"You sound like a drill sergeant."

"I'm in the active Reserves and just got back from camp."

"Got my attention."

He took me to an examination room.

"If you'll just wait here, Dr. Medina will be right in."

I paced back and forth. A pastoral landscape painting on the wall gave me a second of comfort. Someone had realized that a lyrical setting might give a patient a momentary reprieve.

When Dr. Medina came through the door and introduced himself, he immediately reminded me of a Herrera. He was from Spain. He could easily have been one of my father's younger brothers. My father's grandfather was from Cadiz on the southwest coast of Spain. His mother was born in Madrid. Dr. Medina's profile, and even the shape of his hands and fingers could have been from the same gene pool as my paternal grandparents, but the physical traits were where the Herrera resemblance ended.

Dr. Medina was calm in his manner and self-assured in his approach. He didn't rush. He looked at me directly and spoke clearly and to the point. His confidence and intelligence inspired a sense of trust. He explained what he hoped we could accomplish.

The mini-allogeneic transplant would be less toxic because less chemotherapy would be used. At this point of relapse the amount of disease was minimal because of the four rounds of fludarabine I'd begun in November. The objectives of this transplant were:

1. For my brother's immune system to **engraft** in my bone marrow.

2. For the new immune system to **assimilate and to fight** the Mantle Cell Lymphoma and kill it.
3. For the new immune system **to keep the cancer out** of my body.

Each step of the process would be difficult, and with each step a lot of things could go wrong: a new set of hurdles to be cleared.

First, they would have to repeat certain tests that I had had for the autologous transplant in 1997. My heart and lungs had to be checked to see if these organs could endure a second transplant.

My brother John never did drugs or smoked; he had the occasional beer and that was it. At forty years of age he was still an active athlete. Even so, he had to undergo a battery of tests to qualify as a donor.

The allo-transplant itself, if insurance, my physical condition and my brother's tests all worked out, would:

1. Require a three to four-week stay in the hospital.
2. Require me to stay in Houston, within fifteen minutes of the hospital for the next one hundred days.
3. Require someone to live with me during this time, not a health care professional but someone close to me on a personal level.

When he finished his summary of what was to happen next, we stood up and shook hands. Dr. Medina smiled.

"Very nice to meet you, Mr. Herrera. I wish it were under different circumstances."

"Dr. Medina, it has been good to meet you. I want to get on with this, and I'm glad we didn't hate each other because you were the end of the line."

* * * * *

That night I met John and sisters Monica and Carla at a Houston steak house. I proposed a toast.

"I appreciate your help and support, which I accept on one condition: that our mother, or our father, or all the agony we went through being 'Johnny and Theresa's children will never be discussed.'"

Monica's glass came up hard and fast and a little wine sloshed-out as all four glasses clinked together. She exclaimed, "Yes. Oh, yes. I'll drink to that." John joined in with "Great idea!" and Carla with a "Yes, let's all drink to that." The food was good and our sibling reunion upbeat.

Later in the kitchen at Carla's house, her husband Walter didn't yet know of our pact and started talking about our father. Walter had been advising him on some IRA's, and told the story of when Johnny had buried eight thousand dollars in hundred dollar bills in a piece of plastic pipe. When he dug it up five years later, the moisture had fused them all together and he couldn't peel the bills apart. That was one of the funny stories. I slipped into the old pattern and brought up the fact that most of the fights that took place every night Daddy was home and which often lasted until after midnight, were about money. He hadn't contributed to my support since I was twelve. My brothers or sisters earned all of their expense and clothes money through high school, and put themselves through college.

My nightcap had kicked-in and I remarked, "The only thing likely to upset the old man about my illness was if he thought he would die before I did."

John just looked into the middle distance. "You know, you're right, it's sad but you're right."

We then changed the subject to sports and show business, and had some laughs before sleep.

* * * * *

25

One cold and rainy night just before I left New York for my stay in Houston, Basha and I had been to the movies. We were in front of the Millenium Hotel across the street from her apartment on 44th Street. Basha told me to stay under the canopy and hailed a taxi. As a couple climbed out, I jumped in and I saw a young woman running towards me. As I started to close the door, I noticed her feet; she was wearing high-heeled dress sandals and thin white socks. Without looking up I said, "Get in."

She did.

"You're not dressed for this weather. Where are you going?"

"To 74th and Columbus."

"I'll drop you. Driver, let's take this young lady to 74th and Columbus and then I'm going on to 82nd and First Avenue."

"I was about to freeze."

"Where are you from?"

"California, Newport Beach, I'm a buyer here on business. I work for a chain of clothing stores, and I'm not prepared for this kind of weather."

"I lived in Malibu and Beverly Hills from 1975 to 1980."

"Oh, really, did you ever get to Santa Barbara? That's where I'm from originally."

"Yes, in fact one of the most beautiful places I've ever seen was the Old Spanish Mission Church there. My oldest friend in California is from Santa Barbara, Sondra Baker, her daughter got married there."

For the first time the young lady and I really looked at each other. She was very attractive. She gave me an incredulous look.

"You were at Thais' wedding!"

"Yes. You mean Thais, Sondra's daughter. Yes I was there."

"Oh, my God, so was I. Sondra is my first cousin."

"Unbelievable. I haven't talked to Sondra in, probably three years."

"So you don't know that Thais had cancer. Sondra's spent the last three years taking her to every clinic in Europe and the States."

"Is she all right? I mean I've known Thais since she was four years old. She's had cancer?"

"She nearly died, but she's in remission now. They have both fought hard for three years."

We arrived at her stop. I wrote my cell phone number on one of the flyers from my one-man show and gave it to her.

"Please have Sondra call me; the last number I had was the old one in Malibu."

"Yes, I will. Thank you for the ride."

"Please don't forget."

"I won't."

What an extraordinary world! Hardly anyone shares taxis anymore. Without the freezing wind and rain, no young woman would hop in a cab with a stranger. Bizarre, how I learned a very special friend of many years and her child had been suffering through the same battles I had been fighting. I shouldn't have let so much time go by without finding Sondra. If she gets my number she'll call me. Thais once stayed in my apartment years ago when she was in New York. She used to call me Uncle Anthony. I hope she's still in remission.

* * * * *

26

Two days later I was in Houston. Brother John had come through all his tests with flying colors. He had started the Neupogen shots, which would stimulate his bones to overproduce cells for his stem cell harvest. He was driving in from Austin, and we all met at La Quintana, a magnificent Mexican restaurant.

I had warned him that the Neupogen would probably cause him a good deal of pain and to make sure they gave him some Tylenol with Codeine. His reply sounded just like our father.

"I've talked to a nurse and a doctor friend of mine. I know what to expect."

Our father knew little but liked to be an authority on everything. He was simply never wrong. If one of us dared to express an opinion he would make us feel like a fool, or at best declare "You think you know, but you don't know." He always knew "a fella" who was an authority on any subject at hand, and discounted any knowledge or idea put forth by his wife or children. We never got the name of that "fella" or any of his sources. As my siblings and I grew older and my father was threatened by our discussions or felt he was unable to control the situation, he would get up and simply leave the room.

John's remark about an outside authority sounded just like our father, and he couldn't recognize the pattern of his behavior because he'd had never had psychotherapy.

When he arrived for our dinner he looked very uncomfortable and moved like a robot.

"I hurt. It comes and goes. It's weird."

"Did you get any Tylenol with Codeine?"

He kind of laughed. "No."

We had a lighthearted evening. John was the brunt of a few jokes from his older siblings, no sarcasm, nothing cutting, just fun.

* * * * *

The next morning, getting out of the shower I heard Carla in the hall and called out.

"Carla . . ."

When she heard my voice, frightened, like Pavlov's dog she responded, "Yes, Sir?"

I put a towel around me and came out of the bathroom.

"Carla, please, I am not our father. I am your brother."

"I know. I'm sorry."

"Sorry. Don't be sorry."

"I can't help it."

Then her two little boys ran out of the kitchen and started pulling on her. Again she apologized.

"I gotta feed these kids before we go."

* * * * *

Carla dropped me off at MD Anderson for my first meeting. Desiree Howe had introduced me to Lynda Mundy in the Office of Patient Affairs. Lynda was originally from my hometown, Wiggins. It was great to hear her exclaim,

"Oh yes, your grandparents were fine people."

She set me up with Andrea McMillan who would be my social worker/psychologist and help with logistical problems like housing and scheduling conflicts. I was right on time and she didn't keep me waiting. She struck me as a personable, pretty redhead but I wondered if she was smart. Andrea was very smart. She asked me questions about my psychological history and experiences at Sloan-Kettering.

She was very direct.

"Will you be able not to drink alcohol during treatment?"

"Of course. I don't want to die."

We went over the fact that my parents would probably not be visiting, which she found strange but accepted it. We talked about my relationship with Patsy, my sisters in Houston and my affection for Basha.

Then she asked me about money, caretakers and my practical living situation for the hundred days I'd need to remain near the hospital.

I briefly told her about **Smoke & Mirrors** and the plan to produce it off-Broadway in October. I explained that since I'd worked on **As The World Turns** until I left for Houston, I was in relatively good shape for rent, food, taxis and any expenses my SAG and AFTRA insurance wouldn't cover. Also that Felicia Behr, the executive producer was putting me back to work in the fall as soon I had the strength.

"You are very fortunate to have all of those positive things in your life to look forward to."

With regard to caretakers, I told her I'd lined-up my actor friend Patrick for the first week, Basha for the month of May and I'd also scheduled my old roommate from Malibu, Frank Sacks, Patsy, Tandy Cronyn, as well as a life long friend, Malcomb. If there were any gaps, my sisters or my brother John would be able to stay with me.

I went on to tell her about Malcomb, and how far we'd gone since we'd left Wiggins. We would have a lot to talk about.

When we concluded, Andrea commented,

"I think you are planted in reality and ready to face what is ahead of you."

"You mean this was an interview to see if I qualified for a transplant on an emotional level?"

Andrea looked right into my eyes and smiled,

"Yes. Some patients are not emotionally strong enough to make it through a transplant. I think you are."

* * * * *

I met with Dr. Valentine, a psychiatrist. He was tall, lean and seemed a little shy. I summed up my psychiatric history much as I had done for Dr. Holland at Sloan-Kettering. He told me that she was his mentor and that Dr. Holland was the pioneer of Oncological Psychiatry. He said there would be many emotional *"ups and downs, or hills and valleys"* during treatment, but stressed that whatever difficulties lay ahead, "we" would deal with them.

I paused, stared at the floor for a second, then looked him in the eye, "I could die. There is that chance."

"Let's hope not, but - yes - there is that possibility and if it becomes necessary, we'll deal with it."

I had to have tests for my lungs and heart. As I found my way to that floor, I thought how fortunate I was to have such a bright and perceptive psychiatrist as Dr. Valentine right there on staff for me. Next, another bone marrow aspiration, and the memory of Dr. Levine's "This is going to hurt" made me cautious. Because of Dr. Gabrilove's consideration for the patient during the procedure, I knew the difference.

MD Anderson is a giant complex with blue zones, red zones and green zones and a nurse escorted me to the clinic. I asked, "Do they use anesthesia?"

She thought a second.

"I don't know. I don't think so."

Without getting upset, I simply replied, "If they don't use anesthesia, then I'm not doing it."

She gave me a questioning look,

"I'll be right back."

A couple of minutes later she came back with a pleasant looking black man, who put out his hand,

"I'm Larry. I hear you have some concerns."

I briefly told him about Dr. Levine's drilling me without giving me anything for pain and he grimaced.

"No. We don't do it that way here."

A middle-aged woman who was one of his patients who was just leaving caught my eye. "He's the best. I've been going through this for six years and Larry's the best."

"That's good to hear."

Larry patted my shoulder, "It'll be just a few minutes. We'll get through this; don't *you* worry."

Even though I had been assured, I was nervous as I crawled up on the table and lay face down. I could hear two other people in the room. Larry's voice was comforting and reassuring.

"These two ladies are going to help me. I understand you are on TV."

As they prepared, Larry told me he was interested in film making, had taken a course and directed a documentary. He wiped the top of my buttock with something cold.

"Okay. Here we go. You are going to feel a little Bee sting."

He was correct. It was sort of like a bee sting; it didn't hurt as much or as long, but I felt it. He continued to talk me through the procedure in much the same way Dr. Gabrilove had.

During the pauses I told him that I had also made a documentary film and he said he'd like to see it.

"If we get through this and nothing hurts worse than the bee sting, I'll give you a copy."

I heard a little laugh.

"There we are. All finished."

As I started to get off of the table, Larry and one of the assistants helped me keep my balance.

"Take it slow Mr. Herrera."

I shook his hand.

"Larry, I'll bring you a copy of **Delta Blues**. Thank you for not hurting me."

* * * * *

27

4141 Oberlin Drive was the address of an unfurnished house for rent near Rice University. Fortunately Monica had found it and it was perfect for my stay. It had two bedrooms, two baths and a big backyard. I could be at MD Anderson within fifteen minutes.

In recent years University City had become one of Houston's exclusive areas; many modest houses built after World War II were being torn down and replaced by luxury homes. The lawns were neatly groomed, the neighborhood was very quiet and the rent was within my budget. A park and pool were two blocks away and the township's police force was like having a private patrol. The owners, Chris and Judy Simon were very polite and she pointed out that my next-door neighbor, Dr. Paul Spring, was a surgeon at MD Anderson. I rented the house.

During my stay at Carla's it was impossible to have a conversation with my sister because her boys were constantly pulling on her and whining. I suggested we go outside because they kept turning up the television. They had a lovely backyard, and we sat at a picnic table under an oak near the tool shed. Carla had met Basha when we were married, and knew we were still friends. I told her a little about Patsy and asked if she would keep both of them informed if I was not able to communicate. There was also the practical; bills in New York, how to contact Landy Teller, a Sigma Chi brother and my lawyer in Mississippi and Dr. Sudarsky in New York in case they needed to pull the plug.

We had less than sixty seconds of privacy before her oldest boy started bouncing a tennis ball against the side of the tool shed. I was not used to kids, and my sister could not control her children.

"Carla, we can go over this in the car. I don't want to be late."

"Okay. I'm sorry."

"Damn it to hell, quit saying 'I'm sorry'. I didn't mean to yell at you, but your kids need to mind you. They pay no attention to anything you say."

"I know. I know."

Carla got upset and began to gesture like a mechanical doll.

"I just don't want them to have to jump to attention like little soldiers the way we had to."

"There's a middle ground. Look I haven't been around for years. I haven't been any kind of an Uncle to these kids."

"We'd better go. We might hit traffic."

Unlike her husband's car, which was brand new and cool inside, Carla's car had a large dent in the door, a torn headliner and the air conditioner didn't work. In Houston, Texas, every summer day is 95 to 101 degrees and she chauffeured her kids everywhere. She apologized for her car and she apologized for the heat. It was sad for me to see my beautiful sister embedded in the female victim role established by our mother.

Soon we were on Holcombe Boulevard just a few blocks from M.D. Anderson. Carla was shaken.

"Are you going to be in a lot of pain?"

"Pain is part of it. Dr. Bobbie MacGuffie told me that the body has built-in amnesia when it comes to physical pain. Otherwise a woman would never have more than one baby."

"She's right about that!"

"I just want to get on with it."

"Are you scared?"

"No."

"I would be."

"I'm not afraid of what's ahead, I mean the transplant."

Carla looked very distraught.

"I don't mean that I'm not afraid of dying. I am -- I think. But at Sloan-Kettering I tried very hard to see the experience as an adventure. May sound strange but if I could stay in that mental state for most of the time, I did okay. And as Peter Pan said, *'To die must be an awfully big adventure.'* But I hope to wait on that."

* * * * *

The lady at the admissions desk told me Dr. Medina wanted to see me before I checked into my room. When I went to the eighth floor, Darnell came right out and showed me into an examination room.

"I'll let Dr. Medina know you're here."

I was sitting in the same chair, looking at the same painting, when he came in. "Mr. Herrera, the lab found an antibody in one of your blood tests."

"What's an antibody?"

"You have been exposed to hepatitis."

"Doctor, this is no time to dodge the truth. I have never done intravenous drugs."

"You can also be exposed by blood transfusions or sex."

"I had a transfusion Saturday before I left New York."

"That's not enough time for it to have shown up on this test. I don't think it's an active antibody. I think there's only a one or two percent chance that it is active."

"So what does all this mean?"

"If it is active, and we proceed with the transplant, there is a 50% chance you will develop Hepatitis."

"And that could kill me?"

"Yes."

With the trigger finger of his right hand, Dr. Medina pushed back the tip of the middle finger on his left hand as he talked. Then he started playing with his wedding ring. He was a bit nervous and I felt that he hated having to relate this potentially very bad news.

"And, if we don't proceed with the transplant, the Mantle Cell Lymphoma will definitely kill you."

"What do we do?"

"You have to decide if you want to wait until we get the results of the lab test back, or proceed now."

"How long will it take for you to get the results?"

"Nine days."

"Nine days? What takes so long?"

"They have to grow the cultures and then perform the test."

"Doctor, what do you think I should do?"

"Mr. Herrera, I cannot decide that for you."

"I have a doctor friend - she's a surgeon . . . she's like family and has practiced medicine for a long time. Perhaps you could talk to her."

"That won't change any of the facts. You have to tell me."

"Will the lymphoma grow a lot if we wait the nine days?"

"It shouldn't. There is very little disease at this time."

"I'll have to think. I'll call you tomorrow."

I made it into the waiting room. Andrea McMillan approached me.

"How's it going, Mr. Herrera?"

I told her. She suggested that I talk to Dr. Valentine and that I could call her anytime. But then, what next? I just stood there in the waiting area. I could either fall on the floor and cry and scream and cuss, or do what? I managed to get in the elevator and push "1". In the lobby, there were a lot of people rushing around; patients, nurses, young doctors in serious conversation, orderlies, a beauty parlor-coiffed, gray-haired lady with a coffee cart, a guard. I was about to crack. Who the hell were all these people? I found my way outside, looked up at the sky and said, 'Look Universe, I don't know how much more of this I can take.'

I called "B" Spears, Willie Nelson's bass player. The last time I'd called him, they were in Hawaii. They could be in Oregon or Maine. I had no idea where they were now. He answered on the second ring and I told him what I was up against. They were in Austin and headed to a casino in Louisiana just the other side of the Texas state line for a three-day gig.

"Just come over."

"Well, I'll try and see you in a few days."

"We'll be there tomorrow. Come over tomorrow."

Later at Carla's house, I went out into the street. This was Middle America. Other than a few young kids playing in the yard next door, the street was empty. How the hell would I get through the next hour?

Dr. Valentine called me on my cell. I explained that the atmosphere in my sister's house was driving me crazy and that I had an invitation from the Willie Nelson band. I was so panic-stricken that he had to say it twice before his advice sunk-in.

"It is a work in progress, this struggle; one day, one hour, one minute at a time. You cannot solve it immediately. You have to deal with it as best as you can and think how privileged you are to have an invitation to spend this difficult time with good friends."

* * * * *

Walter and Carla offered to drive me to Louisiana, and on the way, my brother-in-law asked three times, "Do you really know these guys that well? I mean, that you can just go and get on the bus with them? How do you know Willie Nelson?"

My mind needed a break from the antibody question anyway. I explained that I had written a screenplay, **Hands On The Wheel**, and that's how I'd met Willie in 1987. The title came from a song on his album, **The Red Headed Stranger.**

> *"I've looked to the stars,*
> *I've tried all of the bars,*
> *and I've nearly gone up in smoke.*
>
> *Now my hands on the wheel of*
> *something that's real,*
> *And I feel like I'm going home."*

It was set in 1953 rural Mississippi, and was a prodigal son story about a white family with a destructive father and a black family, living on a dirt farm. They made moonshine during the depression to keep from losing the farm. The name of the leading black character was "Crip" and Cleavon Little had agreed to play the role. I was attempting to relive some of the glory of my early childhood hero by way of my friend, Mister Little.

From 1987 – 1990 I spent a few months a year working on **As The World Turns,** and the remainder flying back and forth to Hollywood. I never got the money together to make the film and learned painfully that the money side of show business was not my forte.

I remained friends with Willie and "B". Over the years of "on the road" visits, I became friends with the crew and the rest of the band, even the legendary "El Diablo" - Paul English. He always wore black. He had been with Willie since 1956.

For the first five years I knew them, Paul did not even acknowledge my presence. He never spoke or nodded; it was as if I didn't exist. Then one summer day in a big, open public park in New Jersey, Paul climbed on the band bus, gave an update on show time and then turned to me, "Anthony, you want to take a walk?" He scared the hell out of me but . . .

"Sure."

We strolled around the edge of the park for over an hour and he told me that when he started with Willie in 1956, they'd played for eight dollars a night, and how Willie wrote all the songs on the album "Yesterday's Wine" in less than a week. The stories just flowed out of him. This was American folk history and I was hearing it from the man who lived it. I was flattered and kept wishing I had a tape-recorder. From that day on, Paul was a friend and I felt that I was now accepted by all of Willie and Family.

* * * * *

We arrived at the casino, and a guard directed us to the band buses in the back. I didn't know if my show business tale had interested my sister and her husband, but it took my mind off cancer for a few minutes. Those memories were important – at least to me. Just a few hours before it had taken all of my effort just to get on an elevator, to put one foot in front of another.

There they were - the three band buses, Willie's bus and the two band buses. These buses are big forty feet long. Moving houses. I knocked on the door of the middle bus and "B" Spears opened the door. Walter, Carla and I climbed aboard. Hugs, introductions and the latest jokes went around. Billy English plays percussion. Paul English, the drummer, has been with Willie since 1958. Mickey Rafael, the harmonica player, came out of the back with a book in his hand. He reads a lot.

A few hours later Mr. Nelson stepped up to the microphone.

"Whiskey River take my mind . . ." starts every concert. Carla and Walter sat out front in the audience. I was backstage with Pudie, the stage manager, Tommy the tuner, the crew . . . and the music.

Without any to do, it was as if I was a wounded pup, being carefully watched over and taken care of. I left the backstage area for a few minutes and went to get a vodka and tonic. When I got back Tommy asked, "Where have you been? "B" was worried about you."

"I just went to get a drink."

"Oh, good."

"B" caught my eye from the stage and gave me a wink. These guys had been on the road so long that they could communicate without words. I stayed until the closing song, which is usually Bob Will's **Milk Cow Blues**. At this particular show Willie had to stop after two hours. Often, if there's no time restraint, he just keeps playing his Martin guitar with the hole in it and keeps on singing. Years back, I saw him perform without a break for nearly four hours.

Walter and Carla wanted to go and gamble, and I went with "B" and Mickey to a crawfish house across the highway.

After dinner "B" said, "Let's see what Mr. Nelson is up to."

We knocked on the door of Willie's bus and LG, Willie's bodyguard and former Hell's Angel, welcomed us aboard. More handshakes and hugs and soon I found myself in serious conversation with Bobbie Nelson, Willie's sister. She'd been through a lot, knew loss and how precious each day was. Willie was sitting to my left. Suddenly I saw his hand come toward me holding a joint. The rolling paper on one side was hanging down. My mind swiftly computed that I didn't like pot but I could not refuse a toke from an icon. I thanked him, inhaled a small puff and passed it on to Bobbie. We really never stopped our conversation. About two minutes later the joint came around again; another toke, and I passed it on to Bobbie. The third time he handed it to me I finally had to say,

"I apologize, but this just isn't my drug. You have any alcohol?"

Without missing a beat Willie turned to his daughter, "Lana, open some red wine for Anthony."

Willie got up and put in a DAT tape of the show they'd performed that night. He reviewed every section with Bobbie and "B". As he listened intently, he picked up a fifteen-pound barbell and started doing curls with one hand and smoking a joint with the other. Then he would switch. They critiqued the whole show and after the audiotape was finished, Willie put on a video of the show they'd done the night before on **Austin City Limits** with the legendary fiddle player Johnny Gimble.

I thought, don't die, stay alive, get well, and go back to work. No wonder Mr. Nelson and his family were such fine musicians. They worked for decades and never stopped growing and learning. That scene was carved in my mind.

It wasn't Willie's marijuana or the wine that eased my angst, but my friends, who made it possible to rest that night. The next two days were filled with stories, jokes, music and friendship.

On the way back to Texas after the last show, Mickey Raphael and I talked long after the rest of the band were in their bunks asleep. Mickey had lost his father to cancer. We talked about women, music, poetry and finally what was ahead for me: the unknown.

Then I started a sentence, "You know if I were rich I would . . ." I stopped and listened to the hum of the bus tires on the highway. I looked into the dim light of the bus where the men who had taken such good care of me were sleeping. Mickey was silent as I looked back at him; I got emotional but managed to say, "I just realized something Mickey, I am a rich man. I am a very rich man."

* * * * *

28

The antibody was negative; we would proceed with the allogeneic transplant.

The first day in the hospital I had to get a catheter put in my chest. With mild sedation and no complications, the procedure was painless. The bathroom was spacious with handrails near the toilet and shower. The shower stall was large, had a seat and tap handles which made it easy to turn the water on and off. There was a Murphy bed in the wall so a caretaker or loved one could stay the night. The design of this hospital room was well planned for the patient.

I was started on chemo, and there was a parade of people in and out of my room with what seemed like a stream of countless forms and questions. In one group of about six, a young doctor was going over hygiene. To show them that I was a transplant veteran I said, "Yes, Liquid Dial Soap; I'll have my sister get me some."

A striking woman with red hair quickly interjected, "Your skin normally has an acidic ph (acid-base balance) to kill bacteria, and when we change it like some of these soaps do, we destroy the acidic protective environment on the skin surface. If the skin gets too dry and cracks, it creates a perfect way for organisms to enter our body, so for some minutes after using an antibacterial soap our skin has a decreased bacteria count. So, it's best if you use the liquid soap that is in your bathroom."

I couldn't read her nametag so I asked, "What is your name?"

"Joyce Neumann."

"I want you to stay with me through this whole thing."

She didn't even blink.

"All right."

That night Monica, Carla and Ed came to visit. They were uncomfortable. It was considerate of them to make the effort, but they were just standing there, not knowing what to do or say. It must have been strange for them to suddenly have a brother they barely knew and hadn't spent any time with, except for a few Christmases, years ago.

All they could relate to was what they'd seen on television. Ed asked, "Are you going to miss being on the show, I mean it must be fun with all those pretty girls?"

So, I told a story from 1968 when I was Charlton Heston's stand-in. I was excited all of the time and could barely sleep at night, even after twelve and fourteen hour workdays. Between takes, I saw Mr. Heston sketching. He saw me watching with total fascination.

"I do this to relax, for fun."

"Isn't acting fun?"

"Acting is my work."

My sisters and Ed seemed to enjoy hearing a story about Charlton Heston and I think they got the point.

The next morning the chemo hit me and I made it to the toilet before I threw up. This was peculiar. I had never thrown up from chemo. After a moment, I felt okay and got back into bed. My cell phone rang and I heard,

"Hello, Anthony Herrera, this is Sondra Baker. Where are you and what are you doing with yourself?"

"I'm in MD Anderson Cancer Hospital in Houston getting ready for my second bone marrow transplant for Mantle Cell Lymphoma."

"Oh my God."

Between the pills, the blood pressure and temperature checks, Sondra and I caught up on each other's lives. We talked about the early days in Malibu and our dear friend Cleavon. She told me about the three-year struggle with Thais' illness, how close she had come to dying. Thais had divorced her first husband who'd developed a drug problem. A year later she had fallen in love with a wonderful man, Fred. Two weeks after they met, she was diagnosed with cancer. He was still in love with her and they were recently married. Fortunately, Thais had remained in good health since her transplant the year before.

Even though we'd lose touch from time to time, over the years Sondra had become like family to me. We'd met in 1968 when Sondra was still acting. I played her husband in **Wait Until Dark** at the Hollywood Center Theatre. When I moved back to California in 1975, Sondra was one of the first people I went to see. The first time back at the beach in Malibu was a Sunday afternoon and we sat in the sand with a group of friends drinking wine. A black fellow came up and joined us with his two dogs Rufus and Barron. He put out his hand and said, "Hi, I'm Cleavon Little." That handshake started one of the deepest friendships of my life. When Cleavon died I was in Santa Monica. Sondra drove down from Santa Barbara and we went to his memorial together. We both loved and missed Cleavon.

* * * * *

Dr. Medina was on rounds that month so I got to see him the first thing every morning. After five days of chemotherapy, on April 6th 1999, I was infused with my brother John's stem cells. The physical procedure itself is not dramatic. They bring in a bag of what looks like finely ground hamburger, add the bag of cells to the pole holding other IV fluids, turn a little plastic valve and let the cells flow into my vena cava.

The mental and emotional part of the transplant is strange. In less than ten minutes, the stem cells taken out of my brother had been put into my veins. Hopefully they will make their way to my bone marrow, set up shop and kill the Mantle Cell Lymphoma.

Every morning I would ask Dr. Medina how he thought it was going. He assured me everything at this stage was just fine. It was too early to determine if the new cells were engrafting in my marrow. I remarked that I was feeling good, over all, and there was no pain and very little discomfort. Dr. Medina answered,

"You don't necessarily have to suffer."

Things went so well in the hospital that I was released a week early. By that time my sisters and brother had bought basic furnishings for my new home in suburbia. I treated myself to a new television and a VCR. In the yellow pages I found Anytime Piano and rented a piano so Basha could play her repertoire of classical and ragtime.

Mickey Raphael had put me in touch with a young friend he had met on tour, Angela Pillsbury. She had just moved to Houston and had offered to help me in any way that she could. Angela was kind enough to lend me an extra couch for the living room, and one day she came over with her mother, who happened to be a fan of mine and kept calling me "James." Normally that irritates me, but these ladies were too sweet to be annoying. I was also a bit flattered that my screen image as the dashing James Stenbeck had held-up, despite my current, gaunt and scary appearance.

There were no problems to date with the new stem cells floating around in my body, but I knew it would take several months for my strength and energy to return. John stayed with me on the weekends, and Carla and Monica would alternate during the week until my first caretaker arrived. I had a big, comfortable bed, a new TV, cable for the History and Discovery channels and old films.

Life was looking up.

* * * * *

Since things had gone so smoothly, I decided to treat myself to a new laptop. John did the driving and then we had dinner. There I was, a few days after a stem cell transplant, shopping and eating at restaurants.

I was in the house a week earlier than expected, and hoping Patsy might visit and help me get settled. She had a trip planned to New Orleans and I asked if she might be able to squeeze-in a day or two to come to Houston. She made up every excuse she could; the hotel reservations were already made, her friends expected her there on Thursday, dinner reservations were made and she had already committed to coming to Houston for a week in July. I got upset, and it turned into an argument. I needed help, and she wouldn't come. I was very upset.

I called Dr. MacCavoy in New York and she asked, "Are you ready to marry Patsy."

"No."

I saw Dr. Valentine the next day. "Are you ready to end the relationship."

"No."

"Well then." He shrugged.

"You haven't told me what you think I should do."

"Mr. Herrera, take the high road."

I lost it. "You know doctor, sometimes I get frustrated with all this mental health crap. I want to tell her she's a selfish bitch who cares more about getting drunk with her white-trash friends, than taking care of me. To hell with taking the high road."

"Mr. Herrera, that's up to you."

I think he was aware that I was airing-out my psyche. Deep inside, I had known for some time that Patsy was not as involved with me as I was with her. I liked and admired her children and saw the potential for a serious long-term relationship, but Patsy was still emotionally shattered over the failure of her marriage. She wasn't ready or willing to make a real emotional investment in me.

* * * * *

The next night the muscle in my left calf suddenly twisted into a knot. I'd been told to call the Emergency Room if anything at all went wrong, so I called and they told me to come in. My sister Monica came with me, and when the nurse stepped out and called "Herrera" I was standing at the counter. As my sister stood up, the nurse asked, "Mr. Herrera, do you want to come in with your wife?"

"I'm the patient."

"Oh. I thought it was her."

It turned out just to be a cramp, but they emphasized I had done the right thing because it could have been a blood clot. Monica was embarrassed by the confusion over who was the patient; she was pale and drawn and she knew she didn't look well.

"I've always been a little frail and have low blood pressure."

I was saddened by her listlessness. She had never recovered from my parents' abuse and at fifty years of age she still felt unworthy. My sister's symptoms were now physical as well as emotional.

* * * * *

29

The little house on Oberlin Drive had a nice feel to it. I was comfortable and relieved the ordeal was over, but still had a gnawing feeling in my gut that the transplant had gone too smoothly, and something was going to go wrong. I wrestled back and forth with what Dr. Medina had said about
"Not having to suffer."
At MD Anderson, the oncologists work with a team which consists of a Transplant Clinical Nurse Specialist and a PharmD. A PharmD has a Doctorate in Pharmacology, plus a year in Pharmaceutical Oncology, followed by yet another year of study in bone marrow transplantation. The first PharmD who worked with me was Kristin. She had been an officer in the US Navy and presented a no-nonsense demeanor.

Between Dr. Medina and PharmD Kristin, I had been prescribed so many different drugs that I was losing pills and having difficulty keeping track of what to take when. Kristin suggested I get a pillbox divided into little sections to help keep track of my drug schedule. So that night, I stopped by the Eckhard Drug store in the strip mall on the way to my house. I chose one with seven rows across for each day of the week, and four rows down for morning, noon, early evening and night. As I snapped the small compartments open and shut to test them. It struck me, "You are sick. You are very sick. You have to take mountains of pills. You are in a foreign territory holding a plastic box with twenty-eight separate compartments for drugs you have to consume daily hoping to stay alive. What the hell has happened to me? Why am I here? To fight cancer. I don't want a little box! I want to be on a horse with a Colt .45 on my hip and a Winchester .30 -.30 in my hand just like Burt Lancaster or The Duke would carry. But, for now, my horse was an old Mercedes and my weapon was made of plastic. So I bought some bottled water, toilet paper and the damned dinky box with its twenty-eight little lids.

* * * * *

Patrick St. Espirit was my first caretaker. He was in the original tour of **Smoke & Mirrors** I'd produced in Mississippi in 1991. He played the role of Derek; the drugged-out, drunken, jailbait obsessed movie star who was also a very bad actor. Patrick is a wonderful actor and powerful athlete and was very, very funny in the role. We started the tour at my alma mater, Ole Miss in Oxford. The writer, John Grisham, and my major professor, Evans Harrington, were there on opening night. Patrick traveled with his King James Bible and many a night after the play, we would stay up very late in deep discussions of theology and philosophy. These were hard working and strenuous weeks, but fine times.

The Friday night before he arrived, I woke up covered in sweat at 5:00 a.m. My fever had shot up to 103. I went to the Emergency Room and landed back in the hospital. Within the first twenty-four hours they brought the fever down from 103.

The next day it rose to 101.5. I felt that something had gone wrong. Sunday morning a Dr. Kornblau came in my room. He was on rounds for May, and he listened to my chest, felt for lumps on my neck and under my arms. He didn't have on a white coat but did have on the yellow mask everyone was required to wear. He wore tennis shoes and Levy's. He paced back and forth without saying a word, a very intense man.

"What do you think went wrong doctor?"

"I don't know."

He paced back and forth two more times and left. I thought, "Who is this guy in tennis shoes?" but then remembered that it was Sunday.

Dr. Kornblau came back the next morning followed by several white coats. He went through his routine and started to pace.

To relate to him, I asked, "I bet you're from New York."

He paced and without looking up.

"No."

"I don't mean necessarily Manhattan; Brooklyn or Queens."

"Not even close. See you tomorrow."

The guessing game about Dr. Kornblau's hometown continued. He allowed me one chance per day.

"Chicago?"

"No."

"Los Angeles."

"No."

He was Jewish and with my limited knowledge of Jewish populations, I was running out of options.

"San Francisco."

"Wrong. Tell you what Mr. Herrera, when you come up with the right city, I'll let you go home."

Our little game helped me I realize that his concentrated pacing back and forth was his way of working. I also appreciated that this serious doctor had a sense of humor.

Patrick had to go back to Los Angeles. He had come to see me every day and would hold up his King James Bible and pray aloud that God would continue to give me strength and that the fever would leave my body. The nurses who came in during his prayers would wait politely until he finished. I still had a fever and had not been released, so Patrick left Houston a bit saddened. But his faith had given me strength, and I believe that somewhere in the cosmos, the positive force of those prayers was working. I also knew that I was blessed to have a friend with such strong faith.

* * * * *

My primary drug was FK506, or Tacro. Tacro suppressed my new immune system so that it could assimilate into my system and slowly learn to distinguish between my healthy organs and cells, and the lymphoma cells.

As the week progressed I began to feel better and only had a fever a few hours a day. Emotionally, I was fine. I had a CD player, brought Willie and Louis and added Agustin Lara. Lara was a Mexican composer known as the Irving Berlin of Latin America. His most famous song was **Granada.** I didn't understand most of the lyrics but this romantic music helped me.

Basha arrived in Houston in the late afternoon and went straight to the house to get settled in. I told her it was five or six miles but she said she wanted to walk to the hospital for the exercise and to get to know the area. I had learned a long time ago that if Basha wanted to do something, it was much simpler to say, "Okay, just be careful."

I could see a huge construction crane from my window. From eight until four it moved slowly back and forth, like a giant bird looking for food. How lucky were those workers, even in the Houston heat and humidity? My reality was this bed and this room.

I'd told one of the nurses that Basha was walking from University City. She remarked that some areas she was walking through were very dangerous after dark because young gangs would cruise around looking for trouble.

I went berserk.

"And this is a beautiful woman."

Her reply didn't exactly comfort me.

"She could be short, fat and ugly with a pockmarked face, and still be in danger with these gang types."

We waited another thirty minutes and then called the campus police and asked them to drive around and look for her. (MD Anderson is part of the University of Texas.)

Finally, at 7:30 Basha knocked on my door.

"Anthonee, that's me."

"I was worried about you."

"Ah. My feet hurt. It was a long, long way."

* * * * *

Basha and I had many adventures from the day we were married by Judge Jack Strong in Searchlight, Nevada to the day we crossed the Iron Curtain by car in 1988. That was the most dramatic moment in my life until I was diagnosed with cancer.

In West Germany our passports were taken and put in a suction tube that ran along a concrete barrier on the right side of a single lane bridge that stretched some three hundred yards over ground that was cleared and plowed as far as we could see in both directions. We were crossing the Iron Curtain. On the other side, the East German police asked in broken English if the radio in the car would "transmit?" I used my arms as if I were conducting an orchestra, "NO! Music. Music." and then he held up his hand as if it were a pistol,

"You have bing-bing?"

"No. No bing-bing."

And here we were over ten years later in Texas. She was as funny and as beautiful as ever.

Two days later my fever was down to 100 or 101 and only for a couple of hours a day. Dr. Kornblau let me go home on the condition that I came to the bed unit every day.

He signed the release papers and started out.

"San Diego?"

"St. Louis."

"St. Louis?"

"Yep. St. Louis."

* * * * *

30

That night Basha prepared broth with vegetables. My portion had half a carrot in it. I finished the broth. Basha wanted me to eat the carrot. My system was fragile, and I explained that my stomach was uneasy, but she insisted the carrot would be good for me and that I needed to build my strength. The exchange went back and forth and I ate the carrot. Two minutes later, I was in the bathroom throwing up. As I got back into bed, Basha exclaimed in an innocent tone, "psychosomatic."

We both laughed.

* * * * *

The bed unit consisted of twenty-six fully equipped hospital rooms in a big square around a nurse's station. If anything went wrong there was oxygen and all the equipment necessary for an emergency. A nurse's aide would take my temperature, blood pressure and weigh me before I was put in a room. If it took four hours to infuse the drugs and fluids ordered for that day; that's how long I would stay in the room. The bed would be changed so another patient could receive their treatment. Our appointments were staggered throughout the day, but often they would get backed up. In the waiting area for the bed unit we got to know each other; we became a club whose members all wheeled around their poles of fluids and waited for results of blood counts, Gallium Scans and CAT scans. We all had cancer, lived with the dread of our conditions taking a turn for the worse.

My routine was the same every day. After I would wake up I would just lie there for a moment and then make up my mind to get out of bed and go to the hospital. Before I could shower I had to tape a piece of plastic on my chest to cover the three lines that went into my port. Most of the time I could get some cereal to stay down; then I would call a taxi.

First, I had my blood drawn in the Diagnostic Clinic. Most of the technicians knew me from **As The World Turns**. Regina claimed me and I would wait for her. I nicknamed her "Miss Priss." She would greet me, put her arm around me and walk me to her little room where I would sit in a big chair and she would draw blood from my port. This would be sent to the lab and the results would be ready before they started my infusions for the day in the bed unit. If there was a significant change in my blood counts, there would be a conference between the PharmD, Joyce Neumann and Dr. Medina, to decide what drugs to change or add.

* * * * *

In the bed unit waiting area, a big tough-looking redheaded fellow kept staring at me. His wife was the patient, and he was with her every day, usually in a T-shirt with the sleeves rolled up. Each time I looked in his direction, he'd be glaring at me. One day my nurse Rosalie asked, "Mr. Herrera, you see that man over there?"

"Yeah, I think he has a problem with me."

"No, actually, he and his wife are huge fans of yours and they are just too shy to ask to meet you."

I felt small. I went over and introduced myself. Their name was Robinson and they were from Waco, Texas; over the next couple of weeks we talked. They didn't have insurance. He owned a sign company but had spent everything on her treatment. She was not doing well; she had no hair and her skin was a pasty gray. He always either held her hand or had his arm around her shoulder.

"Her doctor isn't very nice to us."

"Then to hell with him. Get another doctor."

"Well, we're meeting with another specialist next week about some kind of new experimental treatment."

Without a trace of self-pity she simply stated, "I don't know if I even want to try it. We've lost everything and I'm just so tired. I have been in pain so long and my quality of life is so miserable, I just don't want to fight anymore."

Then one day I didn't see them in the bed unit or in the halls. But I often thought about them. This big rough man had sacrificed everything he had for her. He was not bitter at all about losing his money. The last time we talked he was suffering because of the extent of her constant pain and he felt he was going to lose her. As a man and as a husband I became a fan of his.

* * * * *

During the day Basha swam in the community pool and walked in the park. The cats were kept out of my room. With my immune system bouncing all over the place one scratch could have caused infection. John had gotten her a bicycle and she explored the Rice University area and used the bike to do our shopping. She loved the tree lined streets and boulevards. "It's like having my own private woods and place to swim."

Most nights I would get a fever and chills and then vomit. For the fever Basha would put cold towels on my forehead. At the end of the second week I had another bone marrow aspiration, CAT scan and a Gallium scan. Fortunately all came back negative. No evidence of lymphoma; however, everyday I still had a low-grade fever.

I was in the bed unit seven days a week. So was Larry Pace, a pleasant man in his early forties from South Carolina. He was also a patient of Dr. Medina's and had recently gone through stem cell transplant. His white counts were very low and he was having trouble with swelling in his calves and ankles.

"I can hardly step up on a curb."

"But, Larry, you don't have any lymphoma in you."

"No."

He owned a computer business and always had his laptop with him. We would talk computers in the waiting area and at times when he finished up he would come to the room I was in and we would talk. He was very shy and sometimes he would just stand just inside of my room and be silent. I think he needed company and so did I.

Dr. Medina sent in a specialist from Infectious Diseases to try to find the source of the fever. The doctor was a woman, accompanied by a Fellow, Dr. Yee. He was very polite and told me his wife was a fan of mine. She thought there might be an infection at the tip of the catheter and wanted to change it from the right to the left side of my chest. But my main nurse in the bed unit, Rosalie, had changed the dressing that morning, and remarked that the incision and stitches were very clean, and there was no redness which was one of the first signs of infection. I told the doctor about the nurse's observation, but she dismissed me with a look, as if to say, ***"What do you know?"*** and ordered the procedure.

When they'd gone, I got out of bed, unplugged the pole from the wall socket and found Rosalie at the nurse's station. She didn't think switching from one side to the other made any sense at this time, but concluded, "She's the doctor."

"And I'm the patient. I think she insisted, despite my input and yours, so that we would know, and she could confirm, that she's a doctor."

"I just called and they can't schedule the procedure today; they are booked and it is 4:30 on Friday afternoon."

We smiled at each other and silently enjoyed our moment of victory over abrupt authority.

* * * * *

My sleep was erratic but when the fever subsided, I would usually drift off. One night I woke up and heard Basha in the living room playing Scott Joplin's "Solace." There was one section that she always rushed. I put on my robe and joined her.

"Basha, I've never directed you, but I want you to start the piece again and I want to give you some input."

Perhaps because of my condition, she readily agreed. We went through the piece several times. To be into the music and able to have input into something creative was fun for me.

The next afternoon John came and grilled a steak and some fish on the deck. I was able to eat a little and Basha even celebrated and had a beer. I sat and watched as my brother and Basha cooked and joked. We enjoyed each other's company. I snapped several pictures and savored the moment. It occurred to me cooking in the backyard, enjoying stories, each other's company and laughter – this is what emotionally healthy people do. It was a very rare event for me to get such pleasure from family. I liked the feeling.

* * * * *

Every Monday and Thursday I was treated in the bed unit with ampho. This was done in a special room, and I had to inhale drug mist spewing out of an atomizer for twenty minutes. A recent X-ray had shown no evidence of pneumonia, and that was their big worry at this stage of treatment. With a compromised immune system, if I were hit with pneumonia, it would probably be fatal.

I finished the ampho and moved into room 17 to get fluids. Joyce came in and we went over my counts. The creatinine level in one's blood shows if the kidney is functioning properly. My creatinine level was high and they still had no clue as to what was causing me to run a fever of 101 to 102 every day for two or three hours. I appreciated Joyce's straightforward manner, "The mini-allo transplant is a relatively new treatment and there are many side effects that are a mystery to us. We just don't know yet, why certain things happen to the patient, but we are learning more every day."

She patted my ankle and left.

After ampho I felt more lousy than usual. I checked my watch- two more hours in bed. After a while Dr. Yee came to inquire about my counts. He started commenting on the kidney and what could happen if my creatinine level went up too high.

"If the condition continues to worsen, it could become very dangerous; of course there is always dialysis."

This was very upsetting and I said I didn't think I was anywhere near that point.

"No, not now, but if . . ." and he went on speculating about kidney deterioration, as if he were reviewing chapters in a medical textbook, with each scenario worse than the one before. He concluded in that certain situations, "a patient like you would die." On that cheerful note he left my room.

My imagination took-off, and within seconds I was frantic about dying from kidney failure. I jumped out of bed, and yanked-out the plug to the pump on the pole with its four bags of fluids, rushed down the hall and stopped Dr. Yee at the nurses station.

"What the hell do you mean coming into my room and speculating on something that is not even happening?"

He made the mistake of saying, "You don't understand."

"I understand English very well, Doctor. You took off on a tangent and ended with 'a patient like you would die.' My creatitine is only up to 1.8 and it's never been above 2.0."

"You misunderstood."

"What did I misunderstand?"

He started to squirm and turned to Rosalie, "I was explaining that under certain conditions if certain things aren't treated, that it could be fatal."

"Doctor, gonorrhea can be fatal if it goes untreated. I've got enough to deal with without your speculative crap."

I went back to my bed as I attempted to calm down, Rosalie knocked gently. "I'm very sorry, Mr. Herrera."

"Why? You didn't do anything. He's the jerk."

"I'm sorry to see you upset."

"Please, don't you feel bad; all you do is try to take care of me."

She checked the levels of fluids in each bag and adjusted the lines.

"You only have about another hour."

"You're a good nurse, Rosalie."

Her professionalism and kindness helped. But then I began to obsess about his remark. I called Patient Affairs and Christine was in her office. I related the incident and asked whether she could handle the situation or I should ask Dr. Medina. She thought it best if Dr. Medina spoke to him.

The next day when I saw Dr. Medina, the first thing he said was, "Mr. Herrera, I am sorry about what happened yesterday."

Again I replied, "You didn't do anything to be sorry about."

"He's still learning. What do you want me to do about it?"

"Maybe he'll learn and maybe he won't, but I don't want that son of a bitch back in my room, ever."

Dr. Medina went over to the sink to wash his hands.

"I'll handle it, Mr. Herrera."

I never saw Dr. Yee again.

* * * * *

31

My days were filled by the hospital schedule and the nights were a combination of sweats, fever and chills. Every morning I walked down the long hallway to the Diagnostic Clinic to have blood drawn. It was a grind. One day I began to wonder what the hell am I doing all of this for? I may never get well. I started to sink and thought why take another step? Then I pulled up in my mind from my favorite film, where John Wayne is asked,

> **"Do you want to quit, Ethan?"**
> **"That'll be the day."**

I kept walking. From then on every day as I started down this long hallway I repeated that dialogue. This mantra became part of my routine and always gave me a boost of energy to begin the eight to nine hours in the hospital.

Time seemed a constant. It didn't move either fast or slow. My world was a low-grade fever, MD Anderson and Basha's company in the little gray house on Oberlin Drive.

My next scheduled caretaker was Frank Sacks but he had to postpone his arrival so Basha stayed an extra week. For five weeks we had lived together under the same roof in total harmony, with the humorous exception of the carrot. Basha and I were no longer man and wife or even lovers but we were family now. She had made up her mind to take care of me and that is exactly what she had done.

* * * * *

In the bed unit there was a new lady behind the sign-in counter. Nora was a black lady, an impeccable dresser and all business. A nice young man named Marco usually signed me in and he was always upbeat. But I accepted Nora's formality.

I noticed a tall fierce looking-man with olive skin, black hair and a full but neat mustache. His formidable appearance made him look as if he could walk into the toughest waterfront bar in the world and everyone would give him plenty of room.

He was standing next to his son, about ten years old, who was the patient. This little boy was in very bad shape. As this man looked at me, I thought he could be Argentine Caballero but I never heard him speak.

Within a few days I learned that he was from Turkey. His son's eyes were blank yet his face and body were filled with agony. The father caught my eye and then gestured with his hand as, to ask, "How are you?" I motioned back "okayish" and nodded and tried to show with body language that I wished them well. I think we understood each other because for the first time I saw this powerful man smile.

The chills and fever remained constant and for some reason I was vomiting once every night but now the fever came for two to three hours in the early morning. Dr. Medina, Joyce, even after test after test, no one could come up with any clue as to the source of the fever.

* * * * *

Frank Sacks and I met at Paramount Studios, when I first moved to California in 1975. A week later he called, said his roommate was moving out and asked whether I'd like to share his beach house in Malibu. 18964 Pacific Coast Highway was more like a cottage and not too expensive, so I moved in. My room was on the deck. My first day there I told Frank about my friend Sondra Baker who also lived in Malibu. Suddenly, I got the strange feeling that I had been in this house before. I picked up the phone and dialed Sondra.

"In 1969, you had a beach house and I came to a party and ended-up spending the night on your couch. What was that address?"

"18964 Pacific Coast Highway."

"I just moved in and my room is on the deck!"

"Yes, I added that a year before I moved."

"Incredible."

It turned out Cleavon Little lived about a hundred yards down the beach, and Frank and I have remained friends ever since Malibu.

When I told him I had relapsed and would need caretakers in Houston after the transplant, he immediately volunteered, "I've got plenty of work I can do on my laptop. Sign me up for a week."

Frank had been a Hollywood producer and agent, and in the early nineties; had written and produced **Extreme Justice** with Scott Glen.

He arrived in Houston, and settled in quickly. He took an inventory of household and food supplies, and went to the supermarket to stock up. The knob on the shift in my car had come apart; he purchased some crazy-glue and fixed it. He got a kick out of driving my old diesel Mercedes because he traded every year for the latest, most powerful vehicles. Had there been a hidden camera, one would have thought Frank was a professional caregiver he was so thorough.

We reminisced about those days on the beach on the Pacific and couldn't remember the names of most of the "girls we loved before."

We talked about Noel, Frank's dog. He was eighteen years old when I moved in; the red hair on his muzzle was now grey. Every afternoon Frank and Noel would take a walk on the beach. The last six months I was there he spent most of the day sleeping by the door waiting for Frank. His eyesight was such that he couldn't tell the difference between Frank and me until he was close and was sniffing our hand or leg. We would time him on how long it took him to get to his feet. Often it was a two to three-minute struggle.

I thought Noel had great dignity and used to kid, "Frank do you think Noel is CIA?"

Frank would laugh, "I suspect he is. But he won't talk about it."

As time went on, Frank had to carry him out and put him on the beach. The ocean air would lift his ears and he would close his eyes as if to fly away in a dream. One day he shook his head and took off running toward Cleavon's house. Frank couldn't believe it. He exclaimed, "Noel just ran over a hundred yards and then stopped. He's a very old man." Noel died that night.

* * * * *

A month after Barbara Steele and I moved into the flats of Beverly Hills, there was a bad storm and it washed away most of our little beach house. Frank moved into "town" and a year later married his downstairs neighbor, Paula. Their marriage worked and Frank adored his wife and his son, Spencer.

The second day after Frank arrived there was a heavy rain and the streets flooded. The water was a foot deep and covering the sidewalks. We waited an hour and the water went down some. Frank drove slowly and as we would pull away from the intersections, the exhaust from the tail pipe would sputter in the water.

"Sounds like a motor boat," and we would laugh.

Medically not that much happened that week. I would have bouts of vomiting at night along with a fever of 100 - 101.

Frank had to leave on Sunday and I would be alone most of the next week, but that was all right because John was coming on the weekend.

Monday I called England to ask Joe Harmston about the production of **Smoke & Mirrors**. He was having problems getting Dasha Epstein on the phone at her place in Spain. This was not a good sign. He blamed his bad Spanish for not being able to get through. I reminded him that when someone wants to get in touch they find a way.

Some good news health wise - the preliminary report from a recent CAT scan showed no evidence of disease.

* * * * *

My next caretaker was Malcomb, also from Wiggins. I was so looking forward to talking about where we came from, what we had learned. I wanted to go back in memory to our innocent teenage years when we went to record hops and danced to The Platters, Chuck Berry and Fats Domino. Recount the Sunday we sat in front of Robert Watts' Pure Oil service station and watched Highway 49 all afternoon because we had heard that Elvis was driving from Memphis to the Gulf Coast. That meant *he had* to drive through Wiggins. We were vigilant until dark. We never even saw a Cadillac.

He was a year older and enlisted in the National Guard for six months when he finished high school. After the football season my senior year, I was at a loss as to what to do with myself. I wanted to *"do something"* with my life but I didn't have a direction. When Malcomb came home after Guard camp we made a very bold plan for ourselves. We were going to go to Ole Miss! We met every Tuesday and Thursday night to learn new vocabulary words like, ***gregarious*** and the difference between ***etymology*** and ***entomology***. We memorized the titles of great novels and their authors. We didn't necessarily read them but we knew that F. Scott Fitzgerald wrote **The Great Gatsby**.

Our plan was so daring we didn't tell any of our friends because we knew we would be ridiculed. Did we think we were better than they were? Who were we to think we could go to Ole Miss?

In that era in my home state, the mystique surrounding the University of Mississippi was the equivalent of Harvard, Yale and Princeton rolled into one. Every doctor, lawyer and Indian Chief in the state had gone to Ole Miss since 1848. They had one of the strongest football teams in the SEC. And two beautiful young ladies from Ole Miss, Mary Ann Mobley and Linda Lee Mead had won the title of Miss America, in 1959 and 1960. It seemed unattainable.

Malcomb became a lawyer, moved to Washington D.C. early in his career and became very successful. He retired early and spent his time traveling and studying philosophy and religion.

Before he arrived in Houston, I told him my car was available, but he wanted to drive a new car so he rented one at the airport. The first night my energy was low, but he wanted to go out to a French restaurant in the University Village. He commented on how it gave him pleasure, "to be able to order in the language of the country."

I made the mistake of having a seafood salad and later spent most of the night throwing-up. That's how his stay started and it went downhill from there.

He would spend three hours out for breakfast, return briefly and then spend another three to four hours out for lunch.

The second night he came in with a film he wanted to see "**Dancing at Lughnasa**" and mispronounced Lughnasa. I said it correctly but he said I was wrong and mispronounced it again. As the story unfolded, Meryl Streep's character said Lughnasa the way I had. He mumbled something about spelling and enunciation. I felt too tired to explain that I'd seen the play on Broadway, several years before the film was made.

He was full of advice. "Yes, well, you have a lot of time now. You should be writing."

"I don't have the energy."

"Why are you wearing those bracelets?"

"One is my hospital identification and the other is a Medic Alert."

I turned over the medallion and read it. "Stem cell transplant. Use irradiated blood products only."

"Oh. Okay." He seemed relieved that I wasn't wearing jewelry. He told me I should go to the mall more often. He'd found a great place to sit and have a cup of coffee and read a book. He expounded on how learning had enriched his life, "For instance race - I see no difference in the races."

I was growing weary, "Malcomb, if you walk into a room and there are a Chinaman and a Massai Warrior standing in front of you and you see no difference . . . have your eyes checked."

"Anthony, you seem very impatient. You need to be more calm about things . . . Do you think you're angry with God?"

"I'm not angry with God or Nature or the Universe. I do get very angry with inept people, rude people and people who don't seem to give a damn when they're taking care of me and have my life in their hands. There is a big difference between the emotion of anger in specific situations and being angry with God."

I needed to feel at one with him about where we had been, what we had learned, mistakes, women, and what our journey had meant to both of us.

It was as if he could not or did not want to deal with the fact that I was very sick. And he couldn't deal with the fact that he couldn't deal with it.

My life experience and achievements counted for nothing. It was as if he preferred to continue thinking of me as that poor scared kid in Wiggins, with nothing but dreams to hold onto. He was unwilling to acknowledge that I had made some of those dreams come true. Not all, but some.

He left two days earlier than planned.

I was too sick to be sad but I couldn't help comparing his behavior with that of Frank Sacks. To my recollection Frank and I had never discussed the meaning of life, religion, philosophy, but he took great care of me and we laughed a lot.

* * * * *

32

Tuesday morning started out with my usual daily schedule; some breakfast, a taxi, Miss Priss, blood drawn, the bed unit, fluids and medication. Then the next seventy-two hours were like falling into a dark hole with nothing to grab onto, just a continuing fall in downward spiral. With no reason, Dasha Epstien backed out of the production. **Smoke & Mirrors** would not be produced Off-Broadway with a Tony award-winning actor in the starring role. The next morning I got a call from the studio; Felcia Behr and the head writer on As The World Turns had been fired. That meant a new executive producer, a new writer and no guarantee of being able to go back to work. Professionally these were big setbacks, but within a couple of hours those two bits of bad news meant nothing.

There was a second reading of the CAT scans I'd done three days before. The official CT report showed that the lymph nodes between my stomach and liver had significantly increased in size.

I wanted to believe that there was a mistake but I feared that there wasn't. Then an hour or so later Joyce came in my room followed by a young doctor I'd only noticed at a distance before in the hallways. His hair was not much longer than a crew cut. He moved quickly to the left side of my bed, stuck out his hand and introduced himself as the poor man's Dr. Medina.

As he circled the end of my bed and approached my right side, his next words were, "Your tumor's back. That's been the source of the fever. We've got to get on this fever."

I was shocked and instantly angered. "Well Doctor, if the tumor is back, I'll be dead in ninety days. Why the hell worry about the damn fever?"

He was taken aback for a split second, and then went right on about how they'd have to do a biopsy as soon as possible. It would be a bit complicated because they would have to maneuver under the liver to access the porta pena area to biopsy the tumor; hard to get to, but needed right away. Joyce would set everything up. And he left.

Joyce gently started to explain why they had reached their conclusion. She showed me several pages of lab reports from my blood work and said they had been tracking the liver enzyme, LDH. The normal range was 450 to 625, but over the past two weeks, mine had more than quadrupled to over 2400. My increased LDH rate indicated tumor growth, which meant renewed activity of Mantle Cell Lymphoma.

Joyce continued to decipher my counts. I wasn't computing much by then, and interrupted, "I don't want to work with this doctor. I want to work with Kornblau until Dr. Medina gets back."

"I'll find him and I'll be back this afternoon before you are finished."

I thought, *'I'll be dead by Thanksgiving. Not much else to do but to see what they have to say.' The transplant didn't work. This crap grows fast. I calculated that it would take me out in three to six months.*

I decided I wasn't going to die, a bag of bones, up there on the eleventh floor, so I began to formulate a plan. If these doctors failed to slow-down the growth of the lymphoma and there was no hope, then I would go back to Africa.

I would go to the Karoo Desert with my brother John, Tandy, Patsy, and Basha. I would ask Nicki Van Reenen to guide us. We would drive the desert for a few days, then one night around our camp fire, we would cook, drink champagne and listen to Willie Nelson, Louis Armstrong and Agustin Lara. We would tell stories, and laugh a lot. I would put my head in Basha's lap and hold her tightly around the waist. Then I would slip away into the night, and kill myself. I wasn't sure how; not with my pistol. I wouldn't want to do that to those who would find me. I could buy some poison on the black market in Cape Town. That would work.

In my mind I saw this like a little movie. Knowing that it was made, I could put it up on a shelf. The comfort of knowing it was there enabled me to go forward on a clear path without debating what to do and how to do it. Joyce came back with Dr. Kornblau.

My anxiety took over. "Doctor, I asked for you because you've taken care of me before, but I want you to know I am in this hospital for one reason, Dr. Medina. But, I trust you and Joyce until he gets back."

"Mr. Herrera, I just talked with Dr. Champlin for an hour and fifteen minutes about you and your case. Do you know who Dr. Champlin is? He was flown to Chernobyl after that tragedy. He was also flown to Johns Hopkins to consult with King Hussein to see if there was any chance of saving his life. You are in good hands until Dr. Medina returns."

"Thank you, Dr. Kornblau."

"You're welcome, Mr. Herrera. We are taking you off of the Tacro as of now. Tacrolimus suppresses the immune system. Let's find out what your immune system will do on its own. I'll see you in the morning after your biopsy. Hang in there."

He left. Joyce stayed. I had to swallow hard to hold back my emotion. I turned my head away, afraid that I was about to cry.

"I wish I could get drunk."

Joyce was kind but firm.

"You know you can't do that."

"Yes, I know."

"Don't smoke any dope either."

"I don't like marijuana."

By then I could look at her.

"Do you want me to call your sisters?"

"No."

"Why not?"

"Joyce, my sisters have shit for brains."

"You're not going to hurt yourself are you?"

I had to take a deep breath on that one.

"No. And if I do start thinking about it, I promise you, I'll call you before I do anything."

In silence we just looked at each other. After a moment she reached down and patted my foot and started out of the room.

As she opened the door I said, "Joyce?"

She stopped without looking back. "Yes."

"You said no vodka. Does that also mean no cocaine?"

She spun around. "Anthony!"

"It's a joke, Joyce. We might as well have a giggle."

She didn't even smile. She just stared at the door for a second. She was suffering for me. Without a word she left; it was as if she passed through the doorway in slow motion. She was upset but tried to cover. I felt very low.

I went through the motions of getting unplugged from the bags of fluids and drugs, putting on my shoes, finding my car in the garage, driving down Holcombe Boulevard and after making a couple of turns, pulling into Oberlin Drive. Sometimes it took me a while to get out of my car; I would just sit there in the driveway and did this night. The grass had grown tall in the backyard, and I liked that. I finally opened the car door, went inside and eased into bed alone. It felt right; this night I wanted to be alone.

* * * * *

33

Tandy Cronyn arrived two days later and as luck would have it, the first night she had to take me to the Emergency Room. The chills and fever got out of hand and I was shaking so badly that she couldn't hold the thermometer in my mouth. After a few hours in the Emergency Room my temperature dropped to normal.

Before Tandy flew down, I told her I wasn't strong enough to drive and asked whether she could drive a standard shift.

"What do you think I am, a privileged urban type? Of course I can drive a stick-shift."

She quickly learned how to operate the clutch and change gears smoothly. I compared the meshing of the gears to what my new immune system was attempting to do; to connect with my system and move forward. She drove me in every morning, and I'd call her shortly before I needed to be picked-up. She was very concerned about my budget and didn't want me spending money on taxis.

Dr. Medina returned from Europe. When he came into my room I could see that my relapse was also tough on him. He listened to my heart and stomach.

"I've seen the biopsy report. We will try a DLI (donor lymphocyte infusion) to boost the immune system. Is your brother still available and willing?"

"Yes, he is."

"Schedule him as soon as possible and I'll talk to Dr. Korbling about another harvest. We'll add some more of his cells and wait six weeks."

"Will it take that long to find out if it works?"

"There's no way of knowing that at this point."

"What if there is no response?"

"We'll do another DLI and wait another six weeks. If we don't get any response, we'll do another DLI with chemo and wait another six weeks. So we have a plan. You are going to be with us in Houston for a while, Mr. Herrera."

"What if all of that fails?"

He was washing his hands at the basin.

"As a last effort, we will try a third transplant."

I hesitated for a second and then said,

"No we won't."

Dr. Medina heard me but didn't respond directly. He dried his hands. His parting comment was.

"Well, we have a plan."

* * * * *

I could be in Houston for many months, if everything worked and I lived.

The next day Tandy came early to pick me up because she wanted to see the bed unit. She was in my room when Joyce, PharmD Kristin and Dr. Medina came in, and heard him say that I needed to put on some weight. That night we stopped by a supermarket and loaded-up on food. My system was in a strange state; I would be starving one minute, and then completely lose my appetite after a few bites. Tandy saw a strawberry cake and said, "Ah Ha. Calories."

That night she cooked me steamed vegetables and broiled fish. She was steeped in the classics but indulged me by watching a John Ford's, **The Man Who Shot Liberty Valance**. Tandy was not a fan of the western but had to admit she enjoyed Lee Marvin's performance.

"I'll get you a piece of cake."

"Tandy, I'm really not hungry."

"Dr. Medina said you needed calories."

I was tired and agreed. She brought me a big helping and retired to her room. I was worn out and I drifted-off to sleep, which lasted less than an hour before I found myself in the bathroom puking up strawberries.

* * * * *

Tandy helped me face the realities that there was not going to be a production of **Smoke & Mirrors**, I was not going back to work on the soap in the fall and my money was going to run out. I still had some of my early redneck hang-ups about "government money."

"I'm not going on welfare."

"Listen, Anty, it is not welfare, it's Disability Insurance. It's your money. Do you remember the money that's been taken out of your paychecks since you were fourteen? "

"Yes."

"That's called FICA . . . your money."

"I just don't like to think of myself as "Disabled.""

"Face it, Anty."

I never liked dealing with bureaucracy. I thought everyone who worked as a bureaucrat was lazy and could care less. I was wrong. The people I dealt with at both of my unions, Screen Actors Guild and the American Federation of Radio and Television Artists were superb. They were understanding, considerate and moved the paperwork fast. The lady at Social Security in Houston was also wonderful. When we spoke on the phone I tried to explain about what my work requirements were as an actor on a television set. The form was so long and the questions were very specific, that she finally kindly offered, "Mr. Herrera, can you get downtown to our office?"

"Yes, I certainly can."

She and I went through the form line by line; she was very understanding and helpful.

"In your work, do you ever have to operate machinery?"

"I've had to drive a car, an ambulance, a boat and fly a plane."

"Do you ever have to crawl in tight spaces?"

"Yes."

"Do you ever have to climb ladders?"

"Yes."

"Do you ever have to lift anything over one hundred pounds?"

"Yes."

"For instance."

"Uh – Elizabeth Hubbard."

At this point she laughed out loud and shook her head. Because of the variety of things an actor might have to do and the specificity of her questions, it took over three hours to complete my application. Not once did she make me feel rushed.

I needed a letter from Dr. Medina and my hospital records, so I phoned the Records Departments at both hospitals and stayed on-hold until I got a real, live person on the phone. I asked for their names, wrote them down, explained my situation and asked each for their help. It worked; within a week I had all the documentation I needed. I hand-delivered it to the helpful lady in the Social Security office and asked her, "Do you think I'll qualify?"

She took off her glasses and looked right at me, "Mr. Herrera, when our doctors review this and see lymphoma, and that you've had not one, but **two bone marrow transplants**, trust me, it'll fly through."

And it did. Within three weeks my disability benefits kicked-in, and I had enough money to live on, coming in like clockwork, every month.

The system worked and fortunately I didn't have the additional stress of "how am I going to pay my bills."

During Tandy's stay we had three late night trips to the Emergency Room. She took it all in a cheerful stride. When it came time for her to leave she even had an upbeat farewell.

"Anthony, hope you're over those shaking chills."

"Well, at least you helped me get past my redneck ideas about the government and my money."

"We had a chuckle or two. I'm faster with a four-speed floor shift and I know more about John Ford westerns than I ever dreamt I would. Hang in there. I'll call and check on you."

* * * * *

For the next few days I took a taxi to the hospital. In the bed unit I had my infusions, visits with Larry Pace and silent conversations with the Turkish father.

It was time for Patsy to arrive. When my taxi rounded the corner on Oberlin I could see Patsy sitting on the front porch with a gin and tonic just like a Mississippi Delta Lady on the veranda.

"This place is so cute I could live here."

"Happy that you're here."

I was always a bit high-strung and she found it strange that I moved around in such a slow and deliberate manner but accepted it.

Her favorite dish to prepare was pork roast. She did an excellent job and it tasted very good. I could only eat a small portion and I had to assure her, "It is tasty, I just can't eat that much . . . No, it is very good."

Some people think it helps if they don't treat you as if you are sick. She would lie on the bed as we watched movies and when she saw me sweating she would touch my forehead and say, "You're burning up!"

"It comes and goes."

She didn't want to talk about "IT" and that was fine. There was a hard rain that night. The next morning, as Patsy backed out of the driveway the tires slipped off of the concrete ramps and got stuck in the mud. The more she gunned the engine the more the rear tires dug in. I got out and pushed. I didn't have the strength to move the car and the wheels went deeper into the mud. Patsy got out.

"Let me try. You can see if you can get the tires to grip if I can rock it some."

I didn't resist. Patsy leaned against the hood. I shifted into reverse and she pushed. The old 240D started to move. I worked the clutch and we got it back out of the driveway and onto the street. Under normal circumstances it would have been a big joke that she could move the car and I couldn't, but she didn't say a word.

She cooked and fed me every night. I wasn't throwing up as much and the fever was getting under control. We watched old movies; Hitchcock's **Rear Window** was her favorite. When she visited New York she could sit for hours watching life on the street from my apartment window. She did the same in Houston. There was a blind man living next door and Patsy chronicled his daily comings and goings. He lived alone as far as we could tell and she was fascinated that there would be a light on in his house at night.

"Why would a blind man need a light? Maybe he has a pet. I've never seen him with a dog, just a cane, but would a dog need a light at night? I don't think so."

Pondering the activities of my blind neighbor was a lovely diversion. She cooked every day and was supportive and positive. The days slipped by until it was time for her to leave.

* * * * *

The next morning in the bed unit Nora greeted me with a smile for the first time. I smiled and nodded back.

"Nice to see you today, Nora."

"Nice to see you too Mr. Herrera."

There was a moment of fun in her voice and I caught a glimpse of a little twinkle in her eye.

"Nora, if I had to guess, I'd say that politically you are a liberal."

"You are right about that." Still upbeat, "And you?"

"Nora . . . I'm conservative on some issues, I believe in the right to bear arms and liberal on others, we ought to legalize drugs . . . William Buckley said legalize all drugs and execute anyone that sells drugs to those under twenty one years of age. I think that teachers should make as much money as lawyers. If we had a higher standard of education we wouldn't need as many lawyers."

Nora, elegant as ever, "Can't disagree with you on that point."

"Nora, left wing – right wing politics really are a minor point at this moment. I mean in this room. I'm standing here with plastic tube hanging out of my chest waiting for those lovely nurses to start pumping fluids and legal drugs into my body. And when I look around this waiting area I see real democracy. I see male, female, Mexicans, Blacks, Caucasians, Jews, Arabs, Asians and folks -- that I don't have a clue they're from. But here we are all equal. We all have cancer. We are afraid. We don't want to die. We just want to get well and go home.

Then a nurse opened the door from the bed unit and motioned that they were ready for me.

The twinkle was still in Nora's eyes.

"We are all grateful for your expose', Mr. Herrera."

* * * * *

I had finished my infusions and was lying in bed resting when a nurse hurried into my room, "Quick, Mr. Herrera, Dr. Medina's coming down. Get up."

He appeared through a side door I had never noticed before. He had two CAT scan films in his hand and held them up to the light. "Look, Mr. Herrera. Look."

"Doctor, they looked like fancy coloring books to me."

He pointed to one of the shapes in the abdomen, "Look, here. *The tumor has shrunk*! It is at least twenty-five percent smaller, maybe thirty."

Just two and a half weeks after Dr. Kronblau had taken me off of the immune suppressant, Tacro, my new immune system was killing the lymphoma. Dr. Medina was ecstatic and I'd never seen him so enthusiastic.

Later, I passed Dr. Valentine in the hall; when he saw me a big smile hit his face. "It's a work in progress, and I'm very happy to hear about the positive developments." It was their excitement that made me think, *"This might really work"* but I didn't want to get too optimistic.

In New York City people walk fast, but Dr. Martin Korbling is the fastest walking man that I have ever seen. He's a German, very German, with a great sense of humor, and a giant in the world of cancer treatment. He pioneered taking the stem cells from the blood stream rather than drilling into the bones and sucking out marrow to collect the stem cells. We'd had a few brief exchanges in the hallways, but this day, he actually stopped, spun around and addressed me directly, "Ah, I have heard the good news. Your case is very important because you survived both transplants and now the donor cells are killing the lymphoma. I understand that your brother is coming back to give some more lymphocytes for a DLI."

"Yes, he's coming in from Austin tomorrow."

He clapped his hands together as for a little applause, "Good, tell him to hurry on down. We'll have some fun."

He gave a little laugh, spun around again and disappeared into the crowded hallway.

He moved like the Roadrunner. I was a bit frustrated. I wanted to pick his brain. He was very excited. Dr. Medina was very excited. I let myself begin to hope that this new immune system and these smart people *might put me back in remission.*

* * * * *

34

John had to be at the hospital at 7:00 a.m. to donate his cells. I arrived at nine. Andrea McMillan came with me to see my brother. He was on the far side of the room and when we got closer, I saw that his face was ashen and he was extremely uncomfortable.

"What's wrong?"

John glanced to the side and mumbled, "It's all right. It's all right."

"What happened?"

He nodded to his left.

"The needle in this arm is in at an angle and it's rubbing against the inside wall of my vein. It hurts a little."

I sensed there was more he wasn't saying.

"What else?"

"Well it's all right now, but . . ."

"But what?"

"They took the wrong cells out for the first hour and we had to start over. The nurse caught it, but we had to start over."

"Which nurse?"

"It's all right."

I got very angry.

"No damn it, it is not all right! Where is she?"

A middle-aged nurse came up behind John's bed and checked the aphaeresis machine.

"Are you in charge?"

"Yes."

"Did you catch the mistake when they took the wrong cells out of him?"

"It wasn't exactly a mistake."

"What was it?"

She didn't answer me, or even look at me.

"Who hooked up this machine and set this procedure in motion?"

"It's fine now."

"You didn't answer my question."

"It doesn't matter; it's fine now."

"It does matter. Are you sure you're getting the right cells now?"

And then I heard the phrase that really set me off,

"Mr. Herrera, you don't understand . . ."

"I understand this. You took the wrong cells out of this man for over an hour, which could have endangered his health, and if the mistake had not been caught, you could have endangered my life. That, I do understand."

Andrea didn't say a word. John was silent and looked embarrassed at my outburst. Dr. Korbling suddenly appeared.

"Doctor, this nurse made a mistake and thinks telling me what I do and don't understand is going to assure me that another mistake has not been made." Dr. Korbling dismissed the nurse with a sharp nod and inspected the machine.

"I just want the right stem cells taken out of my brother so when you put them into me, hopefully they will help kill the lymphoma in my body and not kill me."

Dr. Korbling assured me, "You'll get the right cells, Mr. Herrera; I'll see to it myself."

* * * * *

Six hours later I was in a bed in the Aphresis unit just feet from where my brother was earlier that day. Dr. Korbling came in with a nurse I hadn't seen before, and they proceeded to hang a bag of John's stem cells on the pole and hook up its line to my port. Dr. Korbling looked everything over, pulled up a chair and sat down. I knew that he was concerned about the mistake earlier and that he was sitting beside my bed to assure me that the procedure was being handled correctly. Now I had my chance to get as much information as I could absorb.

"Dr. Korbling, I've heard that you are a pioneer, that you devised the technique of taking stem cells out of the blood stream rather than the bones fifteen years ago at John Hopkins."

"That is correct."

"Dr. Janis Gabrilove was in charge of my autologous transplant at Sloan-Kettering and she developed Neupogen. You two doctors revolutionized cancer treatment."

He was confident in his German dialect.

"Ahh . . . an intelligent patient with interest in what we are doing here. Yes, with the non-myloablative transplant there is less chemo given, less toxicity to the body and therefore less risk of fatality during treatment."

"Doctor, I have never really understood the term, non-myloablative."

"It simply means that we did not burn your immune system out to zero with chemotherapy as they did with the autologous transplant. In your case we burned out a little more than half. What we counted on was that the donor cells would engraft and then take over and push out the rest of the old immune system. And in your case it worked. Your immune system has been replaced 100% by your donor. So this infusion of more donor cells will boost the strength of your immune system, which has already reduced the size of the tumor."

"Am I the first in the treatment of Mantle Cell Lymphoma to have had an autologous transplant with TBI, followed by an allogeneic transplant and **now** a donor lymphocyte infusion?"

"Correct. We are learning a lot from your case. You have already been written-up. We didn't use your name of course."

"Use my name! Use my name! I am an actor, and with a role like this, I want the credit."

Dr. Korbling chuckled.

"I've read that you went to medical school in Germany and Joyce Neumann tells me you maintain a chair at the University of Heidelberg."

"Right."

"And you fly to Europe and back every four or five weeks; isn't that stressful?"

"Ah stress, who cares."

He stood and in a grand gesture toward his clinic.

"It's this place. For my work, this place is a paradise."

I deliberately chose the word *"we"* for my next question.

"Where are we, in finding a cure?"

Dr. Korbling is normally a highly energetic person, but with this question he became electric.

"In this country, with a dynamic leader, we could have a cure for most cancers in three to five years. This country has the scientific and medical brains. We need the focus, funding and leadership."

He was pacing back and forth.

"Like Kennedy in the sixties, you put a man on the moon. Why did this country put a man on the moon? Did you need a man on the moon? No. You did it to show up the Russians. With that kind of leader, this country, we could have a cure in three to five years."

That night I ate alone and then sat at my desk in silence and stared at the Magnolia tree and thought to myself. Look what you are part of - medical history. Cancer history. This indeed is *a lead role*. You are working with giants, geniuses – the best in the world. No matter what happens next, all of the pain and suffering have been worth it. I must remember this moment, this feeling and cling to it.

* * * * *

35

The next day was a long one in the bed unit and I was in my room, working on my laptop when suddenly, all hell broke loose in the hall. I could hear nurses running and shouting. ***"Code Blue. Code Blue."*** Some twenty minutes later my nurse came in and unhooked all of my lines. She was quiet.

I ventured to ask. "Is the patient doing all right?"

"She's in her sixties and had a rough time with her chemo tonight."

I hurried out of there. After I'd been back at my house for a while, I realized that I'd left my date book in the bed unit. When I called, they said they'd found it, and I had some energy, so I drove back to the hospital. In the bed unit I asked a nurse, "How did the little lady do?"

"She didn't make it."

She handed me my date book and we looked at each other in silence as if to say a little prayer.

I drove out of the garage and started out onto Holcombe Boulevard. I stopped the car and just sat there. Someone had died just a few feet from me. I had never seen her. I knew nothing about her except that she was alive at 7:00 p.m. and now it is 8:15 and she's dead.

It was a hot night. My sunroof was open and there was a sprinkler spraying water by the street. It gently moved back and forth and rained on me. It was late and I don't know how long I was there, but it was comforting to sit there and let the mechanical machine rain on me.

I thought this is just like war. Nobody wants to be in combat where there seems to be no reason as to who lives and who dies. Cancer is a war. Cancer - I just wish I could load all six chambers of my .38 Smith & Wesson and kill it.

* * * * *

Someone told me on the sly that Dr. Medina had ***"presented"*** my case to the Bone Marrow Transplant team the day before.

"They are impressed."

Two days later I was waiting to see Dr. Medina and the office manager talking about the heat and how pleased everyone was there was No Evidence of Disease on my mid-August scans. Suddenly, I felt a little weird and she took my forearm.

"Mr. Herrera, do you feel okay?"

"Yes. Well. No. Not really."

"I think you'd better come with me."

She led me through a side door and into the hall to Dr. Medina's examination room. She put me on the table and called for Dr. Medina. By this time I was feeling faint. Then they were taking my blood pressure and Dr. Medina was listening to my chest and pulse, looking concerned. My blood pressure had dropped significantly, and so had my pulse.

They called the bed unit to get me on intravenous fluids immediately and begin *"observation."* When they called transportation for a wheel chair I felt a bit better and said I could walk down there myself, but was told quickly,

"No. You'll be wheeled to the bed unit."

Dr. Medina didn't leave the room and kept checking my chest with his stethoscope. Usually, he does what he has to do, and rushes out; I began to realize that this was serious.

"Doctor. What's happened to me?"

"We're not sure."

The transportation fellow had a problem getting my feet onto the footrest and I had a problem lifting my legs. Doctor Medina said he'd check on me later.

After a few hours in bed and some fluids, I was okay, except my left foot would slap the floor as I walked. My right foot worked the way it had for over fifty years. I would lift it, and as I stepped forward, it would ease down. I had no control over my left foot. As soon as my heel hit the floor, the ball of my left foot would slap down involuntarily. It was a strange sensation, but I thought after everything my body had gone through, I'm lucky the damn thing didn't fall off.

The next morning I had forgotten about my foot flop until I started to the bathroom. Barefoot, it seemed even more pronounced, but I was able to use the clutch in my car just fine, so certain muscles and tendons worked. Some did not.

I went in to see Dr. Medina and after we finished going over my blood work, I asked him to take a look, and got up and walked across the room. He immediately picked up the phone and called a neuro-oncologist. I met with Dr. Rossi twenty minutes later. He said it could be a pinched nerve related to the fact that I had lost weight.

"Do you sit with your legs crossed?"

"Yes, as a matter of fact, I thought about that just the other day. I was sitting with my legs crossed all the way over. That's the way my Grandfather sat."

"That could be it, or, it could be a spinal problem. I don't know if Mantle Cell can get into the spinal cord or not. Do you?"

"No, I don't."

"I'll ask Dr. Medina. You'll come in tomorrow for some tests on your leg and then we'll do a spinal tap and possibly an MRI."

Later, I ran into Dr. Medina. He told me that Mantle Cell could get into the spinal cord. There was about a 10% chance.

"We'll also arrange for an MRI."

"What do we do if it's in there?"

"We'll hit it with chemo."

It wasn't until I was driving back to Oberlin that I realized why I was having "an MRI." The cancer could have gone into my brain. All of a sudden a blast from a car horn brought me back to the present. I was sitting there with the light green. It was 9:30 p.m. I didn't know what to do. This was another time I really could have used a shot of whiskey, but I had too many different drugs in me, so I didn't dare. I started to panic. So I drove out onto the freeway, found a classical radio station, turned it up very loud, opened the sun roof and drove 80 miles an hour, until the speed, the night air and the music helped. A little after midnight I drove back to my house, took a sleeping pill and got some rest.

Unfortunately for him, a young man in my accountant's office in New York, called and woke me up to ask about a check I'd written over a year ago. He didn't realize I was in a different time zone. He also hadn't been in touch in months. I was in a very bad frame of mind and was not at all polite. I told him I could care less about my taxes and added some profanities. I was more concerned about whether or not there was cancer in my brain than about the IRS.

Less than an hour later, I was in a green robe in an examination room when a specialist from Herman Hospital came in. She was from Holland, in her sixties with silver hair, beautiful and spoke with a beautiful accent. I was smitten.

Two young male doctors were with her and proceeded to put suction cups along my left leg from the top of my thigh to my foot. Then they did the same thing to my right leg. This good-looking lady doctor studied a monitor and I was asked to flex and move my legs one at a time. She concentrated, comparing the data of one leg's nerve function to the other.

This flexing and raising and lowering lasted about twelve minutes. Then she informed me, "Our next procedure will be unpleasant. Regrettably, many of the things we have to do to get the information we need are unpleasant."

"I appreciate you telling me."

The younger doctor stuck a needle in the lower part of my calf muscle, and asked me to move my foot back and forth.

Then he proceeded up the length of my leg.

"Doctor, will you be able to . . .?"

"Mr. Herrera, we will finish as soon as possible and I will answer all the questions I can then. Sorry about the little punctures."

When I moved my muscles I could hear a scratching sound like a nail being run over a very rough board. There were about nine more punctures until they got to my upper thigh. Then they did the same number on the right leg. She was right; *"unpleasant"* was the word, but not unbearable. When they finished she looked at me and smiled. "Mr. Herrera, I don't know anything about Mantle Cell Lymphoma or what may be happening in your spinal cord with that disease."

She put her finger on the side of my kneecap.

"I can tell you that the problem with your foot is from a nerve right here. You are very thin. You have had a lot of chemo, and I would bet that you have been sitting with your legs crossed."

"You're right, doctor."

"So. Don't sit with your legs crossed. Continue to exercise and your foot problem will correct itself. And I wish you luck with your health."

36

I still had to go to the bed unit for a couple of hours and get fluids and magnesium, but now with this good news, it seemed like a joyous task.

For the next ten days nothing remarkable happened except one night I was very tired and couldn't find my car in the garage. It had eight floors and even though it was after nine o'clock at night, there were still a lot of vehicles on each floor and it wasn't easy to spot my car. I knew I hadn't left it on the first floor. I thought the fourth. Wrong. Then I explored the fifth. Then the sixth. It was very hot and humid and it seemed that the elevator was taking longer and longer to arrive. Finally I decided to go to the roof and search every floor all the way down to the bottom. I found my car on the third floor, kind of hidden in the corner.

No fever, no chills, no sweats and my counts were stable. When Dr. Korbling would hurry by me in the hallways he would hold his hands up to make a frame like a movie director and quickly say, "Miracle man – poster boy."

I asked Dr. Medina if it would be all right for me to take a short trip to visit Patsy. He okayed the trip.

* * * * *

The flight to Nashville was smooth. I didn't eat the peanuts. Patsy hated to wait and always tried to time picking me up by adding ten minutes to the ETA. I put my bag on one of the barrels used for blocking-off the new construction. Fifteen minutes went by before I called her house. I got the machine. Three calls and forty-five minutes later, I hailed a taxi. I found both her front door and kitchen door locked, but fortunately the gate to the garden was open and I fell asleep on a chaise lounge. I woke up when I heard her drive into the garage. When she saw me at a distance she said, "Yes?" as if she were addressing a stranger.

"I was worried something had happened to one of your kids."

"Anthony, is that you?"

"What do you mean?"

"I didn't recognize you."

"You're kidding?"

"I do now, but not when you came through the gate. Where the hell were you. I've been driving around and around the airport for forty-five minutes like it's the Indianapolis 500."

As it turned out, I'd been waiting on the departure ramp rather than in the arrivals area. I had flown into that airport at least twenty-five times. She calmed down once she realized that I was weak and disoriented. I had to take a nap and wasn't very hungry or very upbeat company, but it was comforting to be in her home with her and her children, both of whom were exceptionally bright.

The next morning I realized that I didn't have enough Tacro. I phoned Kristin and she told me to check with Vanderbilt University Hospital. Being put on hold, and explaining my situation over and over took up the entire morning, and most of the afternoon. They didn't have any Tacro, but referred me to St. Matthews, one of the leading heart transplant hospitals in the Southeast. I got through to the pharmacy and Kristin faxed a prescription from MD Anderson. When I picked it up, I met two nurses who were both nuns, and we got into a long discussion about my treatment. They informed me that a moderate amount of alcohol with Tacro was fine, and I remarked that MD Anderson was founded by a Protestant in Texas, where they believed Protestants differed in their biochemical make up, and shouldn't drink while taking that drug. The nuns were amused.

That night, a sharp pain under my sternum wouldn't go away. I thought that in light of the conflicting opinions about Tacro and alcohol, I would allow myself a vodka and tonic. It helped me to get to sleep, but the next morning, the pain in my stomach was worse. I didn't feel like trying to eat and Patsy said I was looking worse. Kristin called because they had found some sort of virus in my blood, and said I needed to get back to Houston as soon as possible to start medication.

"I can get back to Houston and be in the bed unit by 5:30 this afternoon."

"That should be fine. I think we've caught this in time."

The abdominal pain was constant. I arrived in plenty of time and was given two *"baby bottles"* of Foscarnate to take home. This type of infusion was new to me. The medication was a liquid in a vacuum-compressed bottle, and all I had to do was screw it into the port in my chest, so it would slowly empty into me. This saved having to hook-up the pump, and waking to that little beep every time the slightest thing went wrong.

I woke up vomiting. It was still dark. I had thrown-up a lot in the last four months, but this was different. I was on my knees, and suddenly I couldn't control my bowels. I made the switch and didn't mess up the bathroom. I got back to sleep and then just about dawn, it started all over again. After a violent episode erupting from both ends of my gastrointestinal track, I eased back in bed. This was very strange. I checked my little bottle and it was empty. I disconnected it and tried to get back to sleep. I heard Dr. Spring next door start his Jeep and leave for the hospital about 6:00 am as he did six mornings a week. There was some water on the nightstand and I tried to get some down - a bad idea. I threw-up on the floor before I got to the toilet. Large amounts of dark fluid kept pouring out of me. A few minutes later, I made it to the phone and asked Carla to come take me to the hospital.

In the Emergency Room they put me in a wheel chair, and said they had to take my temperature and blood pressure. I kept stressing, "I am very sick!" When the nurse finally finished, I repeated.

"Please, just get me into a room. I am very sick."

"Now we have to get your blood pressure standing up."

"What? I'm very sick . . . just get me . . ."

"We have to have both readings."

I was losing strength fast. They had to hold me up to get the "second reading" so they could fill-out their damned form, then another nurse started wheeling me down the hall to a room.

"Get me a towel."

"You'll be in your room in a second."

I vomited all over myself, and the wheelchair, and the floor.

"Oh God. He's sick."

Carla got angry, "He told you he was really sick."

They took off my wet clothes, helped me into bed and hooked me up to a bag of fluids.

Dr. Medina had flown to Copenhagen for a conference. I kept trying to get them to call Kristin, my PharmD in the bed unit. Dr. Gomez was on duty and I remembered meeting him once before. I could hear him requesting charts and records over and over, both for me, and for other patients. I heard one confused nurse say, "Is it Mendoza? I can't find a Mendoza."

"No. I'll repeat it one more time. Medina. Dr. M-E-D-I-N-A

Nothing was working right. My fever was shooting up. They started me on an IV antibiotic. I was drifting into a zone of constant pain.

They took my temperature again and it had reached 102.5. They added more hydration. "Please call Kristin, she's a PharmD in the bed unit."

* * * * *

Carla had brought me in at 9:00 a.m. At 4:30 p.m. Dr. Gomez reported, "I just spoke with Dr. Medina himself; he called from the airport. He and Kristin have already talked, and you're going to be admitted, but we have to do an endoscopy first. They'll take you up in a few minutes."

I told Dr. Reddy, the assistant endoscopist, that I had been through this procedure before. Nevertheless, he explained the risks, benefits, indications, complications and alternatives. They checked my vital signs and hooked me up to a monitor to watch my pulse and heart. Those parts of my body seemed to be doing fine, and they told me the intravenous sedation would help achieve and maintain a drowsy state, but would not put me out completely.

Another doctor came in, introduced himself, inserted a bite block in my mouth and started pushing the tube down my throat. I didn't choke or gag. By the time I heard from somewhere "help us, swallow, that's it, help us swallow."

I was so out of it that I didn't mind or worry. Somewhere in my mind I knew what was going on, but it didn't matter. I tried to pass out, but don't think I did. The only physical sensation I was aware of was the intense pain in my gut. I thought I could die right here, at least that would end the agony. If the grim reaper had slipped into the room, I don't think anyone would have noticed. He would have fit right in.

* * * * *

When I started coming around and realized I was back in the hospital on the 11th floor. John and Carla were there and I heard, "multiple bleeding ulcers" and then "No, you can stay." A man in a white doctor's coat was looking at me.

"I'm Dr. Gajewski. I'll be looking after you."

"What do you do here?"

"I'm Vice Chairman of the Department."

"That'll do."

"I'm pleased to hear you approve, Mr. Herrera."

"I've been through too much to have a beginner working on me. Am I going to die?"

"No. I'm not going to let you die. You're going to suffer like hell for a while, like being in a Beckett play."

"I have ulcers?"

"The endoscopy showed that you have Cytomegalovirus, or CMV. This is a virus that 8 out of 10 people have in their systems. But, they haven't been through a stem cell transplant. Your immune system is suppressed, and this can and did activate the CMV. They didn't find any lymphoma in your stomach. We will have to wait and do further testing to see if GVH is involved. The next couple of days are going to be rough, and we'll have to run a lot of tests."

A pretty Latin technician came in with a tray full of test tubes and a tourniquet to take blood. "I can't use your port. I'm afraid I'm going to have to stick you."

"Okay."

As soon as she pulled the needle out of my vein, I told her I had to get to the bathroom. She understood that I had to move fast and scurried out of my way. I made it without an accident.

I closed the door and heard her say, "Wash your hands."

As soon as I got back in bed, the technician came back in and said she had to stick me again. She apologized, and I made an attempt to be pleasant about it. An hour later she came back for another stick with her needle, and I was not as pleasant. I called the head nurse and asked her to explain why they couldn't just take a bunch of blood, put it in test tubes and send it to different labs as the doctors thought of more and more tests. She replied, "It doesn't work that way."

The next time she came in she said, "We need blood from an artery for an oxygen level and it will be painful."

I got mad at the technician and then tried to realize she was just doing her job. I apologized. She accepted.

The fifth time she came in she said, "I told them to get someone else. I told them I'm not going to stick that man again."

An hour later, the sixth time she stuck me, we were both silent.

PharmD Hicks was in charge of the drugs. She dressed as if she was to be photographed for the cover of Vogue and was so beautiful and funny that when she came in my room, for a few seconds, the pain seemed to disappear. They hit me hard with a lot of steroids, Ganciclovir, Foscarnate, other drugs and lots of hydration. I still had a fever. I started getting chills and they brought me some warm blankets. I kept bleeding internally, and had to hurry to the toilet every couple of hours; what resembled used heavyweight motor oil continued to pour out of my bowels.

The next forty-eight hours seemed to just fold together. Lorraine was the nurse in charge. There was a note board on the wall beside the closet, where she wrote down in black, the names of the other nurses who would take care of me that day, and in red, the names of the drugs I was scheduled to take. She explained what they were hoping these drugs would do, both to kill the CMV, and keep other viruses and bacteria from causing infection. An x-ray showed what might have been some pneumonia in my left lung; she said they would have to watch it.

My night nurse asked if I wanted some Dilaudid for the pain.

"No, that's all right, but could I have just a sip of water?"

"Nothing by mouth, Mr. Herrera."

The pain was either bad or very bad. I couldn't get any real rest. They had to keep a close watch on me, and took my blood pressure and temperature every four hours. There were ten to twelve bags of saline, drugs, and platelets, running into my port at any given time. Late Saturday night the nurse let me have a sliver of ice. It melted in my mouth and **was** wonderful, but still, nothing to drink. The pumps timed and regulated the amount of each drug according to the prescribed dose, and the slightest irregularity made the pumps start to beep. It was complicated and difficult for them to synchronize all those drugs flowing into me, and at just the right dosages. Intellectually I knew this, but it was very difficult to be reasonable between the motor oil craps and the "beep, beep, beeps."

* * * * *

John drove down from Austin Sunday morning to give platelets. Carla called and told me Monica had tried to give platelets the day before, but they found her to be anemic. John came by my room for a visit in his yellow throwaway mask and gown. Everyone who entered my room had to wear protective clothing because they'd found a bug in my stool, which could spread infection. John looked like a big duck.

Dr. Gajewski and PharmD Hicks came in with several other white coats. My platelet levels were running very low and Dr. Gajewski wanted them to be at least 50,000. "So if something goes wrong, I'll have room to work. Let's wait for your brother's platelets to be processed. Because he was your stem cell donor, his platelets are the most beneficial."

Dr. Gajewski felt my stomach as the white coat entourage observed.

"You were right about the Beckett play."

"CMV is a tough one. Fifteen years ago it was fatal, and even now, if you're HIV positive, it will blind you."

"Doctor, they've offered me Dilaudid for pain, and I haven't taken any, but I think I want it now. It's worse today."

"I can't let you have any opiates. Opiates can cause the gut to obstruct. One day I want to come up and have you show me New York City. I want to see it through the eyes of an actor."

"We'll start at CBS studios; it was a dairy before World War II."

He looked over at the nurse of the day and the words he spoke sounded like a dream come true.

"Let Mr. Herrera have a glass of water, and order him a cup of chicken broth. Deal with the discomfort as best as you can. Try walking around in the room. See you in the morning."

A cup of chicken broth! A sixteen-ounce T-bone steak couldn't have sounded better.

By 3:00 p.m. I was getting anxious about my platelets. The nurse kept saying she was checking. At four, I asked for the number at the blood bank and called them myself. I got excuses. The woman who answered the phone was a temp, and said she didn't know how to find John's patient number. All the drilling my grandmother gave me on manners went out the window.

"Who runs this place? You have to have someone in charge." We went back and forth until I finally got the supervisor on the line.

"Mr. Herrera, we have several new people, and we're working out our problems. All right?"

"No. It is not all right! I don't give a damn what your problems are. I'm on the eleventh floor with CMV, and I'm crapping blood at least ten times a day. My brother John's patient number is 394929. He donated platelets this very morning, specifically for me. Where are they?"

As it turns out, they were lost. I had to get infused with a random donor.

I had to call about my cup of chicken broth. It was ordered at 12:30. The nurses were getting weary of me buzzing every few minutes. I'd had only one glass of water in the past three days. At 5:00 pm I asked for the number of the kitchen. They hadn't gotten the order for my cup of chicken broth. It finally arrived at 5:30 and I savored every sip. It was my feast.

* * * * *

I woke to find the big bird crane was no longer working outside of my window. There was a knock and Dr. Gajewski came in with the team.

"Mr. Herrera, I hear you're known as 'poison tongue' out there." He tilted his head toward the door that was directly across from the nurse's station.

"Dr. Gajewski, I have been treated by some of the finest minds in Hematology and Oncology in the western world: Chatham, Janice Gabrilove, Martin Korbling, Doctor Medina and you! I have been a patient in two of the finest cancer institutes in the entire world. But yesterday, it took five hours, from the time you gave the order at 12:30, until 5:30 pm, for me to get one cup of chicken broth. And, did you hear about my brother's platelets getting lost?"

Without any further to do, he felt my stomach and ordered a lower endoscopy. Joyce Neumann came back a few minutes after the team left.

"I understand a lot of things went wrong over the weekend. Would you write down, from your point of view as a patient, how we could make things work better?"

"Yes, I will, and I'm honored."

"I'm holding a meeting with the entire floor Friday morning."

Transportation arrived. They didn't have to completely lift me on the gurney, but they did have to help. As we maneuvered the pole and gurney out of my room and into the hall, there stood the nurse who'd forgotten to order my cup of chicken broth. I didn't even try to hold back my anger.

"You didn't call in my meal, my chicken broth yesterday. I waited five hours . . ." She gave me a feeble smile as I was wheeled down the hall.

They parked me in a line of gurneys. We looked like a row of little trucks waiting to be serviced. Ron, a big male nurse with a handlebar mustache, came over to review his paperwork, double-checked my name and date of birth, and then started the IV drug to sedate me. I asked if he could check with the doctor to see if I could have less sedation, and explained that I wanted to watch the procedure and see what was going on in my gut.

On his way back I overheard him talking with another male nurse about his Mercedes Benz, a 1980 model, and the work he'd just had done by a German mechanic. I asked about the mechanic, and when the other fellow wrote his name down for me, I tucked it under my name band. Ron said the doctor would want to talk to me, but he felt he'd be "cool" with the idea of less sedation. I also learned that Ron lived in his motor home, eighteen miles south of Houston, in an RV park called Almost Heaven. He liked it there and said there was a lake with ducks, and about half of the residents were cancer patients. In the event of a medical emergency, top professional support was just minutes away.

I waited on the gurney for another hour until Dr. Frederick arrived. He was about thirty, tall, blond, and "movie star" handsome. He was polite and agreed to my request for less sedation. During the procedure, I asked if he could turn the monitor toward me. I saw the interior of my intestine. It was surreal to be just a bit groggy and watch a color image of my colon on a nineteen-inch screen. It was not a pretty picture; the walls of my intestine were covered with large patches of ulcers, oozing blood. It looked as if someone had taken sandpaper and sanded about two thirds of my flesh away. The visuals made it a little easier for me to deal with the misery.

Back in my room, I was thrilled to see another cup of broth waiting for me, and I hadn't even asked for it. That night I watched a Biography on Bill Monroe, the father of bluegrass music. Lester Flatt and Earl Scruggs had toured with him for years. I learned that out of respect, Elvis had called to ask him personally if he could record **Blue Moon of Kentucky**. Monroe's tenacity was impressive; he had his own sound and his own vision, and he stuck to it. During the program I had to scoot to the bathroom twice. Like Willie Nelson's, Bill Monroe's music and dedication to his craft inspired me.

Get well. Get back to work.

* * * * *

The next morning Dr. Fredrick appeared. He told me the findings from the biopsies were consistent with CMV. One ulcer measured 3 x 2 centimeters. He was a perfect gentleman, and asked how I was feeling. I thanked him and assured him I was doing as well as could be expected.

As he left, he hesitated at the door and turned toward me,

"Mr. Herrera, I'm sorry."

I froze inside. Had he seen something, or did he know something about my condition that no one else had told me?

"Sorry about what doctor?"

It was clearly awkward for him to answer.

"The procedure, having to put you through a lower endoscopy."

"Don't worry about that, Doc. What's a tube up your butt compared to cancer?"

Later a tall, very attractive black lady came into my room and introduced herself, "I'm Dorothy Polk. I run the blood bank. I'm very sorry about all the confusion yesterday; it won't happen again."

"Miss Polk, next time, I'm going to get you on the phone so there won't be any mistakes."

"You do just that. I'll make sure the platelets given for you are followed every step of the way, and if necessary, I'll bring them to you myself."

I thought she was absolutely great. She stepped right up and took responsibility.

* * * * *

The next week crawled by: pain, pumps beeping, fevers and pills. I passed blood ten to twelve times a day. Sometimes my gut would wrench so fast that I'd "have an accident" on the bathroom floor.

One of the jobs I had in high school was janitor of the grammar school. With this job I could still go to football practice right after classes finished, and then in the early evening, clean up what we called the old school. After big events like Halloween, the bathrooms were especially stinky. If I could do this when I was sixteen, for fifty-five dollars a month, I could clean up my own mess now. My condition didn't seem to be getting under control, so I learned to make myself a diaper out of a bath towel.

* * * * *

ParmD Hicks arrived with some good news: there was no Graft Versus Host disease in my gut, but I was losing weight so fast that they had to start infusing me with lipids.

Lorraine came in and ordered me out of bed.

"You need to move around."

Lorraine was black and tough. I adored her. I reached down and wrapped my hands around my upper thigh; it was smaller than the fat end of a baseball bat.

"Look at this Lorraine, my forearm used to be bigger than my thigh. My legs are pitiful."

She came right back at me. "But there's blood running through them, Mr. Herrera."

I started speculating on who I could "take out" if I knew for certain I was going to die.

"Lorraine, you know I'm originally from Mississippi. I've been shooting a pistol since the age of five and a rifle since the age of six. I'm still a good shot. Think about it. Those white trash boys who chained that black man behind their pick-up truck and dragged him to death; I could save the state of Texas a lot of money. While they're walking them from the courthouse to the jail, with a 30.06 and a four-power scope; I could kill'em both."

"Yeah. They aren't worth what it's going to take to house them, feed them and let them watch color television too."

"Who else? I'm on a roll. Let's make a list. What about O J.?"

"Put him on the list too."

She laughed, finished her work and left. It suddenly hit me what Dr. Gajewski meant by **"room to work."**

When he and the white coat team came in, I asked, "Doctor, my system is overall in a very weakened state. We need to keep the platelets above fifty thousand so that if an artery or vein bursts, you'll have time to get into my gut and fix it before I bleed to death, right?"

"That's correct, Mr. Herrera."

He glanced at my computer. I had pulled up the American Poetry Web Site.

"Do you think Ezra Pound should have been tried for treason? He's one of my favorite poets."

"Doctor, you are a scholar. I don't know that much about Pound. I know about Robert Service, **The Shooting Of Dangerours Dan MacGrew**, and a poem or two by A. E. Housman. I do them in my one-man show."

"I'll have to see that one day. I want you to start PT tomorrow. Think you're up to it?"

"Philosophically, I'm against physical therapy. I'd rather go to the gym or dig ditches. But for pragmatic reasons, I'll try."

"Philosophically, I'm for it."

He looked at the nurse of the day.

"Start PT for Mr. Herrera tomorrow, even if they have to come up here."

He noticed a videotape of **People Will Talk** staring Cary Grant as Dr. Petronius, and picked it up to read the jacket.

"I like Cary Grant."

"Doctor, that is a very interesting and entertaining film. I think it should be required viewing for all medical students. Very advanced ideas even by today's standards, and it was written and directed by Joseph Mankiewicz in 1951. Please take it; I have other copies."

"Okay, but it will be a while before I get it back to you; I'm leaving for Japan on Friday."

"You're what? Japan? No, not until I'm over this."

"There's a good man coming in; he'll take care of you."

"But you're leaving me."

"Don't worry, you and I have bonded. When I return, I don't think I'll let Medina have you back." He smiled, shook my hand and left.

PharmD Hicks stayed and went over all the drugs they were giving me. Basically progress was slow. My big question was, "Any indication of lymphoma?"; and as long as that answer was "No." I told her I could stay in the saddle. She laughed, "You'd like my husband; he's a cowboy, too."

* * * * *

37

Dr. Gajewski was right about Dr. Daniel Couriel. He was upbeat and very smart. He came in with the team every morning and felt my stomach, and then PharmD Hicks would report on lab results and drugs. I still had CMV. Susan was my first physical therapist. My entire system was blown-out and my testosterone levels had been very low for months but there was no mistaking that this girl was sexy, good at her job and a very nice person. She took me over to a big padded bench. She asked me to sit, and try to hold my back as erectly as possible; then she handed me two dumbbells. They weighed only three pounds each.

"Oh, come on." I said, "Give me at least fives!"

"I think you're going to be surprised. Now, arms straight and palms down then lift up. First your right."

Maybe I was trying to show off for the pretty trainer. Maybe I was being arrogant out of pride about how strong I used to be. Maybe I was trying to fool myself as to the extent of my weakened state. The reality was difficult to deal with. Holding the three-pound weight I couldn't lift my right arm parallel to the floor. Nor could I lift my left. We went down to two-pound weights and I could barely get five reps on each arm. The one-pound difference shocked me.

"Let's have a rest and some water."

"Okay."

A sinking feeling crept into my middle. Easing our way across the room we passed a team of three therapists helping a big middle-aged, black man out of his wheel chair. He looked as if he could have been a tackle in the NFL, and now he couldn't even stand up. Struggling, they got him on his feet and helped him to the walkway with the handrails.

Next the treadmill; she started it at barely a crawl. I had to hold myself up to keep from slipping. Susan stayed close to make sure I didn't fall. I was feeling sorry for myself.

To my right, two therapists helped a white guy no more than thirty years old onto his treadmill. As they started the machine, the therapist nearest me moved out of the way, giving me a clear view of this man. I saw that he had only one leg. The look on his face was not angry or bitter. As he held himself up, the belt on the treadmill started slowly. I saw a smile as his foot thumped the big belt moving under him. I looked away so as not to stare, and looked back a few minutes later. He was sweating and his smile was still there.

I thought, how small to feel self-pity. Gam would often say, "I complained because I had no shoes, until I met a man that had no feet." As a teenager I thought that was corny. Damn sure wasn't corny in this room.

* * * * *

The next morning after my vital signs were checked, Dr. Valentine walked in. I had worked with many psychiatrists and psychologists over the past thirty-three years, including the great Silvano Arieti. Dr. Alan Valentine was one of the best. He had the ability to zero-in, hit the bulls-eye of the problem and he didn't waste time. He treats patients with cancer.

Without thinking I started talking about the conditions my brothers and sisters had grown up in, and how it was still damaging their lives and I wished they would work on themselves in therapy.

Dr. Valentine stopped me and motioned to the bags of drugs and fluids pouring into me.

"Mr. Herrera, you came to Houston to fight Mantle Cell Lymphoma. You need all the strength you can muster for that fight. I suggest you spend less time with your siblings."

That night as I tried to sleep my brain was whirling. They'd been pumping me full of steroids. Dr. Gajewski said if my gut exploded he'd need "room to work." Dr. Valentine had advised "*spend less time with your siblings.* Here I am in another tough spot and I need to use what strength I have to fight for myself.

I turned on my laptop and rewrote my will. I also wrote out instructions for the design of a bronze plaque to be placed between the head stones of my Grandparents in Wiggins, Mississippi.

Anthony Herrera
Born: January 19, 1944   Died _____

Wiggins	Ole Miss	New York
Left Tackle	Sigma Chi	Actor
Vivian Spiers	Evans Harrington	Stella Adler

I go the errant trail to try,
*   to clutch the skirts of chance*
To make once more before I die
*   the gesture of Romance.*

                          . . . Robert Service

"Son, it is leg over leg to Dover."
My beloved Grandfather – **John Blackburn**

I printed out both documents and signed them. It felt right what I wanted on my grave, a way of saying thank you to my teachers that gave me so much for my life and Bop who really loved me. I eased over and sat on the edge of my bed and gazed at the floor and my big skinny feet. I thought I might not wake up. This night I could die.

* * * * *

On the eleventh day, all of the team and some observers came in, except for the PharmD. Hicks. Dr. Couriel felt my stomach and Joyce Neumann went over my blood work. PharmD Hicks made a grand entrance and announced, "For the second day in a row, CMV cells found in Mr. Herrera's workup ZERO!" There were at least ten people in the room. Everyone instantly burst into applause.

Later Lorraine came in; she was as happy about the news as if I had been her own child.

That night I thought soon this suffering will be over. My chest swelled with emotion when I thought of their faces when Hicks announced the news. I had to get to the toilet; when I finished I looked at myself in the mirror. My body was just a skeleton with some saggy skin stretched over it but not as ghoulish as the figure I saw in the mirror at Sloan-Kettering.

I got back in bed and heard Stella Adler's voice in my mind. "Don't try to remember emotions . . . how you felt. Remember what your muscles did in a particular situation." I didn't have any muscles. But it was a fine moment to rehearse:

> *"To be or not to be. That is the question*
> *Whether tis nobler in the mind to suffer*
> *The slings and arrows of outrageous fortune*
> *Or to take arms against a sea of troubles and*
> *by opposing end them?"*

I quoted the entire monologue without someone coming in to check my vital signs or one of my pumps going beep, beep, beep. That mental exercise relieved the misery for a moment.

* * * * *

Later Lorraine made me out of bed for physical therapy. I looked down at my feet. My legs looked like broomsticks stuck into two big clown's feet. I could have wept or laughed.

"Lorraine, look, I could paint my feet red and join the circus!"

"And you'd be back in show biz. Now get yourself down to your therapy."

"Yes boss lady."

The drugs and the brains of those working on me had killed the CMV virus. It took another ten days to stop the bleeding. I went from 194 pounds to 160 pounds in those 21 days.

38

The third night back in my little house I was sitting on the couch trying to watch television. The room had grown dark except for the glow of the screen. I didn't feel like getting up and going into the kitchen to get the bag of saline out of the refrigerator. I finally talked myself into getting the infusion over-with. I turned on one light and hooked myself up to a new pump. I had used this type of pump only once some months before. The switches worked differently. I clicked around with the remote. Then I looked down at the pump and thought I saw "AIR" spelled out on its little screen. I moved closer to the light; it read, "AIR" so I shut it off.

I couldn't remember the exact sequence of settings, but I attempted to set it again. All the other pumps I'd ever used would beep if anything went wrong and automatically shut off. This one didn't. I reset everything and started over, but again, it registered: "AIR." I shut it off and debated whether or not I should call the bed unit. All of a sudden, I couldn't catch my breath. That was one of the questions they were always asking, "Any difficulty breathing?" I unhooked the pump.

Instead of getting easier, trying to breathe became more difficult. I stood-up and opened the front door; I still struggled to breathe. I didn't want to alarm myself so I went back inside but left the door open. What if I passed out? I was in my sock feet, red pajama bottoms and a t-shirt. I staggered out of the door and across the front yard to Paul's house. Luckily he was home and opened his door on the first knock.

"Paul, I can't breathe."

"Sit down."

He guided me to chair and gave me some water.

"I think I've pumped air into my chest. But the damn pump didn't beep."

He listened to my heart and chest with his stethoscope; then he went to the phone.

"This is Dr. Paul Spring. I'm with Anthony Herrera, a BMT patient. Hold on. Anthony, how do you spell your oncologist's name?"

"Medina -- Medina."

"Call Dr. Medina and tell him I'm bringing-in Anthony Herrera. He's having difficulty breathing."

On the way down Holcombe Boulevard I pushed my foot against the floor to stretch my body and try to breathe.

"Paul, do you think I'm having a stroke?"

He hesitated for a split second.

"I don't think so."

He drove into the ambulance entrance and helped me out of the car. My gut wrenched and I had to crap, and fast. I made it into bathroom, but fell against the wall and slid to the floor before reaching the toilet. I was holding onto the towel rack.

"I need some help."

I was trying to yell, but it sounded to me as if nothing was coming out of my mouth.

"I need some help."

I heard a lot of muffled chatter all around me. I was on a gurney. I sensed a lot of movement, a lot of people, a lot of excitement. I heard someone slap my hand over and over and yell!

"Move it! Move it! We're losing him! We're losing him!"

Suddenly it felt like a drainpipe came up out of the floor, attached itself to my head and the back of my skull flipped open like a trap door. I gasped "***THIS IS IT ...***"

Everything went black.

* * * * *

Something somewhere was wet. I was on my back. A nurse standing right beside me started to come into focus.

"I'm wet."

"You had an accident." She was cleaning me from the waist down with moist towels.

"Did I nearly expire here?"

"Mr. Herrera, let's just say you made this ***a very interesting evening in the emergency room for all of us.***"

"Oh."

I drifted off into a thick sleep.

From somewhere I heard Dr. Medina's voice. He sounded distressed. I thought I saw him standing in a hot mist beside my bed.

"Mr. Herrera. What happened to you?"

He seemed to fade away. I didn't know where I was. A male nurse was taking my vitals. I managed to ask for some water.

"In just a minute."

My throat was burning. The nurse never came back. I hurt. The rest of the world seemed far away. I was in a murky limbo, parched and in pain.

When I woke up I saw my brother John. He was sitting beside my bed. A Dr. McGill was asking me questions.

"Where are you, Mr. Herrera?"

"I don't know. In the hospital?"

"Why are you in the hospital?"

That was a tough one. I had to think.

"I've been sick."

"Are you taking any medicine?"

"I . . . Yes. Some drugs."

"What kind of drugs?"

Another tough one. "I don't know."

As he pointed to his watch he asked, "Mr. Herrera, what is this?"

It took me a few seconds.

"It's a watch."

"Right. What does it do?"

I struggled. "I don't know."

"I'll see you tomorrow."

John got up and moved to the end of the bed. He was smiling.

"Where am I?"

"In the hospital, in your own room. You were in intensive care for two days. I'm glad to see you're doing better."

Things seemed to come into focus.

"Damn, if this is 'better', I'm glad I don't remember what was 'worse'."

"For a while there I was worried that your condition would be permanent. You've had a stroke."

My right side was impaired. Over the course of that day, seven different specialists came into my room and asked all kinds of questions. It was draining, but I could reason well enough to know they were trying to help me.

Carla came the second day and was sitting by my bed when another team of doctors and nurses came in. The doctor in charge had a tiny vase in the pocket of his white coat with a red flower in it. Just as they left, I started to tremble, my body convulsed and I lurched forward.

"Jesus. I don't think I'm supposed to be shaking like this."

Carla quickly realized that I was not praying, ran out and got the team to come back to my room.

I was having a seizure. The doctors and nurses rushed back in and were all over me. Within minutes, they had me stabilized.

The stroke was on the left side of my brain and affected my entire right side. Dr. McGill ordered physical therapy for the next day. They were very tolerant and didn't try to rush me. They started me off working with my right hand, and it took me five minutes to put twelve little pegs into twelve holes on a wooden block.

The physical therapist kept saying, "You're doing just fine."

Then she helped me stand up, and held me while I attempted to walk. That didn't go too well either. I stumbled but she caught me and kept me from falling on the floor.

For the rest of that day and the next, I was still in a haze, but on Monday there was a remarkable improvement. I managed to put all the pegs into the twelve holes in only thirty-five seconds and could walk a few steps by myself, using a walking cane.

Dr. McGill and his team came in and reported that they'd consulted with Dr. Paul Spring but could not pinpoint the reasons for my stroke.

Dr. McGill continued; "We are considering the possibility that you may have suffered an air embolus to your lungs causing an acute shortness of breath. This may have contributed to your ischemic episode, but it would have to have been a fairly significant air embolus to cause enough hypo-tension for a stroke of this nature. We'll have to do an

MRI. An MRI will help delineate the etiology of neurological symptoms."

I explained that I had claustrophobia, but they couldn't give me a sedative because it would interfere with my brain function.

Joyce Neumann arrived just before we started the MRI.

"Would it help if I held your hand?"

"Yes."

"You'll only be going-in about halfway, so I'll be able to hold onto you. I'll talk you through it."

It was very loud; I wasn't prepared for the noise. It sounded like I was underneath the hood of a Peterbuilt Diesel 18 wheeler whose engine was coming apart. Joyce was magnificent; she held onto both my hands and talked to me. My fear was kept under control and because of Nurse Joyce Neumann's kindness I didn't panic.

Later that day Dr. McGill came up to my room and reported on the MRI findings. There was minimal damage to the left side of my brain; it had been a mild stroke. With a lot of work at physical therapy, he saw no reason why I shouldn't make a full recovery, in time.

* * * * *

The next day Mickey and "B" appeared and brought me a black T-shirt with a picture of the band on it. They each leaned over and hugged me. They were playing in Houston that night and then **on the road again** for three months of one-night stands. "B" said, "Willie now has us rehearsing every day before "the gig". We're working in some jazz numbers. Willie's tribute to Django."

"Django?"

Mickey educated me. Django Reinhardt was the greatest jazz guitarist ever. He started it all, in Paris in the thirties. He was a gypsy and only had three fingers on his left hand. Willie's listened to him all of his life. Django's his hero."

After they left I thought how it took them time and energy to come and visit me. I may look dreadful and I'm in bed not able to move the right side of my body, but I'm blessed to have such good friends.

* * * * *

Dr. McGill's prediction was correct. After three weeks of intensive physical therapy, my speech was clear and I could move around fairly well with the help of my cane.

I wanted out of the hospital. Dr. McGill said I could be discharged if I stayed in the Rotary House Hotel for the first two nights, on the conditions that someone stayed with me, and I used a walker. I objected to the walker and asked if I could substitute an empty wheelchair. He was amused and agreed. This plan made sense. Carla said she would stay the first night, and then possibly her husband would stay the second. I got the wheelchair and the pole all lined-up and the nurse helped me to the elevator.

I pushed the button for the second floor. My nurse left and suddenly I had to sit in the wheelchair. For the next couple of minutes I felt as if I had no strength left. The elevator door opened and two attendants wheeled a gurney off with an older man on it. He was pale and thin. His eyes were closed and he wheezed when he breathed. Because of his condition it was difficult to tell if he was seventy, seventy-five or eighty years old. He was in bad shape.

As they passed by me I thought, *"that could be me."* I pushed my wheelchair to the elevator and whispered to myself.

"Do you want to quit, Ethan?"
"That'll be the day."

* * * * *

The Rotary House was expensive, but there were two big beds and I was able to sleep without any interruptions for vital sign checks. Carla and I watched Dan Rather on the CBS network news. There was a world out there. Carla got a call from her husband and said she had to run home for a few minutes. She said it would not take much longer than an hour and she'd be back right after 7:00. I dozed-off and woke up when Carla returned, at 11:30.

"Did Walter have a problem?"

"Walter has a lot of problems."

I went back to sleep.

The next morning when I opened my eyes, Carla was fully dressed and sitting on the edge of the bed in the soft morning light, just staring at the floor. I knew she'd had a rough time with her husband the night before, but neither of us had the energy to talk about it. The next night I stayed by myself. Nothing strange happened.

* * * * *

39

The little house on Oberlin had been torn down. The owners had started construction on their new big house. Andrea recommended the Wellesley Inn, which was less expensive than the Rotary House and close to the hospital. My room there was comfortable with a kitchenette. There was a shuttle service but some days I walked to clinic. It was about a half mile.

After three weeks as an outpatient, Dr. McGill released me, "Mr. Herrera it has been ten months since you came to MD Anderson. You have been through a stem cell transplant, a relapse, a donor lymphocyte infusion, CMV, a stroke, and a seizure. In short, you've been through hell. When you get home: lots of calories and moderate exercise. Good Luck."

Dr. Medina sent me off with concise instructions and reports of all my blood work from MD Anderson for Dr. Chatham. He requested that a weekly update be faxed to him so he could keep a close watch on my Tacro (FK506) levels. I left Houston feeling secure that all those wonderful folks at MD Anderson were still there if I needed them.

I went to the 11th floor and thanked all the nurses I could find.

"I know I was difficult at times."

"We like a fighter, Mr. Herrera."

Joyce wasn't in her office. I saw her coming out of a patient's room. A big hug and "call me anytime" and she was off to see another patient. A pang of emotion hit my chest as I watched her disappear around the corner and I thought, *"I'm going to miss her very much."*

* * * * *

I was in the air at thirty-five thousand feet going five hundred miles an hour. New York City was only three hours away. It was impossible to compute all that had happened to me in the last nine months. In the fight against cancer we made medical history with my case, using the stem cell transplant. I was weak but in remission. How privileged to be alive.

Malcomb was out of my life. Patrick had called and prayed on the phone several times. Patsy's calls were fewer but she was still in contact. Frank and Tandy had been like big rocks that I could hold onto during a storm and still are. John came through time and time again and I want to spend more time with him and his children in the future. Angela Pillsbury had filled in as my sister's interest diminished. Monica all but disappeared after the first few weeks. I feel that Carla grew weary from pressure at home. I think she cares for me but unfortunately we don't know each other any better than we did in March. Basha's support remained constant.

* * * * *

My brothers, sisters and I used to relive and laugh about a lot of "Daddy" stories. Humor can be a way to protect oneself from the anguish of painful memories. One of the more famous was "Go get some Coca Colas." The custom on Sundays was to get up and work on whatever project Daddy had going at the time. We would work until 10:00, change, go to church, come back, have lunch and then go back to work. It was not work with an overall view to start here and end there. Then you will have accomplished a goal. You just did as you were told. Most of the time this lasted until dark; then there was a big meal. There were some rare times when it was pleasant. Most of the time, he used verbal techniques to upset mother. He would make sarcastic remarks, and she would turn to her five children for sympathy. At least once during each dinner, she'd leave the table crying.

This one Sunday, the project was mixing concrete and building a stonewall. Our father had incredible energy that he fueled further with alcohol. This day they didn't stop at dark. Extension cords were brought for lights so the work could go on until midnight if Daddy felt like it. It was late fall, the weather was brisk and it started drizzling rain. Mother started complaining, "Johnny, it's after nine o'clock and they have school tomorrow. These children are getting wet and will catch cold." Daddy finally said, "Okay go get these kids some Coca Colas." My brother Ralph, who is best at telling this particular story, said that he could remember thinking, "Wow, a Coca Cola." I can count on one hand how many times Daddy let us have Cokes, and this time they were big ones -- ten ounces. Daddy handed them each a bottle, "Drink a couple of swallows." He sent Ralph to the garage to get a quart of whiskey, and then Daddy filled each of their bottles up to the top with booze. "Now drink that, and you won't get sick." These kids ranged from the age of six to fourteen at the time, and they worked on mixing concrete and carrying stones for another two hours in the drizzling rain.

They had to perform tasks that were far beyond their ability and if something wasn't done fast enough or just right, they caught hell. He would remind them of their mistakes with cutting, little remarks for weeks or even years after they occurred. When one of them accomplished something outside of "His Kingdom" it was always minimized. "Sure you can tackle on the football field. But what is that? Can you get the sand and water mixture right with the cement? No. I know I'm critical, but one day you'll know I'm right."

John often commented that one week in the fall of 1982, all three of his sons were on national television. John's name was called on ABC when he sacked the quarterback in the Sun Bowl game between the Texas and Arkansas. Barbara Steele had given Ralph a scene with Robert Mitchum in **The Winds of War** and I was acting on **As The World Turns**.

Most fathers would have been bursting with pride. As far as we knew, Daddy didn't watch his sons. He never mentioned it. It was as if it never happened. All six of his children have University degrees. All six children worked their way through high school and university. None of us have ever heard a compliment from him for those achievements. As an adult Monica told me that she couldn't remember a night in that house when she went to sleep without hearing Daddy shouting and mother crying. Growing up in that environment and never having extensive therapy is why my sisters *"have shit for brains."*

* * * * *

As the plane began its descent over New York, Central Park glistened in the December twilight. I was still very weak, but inspired to be back in the city. After an early dinner with

Basha, I was finally back in my apartment and able to go to sleep in my own bed.

At Sloan-Kettering Dr. Chatham seemed pleased to see me and outlined my schedule for infusions of fluids and whatever drugs I needed. I gave her my flow chart from MD Anderson. Kim Cocoran took me into her office and paged Nancy Cody. When Nancy arrived, I was greeted with a big hug. Dr. Goy popped-in, said "Good work" and gave me a big smile and a vigorous handshake. They made me feel like a champion.

It was cold but the sky was a clear blue and I was full of optimism. I walked all the way from First Avenue to the Sailboat Pond in Central Park and sat by the bronze statue of Alice in Wonderland, the Mad Hatter and the Door Mouse. I was upbeat and invigorated from my welcome at Sloan-Kettering, and felt as if all things were possible for me now.

The next day on the 16th floor there was another sweet welcome from my chemo nurse, Elizabeth. As she hooked three bags of fluids up to my port, she took a second, looked at me and smiled, "Congratulations."

"I'm glad you are still here to take care of me."

Mount Sinai on Fifth Avenue was the closest hospital in the tri-state area equipped to test FK506 levels, so the plan was to send a tube of blood out for analysis, and wait overnight for the results. Then they'd fax the lab reports and FK506 analysis to MD Anderson for Dr. Medina to review. I thought it would be simpler to just send the blood itself, with Sloan-Kettering's lab report to MD Anderson, and save 24 or 48 hours. I called my PharmD Kristin in Houston and she assured me there would be no problem on her end. She agreed that it would streamline the process.

The next day I was back on the sixteenth floor. Elizabeth started the fluids. Dr. Chatham came in, pulled the curtain around my chair, took my blood pressure and listened to my chest. I asked her about my idea and told her I had already called Houston and it was fine with them.

She said, "No. I want to keep everything here in New York."

"But doctor, wouldn't it save a step?"

"I want everything kept in New York. You are under my care here."

"Yes. But I thought this way; you'd have the results faster."

"You are under my care. But, if you want, you can call Dr. Medina and he can find you another allo-transplant doctor here, or, you can always go back to Houston."

"I don't want to change doctors."

She shut the curtain and left without another word. I was stunned. After a couple of minutes, Elizabeth pulled the curtain back and said softly, "Give her a little time; a week or so. She'll calm down."

"She'll calm down! What about me? I'm the patient."

"Dr. Chatham just motioned for me to come out in the hall and said 'That man has every right to be upset, he's been through hell'."

"Wait, wait, wait! You mean she knows I'm upset, and she just walked away! Well, Elizabeth, you just hide and watch. I'll haul my redneck butt right back to Houston in a heartbeat."

* * * * *

I flew out of La Guardia on January 2nd to spend a couple of days with Patsy and her children in Nashville on my way back to Houston. Fatigue hit me hard the first night and I slept in the guestroom.

The next morning Patsy loaned me her BMW and I drove to Franklin to have lunch with "B" and Julia Spears. The air was crisp, the sky was bright blue, I was on my way to be with good friends; I felt great.

I returned mid-afternoon and Patsy had started drinking. Lucy, her daughter had gotten herself in a social bind with two sets of friends by going to one New Year's Eve party and not another. She was planning a sleepover with girls from both groups as a way of making peace. She was very upset about the conflict and thought this plan would soothe hurt feelings. Patsy seemed irritated by the whole thing and exclaimed, "When you're twenty years old, you won't remember hardly any of their names."

I interjected. "That's seven years from now."

"Well Lucy, how many do you plan to have over?"

"I'm not sure yet Mommie."

"I just don't want a bunch of She-Devils running all over my house."

Lucy glanced at me. She felt very awkward. I left and went upstairs to the guestroom. It was the booze that caused Patsy to treat her daughter as she did. The pattern of liquor-induced abuse and irrational meanness was too familiar. My father had it down to a fine science with the addition of domination to make him feel superior.

I heard Lucy go into her room, so I went back downstairs and had a drink myself. After a few minutes of chat Patsy excused herself and went into her bedroom. Two hours later, I looked in and she was asleep. I woke her up and told her it was eight o'clock. As she shook her head, "Okay. Okay. Gotta get the kids to school."

"No Patsy, it is eight o'clock at night."

"Oh. Oh. Then I'm going to sleep a little more, and then I'll fix dinner."

Lucy, Kevin and I had dinner while Patsy slept. I left the next day.

* * * * *

40

On my first day back at MD Anderson, Andrea and Darnell welcomed me in the 8th floor clinic with smiles and "good to see you." Dr. Medina asked in a polite manner why I had chosen to return. I was as diplomatic as possible and said I felt more comfortable in an environment where my recent treatment and lab work were readily available. We left it at that.

For the first two weeks, my days were pretty much the same; blood work, the bed unit, infusions, back to the Wellesley Inn, dinner, some television and sleep.

I wrote a letter to Patsy saying that the way she treated Lucy when she drank too much was hurting her child. I also said it was unjust behavior and that I thought she should seriously consider therapy. That letter ended what was left of our romance.

Two days later I went out to explore the Almost Heaven RV Park I'd heard about from the male nurse, when I had the lower endoscopy. It is located twenty miles South of Houston, so I drove down Highway 288 onto County Road 52 and then made some twists and turns on real country roads. Small farms with cows and horses in the fields lined the road, and this countryside reminded me of southern Mississippi where I grew up; it was flat with no rolling hills like Stone County.

Tex and Susan Lawson owned the park and at least half of the residents were cancer patients. Most of the RV sites were around a twelve-acre lake, which was home for some thirty ducks and four bossy geese. The store, except for a modem line for laptops and a VHS library of films, would have been ideal for a movie set from the forties or early fifties. John had been using my motor home since he drove it back from "B" Spears' house in Tennessee in late summer, and brought it down from Austin, so I set up in site number twenty-seven.

I left every morning at eight o'clock for the hospital and usually returned an hour before dark.

I was in the bed unit five to six days a week and saw Dr. Medina in the clinic every Tuesday morning. On January 18th Dr. Medina told me they'd found I had a virus of unknown origin and he wanted me back on Foscarnate. I ran into PharmD Hicks on my way to the bed unit and she referred to this new problem as an occult virus'. She also questioned if Dr. Medina knew I no longer had a port in my chest, but when I settled into my room for the day, my nurse told me she thought that I could take the drug through an IV.

Joyce Neumann came in to check on me and explained that the drug had to flow into the vena cava. She phoned Dr. Medina and reported that he'd said to get a long line. "A long line?" I wondered aloud. Within minutes, I was in the 2nd floor Infusion Therapy section in an examination room, with a nurse holding one end of a tape measure in the middle of my chest and running it down my arm.

In high school Gam made all my shirts, and once even a sports coat. She was a very good seamstress. This nurse was as meticulous as my grandmother with a tape measure. She opened a packet, took out a long piece of plastic tubing an eighth of an inch in diameter, painlessly made an incision in the vein of my right arm, and preceded to slide the tube into me. It didn't hurt and I really couldn't feel anything as she continued to ease the tube in further and further.. Then she asked, "Do you feel anything in your heart?"

"No."

"Good."

She continued and concentrated. "Still don't feel anything unusual in your chest?"

"No. You mean, sometimes you shove this line into the patient's heart?"

"It happens."

"Damn. What do you do then?"

"Just pull it back a little."

She smiled and nodded that she was satisfied she had placed the long line in me successfully.

A trip down to the second floor pharmacy, and I was hooked up with a bottle of drugs flowing into my vena cava through my "long line."

* * * * *

Tandy Cronyn was starring in a production of an Irish play, **The Cripple of Inishmann** in Salt Lake City at the

Pioneer Theatre. I wanted to spend some time with her and see her in this play. Dr. Medina okayed the trip and I flew out for a long weekend. Tandy was excellent in her role of a spinster sister and afterwards we went to a pub with the cast, stayed up very late and "talked shop."

After thirty years of friendship and touring theatre together, Tandy and I were as comfortable together as a pair of old slippers. I told her about my last visit with Patsy, my letter and that I'd never heard from her again. Tandy simply said, "Anty, I'm glad to see you out of that relationship. It wasn't good for you." We talked family, show biz, argued politics and chuckled about calories and strawberry cake.

* * * * *

Three days later, once again my world was Almost Heaven and MD Anderson. My kidneys were still not in the best of shape and Dr. Medina was concerned. I called Braxter Irby in Mississippi because he was a kidney specialist. He explained that my kidneys **"have been through hell"** from the transplant and the trauma of all of the drugs that had been put through my body to deal with the CMV. It was his opinion that in a few months my kidneys would be back to their normal function. I concluded that Dr. Medina wanted all of me back to normal as soon as possible. We had made such progress with the new immune system and the donor lymphocyte infusion.

Ever since I relapsed in November of '98 I've dreaded CAT scans and Gallium scans but it was time for another set. Mrs. Longworth was in charge of scheduling scans. She always gave me a hug that eased my anxiety for the moment. I put my clothes in a locker and put on a robe that tied in the back. In the waiting area I sat next to a Latino gentleman who looked to be in his late fifties. I could tell by his weary but determined expression that this was not his first CAT scan, nor would it probably be his last. He was in the thick of it.

"You know, maybe after we reach fifty-three years of age, they should just take us out back and knock us in the head."

He looked at me and nodded. "I have been thinking a lot about Kervorkian myself."

Contemplating taking one's life is a very private and sensitive subject. But there we were, two men who would otherwise have probably chatted about weather, sports or women -- if at all, but we went right into the heart of the matter. If it got too awful and the end was certain, why suffer needlessly, was our conclusion. Then a nurse's aid came in and called his name, "Mr. Lopez." We shook hands, and like so many other patients I encountered, I never saw him again.

After the scan I changed back into my clothes and noticed that a pen had leaked in my shirt pocket and there was a splotch of black ink, about two inches across, in the green and blue patterned flannel. I had a quick flashback to Wiggins and the holidays of 1995 that I spent with Lucas and his family. This shirt was my Christmas present from them. I never heard from him again, after our conversation in April of 1999. It was his choice, either out of fear or lack of caring about me. Some friendships die during battle.

I finished getting dressed and walked into the hall. The nurse with my chart rounded the corner and when she saw me she said, "Oh no, Mr. Herrera!"

My heart sank. Immediately I thought she had seen my scan with the radiologist, and the cancer was back.

"What? What is it?"

"Mr. Herrera, you've got a spot on your shirt."

She handed me my chart and walked away.

* * * * *

The next morning there were very few people in the lobby of the hospital and the reception area in the bed unit was empty. Nora was seated behind the counter.

"Nora, what is it? Did they find a cure for cancer? Where are the patients?"

"Mr. Herrera -- it's Presidents Day."

A young nurse looked up from a filing cabinet. "I wonder what President Clinton's doing on his day?"

"Oh he's probably found some ugly white chick to fool around with."

Nora gave me a sharp look.

"Mr. Herrera, you should be ashamed of yourself."

"Why? Did I say anything politically incorrect?"

"No. But ugly people need love too."

We all laughed.

The long line and the drugs were working. My blood work showed a large reduction in the occult virus. Willie and family were playing in Las Vegas in early March, not too long of a flight from Houston. Sondra Baker was going to be at her home in Santa Fe. This was working out. Fly to Vegas and enjoy their music and companionship, then ride with the band on the bus to Albuquerque. Sondra would drive down from Santa Fe and pick me up. Friends gave me a feeling of family and support.

In Las Vegas, "B" Spears gave me his hotel room and slept on the bus so I could sleep during the day. Strange to get rest in Las Vegas but I did, thanks to the reassurance and generosity of my friends. The first night after the concert, I had a long visit with Sister Bobbie and Lana. Lana took my picture with Bobbie.

"I'm going to put it on our web site, 'James of **As The World Turns,** back stage.'"

"Lana, I don't know when, or if I'll be going back to work."

"That's all right. We'll just put it out there."

The next night I was invited to Willie's bus after they finished.

"You ought to put your one-man show on the web."

This came out as we were shaking hands. This was Willie's kind of greeting. I didn't remember ever discussing my show with him and I wasn't sure how he knew, but he did.

"The web is powerful. Lana's our webmaster."

"After all those years in the studio, I enjoy the road, working live."

"Nothing like a new audience every night, new energy every night. I get something from every place we play."

We got into a discussion about **Stardust**. I commented that I didn't think Hoagy Carmichael had written the lyrics. Willie came right back, "Are you sure?"

"No, I'm not."

"Lana, get on the web and see if you can find out."

Lana started searching the web, Willie got up to look at the screen of her laptop and then turned back to me, "Do you know the lyrics to the intro?"

"Sort of . . ."

Mr. Willie Nelson himself started quoting them to me.

"And now the purple dust of twilight time
Steals across the meadows of my heart.
High up in the sky the little stars climb,
Always reminding me that we're apart."

There I was sitting on Willie Nelson's bus with my friends and one of my heroes reciting one of the most famous songs in American history to me. Me -- still looking much like a ghost, with a *"long line"* pumping drugs into my chest -- I felt great.

Backstage Sunday night there was a buzz about whether we would leave after the show, or stay the night and leave first thing in the morning. Then, "We're leaving in forty-five minutes."

There it was, just before midnight and we were all rushing around to get packed and on the bus. Paul English sent a message that he wanted to see me. The back sections of the band bus were his bedroom and office.

"Paul?"

"Anthony, come in."

He shut the door. The conversation that followed was brief. Paul let me know in a few words that I was welcome anytime, and no matter how bad my situation might get, I could always count on them.

There are three buses for the band, Willie's bus, the smoking bus and the nonsmoking bus. I rode on the nonsmoking bus and sat up most of the night talking with Jackie King, who was relatively new with the band. Jackie was a Texan who had been on the West Coast for twenty years and had become one of the leading jazz guitarists in the USA. He talked jazz. I talked acting. We understood each other. Then about four in the morning we hit a bad snowstorm, and the drivers had to stop and put chains on the tires.

Willie had to be in Nashville the next afternoon to tape a television special. As I drifted off to sleep, Neil, the driver was on his CB radio with the two other buses debating whether they could make it. Perhaps he should fly from Albuquerque. The next thing I knew, it was morning and I was standing in the parking area of a huge truck stop with my bag. The caravan of busses roared off to Nashville.

* * * * *

I had a big breakfast and waited for Sondra. Once I was in her car and we were weaving our way to Santa Fe, it felt as if we had seen each other the week before. I stayed at the La Fonda Hotel. Its Spanish, pueblo style architecture in the huge dining room reminded me of the main hall in the house I had built in my imagination, when I was drifting in and out of the misery of CMV. I was very comfortable there. Sondra and I had long lunches that seemed to flow right into early dinners. We honored our friend Cleavon Little by trading memories of his warmth and humor.

"One night at Wilson's on the West Side, one of his favorite places, we were joined by a group of New York Italians. Hey, Cleavon, what you doin' hanging around this guy?"

"Who? Herrera?"

"Yeah man, he's from Mississippi?"

"So?"

"Oh, come on man, you're a black man and, I mean down there, those rednecks you know, and the Ku Klux Klan."

Cleavon gave him one of his sly Cleavon Little smiles.

"I was born in Oklahoma BUT my Momma and Daddy were from Mississippi. Shoot, me and Herrera . . . we're probably cousins."

Sondra and I both laughed.

"In Malibu, if he wasn't acting, he'd rearrange his living room furniture on a daily basis. He'd call and say, Sondrena, I need your advice."

"I called on him for help during some very scary times. He got me through a lot of scans and chemo."

Sondra smiled. "Oh. I can just see him." Sondra stared at her wineglass. "I still talk to him, when I get blue."

I know his voice so well, and went into it.

"Herrera, when we're old men, we're going to live out in the country. I'm going to have a house on one hill and you're going to have one on the hill right across the little valley. I'll have a yard full of children, grandchildren, dogs, a couple of horses and a goat; you got to have at least one goat. Every evening, I'll cook up a big dinner and you'll come over . . . and when I don't . . . I'll just come over to your house and eat . . ."

I had to bite the inside of my mouth so my chin wouldn't quiver.

"Sondra, we had a wonderful friend."

"We still have him, Anthony."

At that moment a Mexican guitar trio started playing Agustin Lara's song **Solomente Una Vez** on the other side of the room. Sondra and I sat in silence. Rarely when we are together, do we stop talking, but it felt appropriate at that moment, just to be silent and listen to the music.

* * * * *

41

Two days later I was back at Almost Heaven. I had found a picture of Emilliano Zapata, the great Mexican revolutionary on his horse and pasted it on the kitchen cabinet. On the opposite wall I had an 8 by 10 production still of John Wayne from **The Searchers**. So every time I came into my RV, I saw the faces of two powerful men filled with commitment. I cooked for myself most every night on the terrace next to the RV. Angela Pillsbury came out for dinner several times and our conversations were filled with introspection and reflection. She too had a family that was far from functional.

I fed the ducks every afternoon. I would see the whole flock wobbling toward my RV as soon as I drove through the front gate of the park. The white duck with webbing missing on her left foot was always ahead of the rest. When I poured a little pile of corn, she got there first. Then three feet away, I poured another pile. She'd run back and forth between the two piles, and the others moved in but she would still try to chase them away. When I poured a third pile; she ran to that one too, but after several attempts to dominate the food supply, she realized it was futile. She promptly pecked at her boyfriend who scooted under my neighbor's motor home, walked away, but then stopped about ten feet from the crowd and turned back with a couple of quacks to make sure I saw that she was leaving.

Tex and Sue had two daughters, Megan and Syd. Megan, the oldest, helped in the store; she was fourteen and was shy. Syd was eight and diabetic, but one would ever have known. She was all over the campground on her bicycle, had a horse named Star and was raising some baby chicks and one turkey chick in a cage that Tex built for her next to the corral. Within a few weeks she had enlisted me as her personal aid and photographer. So now along with the ducks, I helped feed the chicks and Star. On Mondays, Syd would sit me down in the recreation room, get out her date book and we would plan out the afternoons of the week. She wanted pictures of Star, of the chicks and of the baby turkey. She had me charmed and in the palm of her hand. I looked forward to our adventures.

This blue-eyed, eight-year-old girl brought a lot of joy into my life.

* * * * *

Across from my parking spot were a pair of big, blue RV's owned by two brothers, Ken and Larry Raper. They knew a lot about RV living. Ken showed me how to turn on the heat and Larry helped me with a plumbing problem. Ken's wife kept going on about James Stenbeck living across the street from her.

Eventually, I was invited over for supper. She served meatloaf, mashed potatoes and butter beans. These were country folks. Ken had been an airplane mechanic for twenty-five years and now was suffering with lung cancer after being exposed to asbestos. During dinner, showing a bit of pride, he asked me, "Anthony, how much do you think I'm worth?"

"Ken . . . I wouldn't have any idea."

"Take a guess."

"Well, this motor home probably cost four or five hundred thousand, so you have to be worth . . . Six or seven hundred thousand?"

He looked at me with a smile, "Anthony, I got four and a half million dollars in the bank. Yes sir! And in cash!"

The delight left his face and his glance dropped down to the right. His voice was soft and calm as he said, "Of course all that money's not going to do me much good. I'm going to die soon."

Stella Adler taught us that if the moment in a script was profound, one should not scream or shout the words - the simpler the delivery, the more powerful. I was sitting across from a man who was realizing his own mortality in an honest, quiet and calm manner. I kept eating to be polite, despite the sinking feeling in my chest.

* * * * *

Larry Pace was back in the bed unit the next day. His white cell count was low and he was undergoing a new procedure. They processed his blood and treated the white cells in it, to build up his counts. He never complained, even though his ankles were so swollen that he couldn't lace up his shoes.

"But Larry you're still in remission. No lymphoma."

"No. No lymphoma.   He smiled, I watch **As The World Turns** when I rest."

"How do you think the show is looking?"

"I enjoy it."

Then he'd be silent for a several minutes.

"I just don't have much energy."

Often he would not say another word and after another few minutes of silence, he'd just turn and hobble away.

* * * * *

I would call Basha about every other night. She had met a Polish director who'd offered her a job designing the costumes for a Philip Glass opera being staged in Lodtz, Poland. Basha was very excited about the prospect, as she had earned her Masters degree at the University of Lodtz. The setting of the opera was a combination of modern and ancient Egyptian. I said, "Basha with your imagination and exotic sense of style, you are perfect for this job."

In the bed unit, I realized that I hadn't seen the Turkish man and his son. There were some days that boy was so gray and thin that he looked as if he were on death's doorstep. Then the pump beeped and Rosalie came in to adjust it.

"The Turkish boy? I haven't seen them lately."

"Oh, Mr. Herrera, what a wonderful father. We almost lost him several times. Then we couldn't get him to eat. His father would tell him funny stories, and when the boy laughed, his father stuck a spoonful of food in his mouth. He would sit by his bed for hours. This went on all through December. That boy survived and they are back in Turkey."

That night as I drifted off, I thought about my first encounters with the Turkish man, with his mustache and fierce demeanor, no one, at first glance, would ever have imagined the depth of tenderness and caring this father possessed.

* * * * *

The boom, boom, boom of a large diesel motor jolted me out of a deep sleep. It was the middle of the night. I tried to get back to sleep, but the boom, boom, boom didn't stop. I pulled the covers over my head and thought 'Who is this rude jackass who starts an engine that powerful and just leaves it running? If he has to leave before daylight, he should crank the damn thing up and drive away.' It seemed endless. Finally I was totally awake and sat up to see a spinning red glow from across the little road. It was an Emergency Medical Vehicle. I thought, **"I am not in pain. I am in remission and just a few feet away somebody is in serious trouble or dying."**

In the hospital that morning, I saw Christine Murasky and was greeted with her charming smile.

"Everything health-wise is improving. I have enough energy that I've started, slowly, to write my book. Putting a Mantle Cell Lymphoma patient in remission using the donor stem cell is medical history. Science is moving forward by leaps and bounds. In Scotland they've cloned "Dolly" and just last week every television network news station and the cover of Time Magazine featured the story of Craig Venter having mapped the human genome. It is all very important."

"You met Dr. Wharton, my boss, the first day you were an inpatient."

"Right. Yes, I did."

"He'll have some ideas."

Dr. Wharton, Christine and I met the next day. I found myself going on about my transplant team. "Joyce Neumann, Medina, Korbling, Couriel, these are very smart people. And Dr. Gajewski knows more about literature and theatre than I will ever know."

Dr. Wharton interjected, "Gajewski is brilliant and easily as smart as Venter. Any of our people you just mentioned, with the money and time, could, and will contribute major scientific discoveries."

"You're right, and until I'm in remission for at least five years, they are mine."

"Mr. Herrera, your work on **As The World Turns** all these years has reached a lot of people, my mother for one. Recently, and unfortunately, we had to put mother in a senior facility. She made doubly sure that the eight by ten glossy you sent her last year, signed "James" was prominently on display in her room.

"I think this hospital should get behind your efforts on your book and getting your story out to the public. I'm going to take this to John Mendelssohn, actually to his wife, Anne. She was a television producer for PBS in New York when he was at Sloan–Kettering. She'll know what to do."

* * * * *

My next stop was the bed unit. Dr. Gajewski was rushing through the door in front of me. I caught him with my voice.

"Dr. Gajewski, there is a rumor in this hospital that you are as smart or smarter than Craig Venter."

Before he turned all the way around, he was speaking,

"Mr. Herrera, I don't want to be smarter than Venter. I just want to be as good a doctor as Dr. Petronius."

By then he was shaking my hand.

"Dr. Petronius? Oh, the Cary Grant film. You watched it."

"I loved it. A little antiquated here and there, but overall a very important message."

"That film and **The Searchers** have helped me so much through all of this."

"Mr. Herrera, art has always uplifted the human spirit. Gotta go. I'll get it back to you."

"No. Doctor, you keep it. Please."

As he rushed away, "Thank you. I will."

Gajewski, a doctor, who is a pioneer in research, travels to Japan and all over the world for MD Anderson, and still takes time to watch a film a patient recommends. I was impressed and flattered. Plus he *"got it."* This doctor knows that it is essential for the patient to find within himself the will to live, and that music, poetry, movies -- art fuels the spirit in the most desperate of times.

"Art has always uplifted the human spirit."

* * * * *

42

My energy level was better. Basha was in Poland. This was her first job in the theatre as a designer, and she threw herself into the work. With the time difference and her late hours I didn't talk to her as much, and would only get her on the phone about once a week.

"Ah, Anthonee, I have a lot of helpers but I give them a task that should be simple to do, and I come back later, and you know what? They mess it up."

In her enchanting Polish accent, it sounded very funny.

I told her that I wanted to be there for opening night. I thought Dr. Medina would probably approve of my taking such a long flight since all of my counts were stable, and the only drug I was taking was the Tacro (FK506).

* * * * *

Larry Raper told me that there was no hope for his brother and he didn't have long. The next morning I went to the 11th floor and saw Ken. His room was crowed with family. When I shook his hand he didn't try to speak. He looked into my eyes and I into his. He gave me a little nod as a goodbye. I left. As I made my way to the elevator I thought of his comment "all that money." I had to steel up not to wander into sadness. In the world of cancer, death is part of it, and the end of the agony and the pain.

* * * * *

Dr. Medina okayed my trip to Poland. I was excited. I would fly to New York and rest for two days before going on to Europe.
Basha had been so supportive through all my treatment. I was looking forward to being there while she had her moment of glory.

The afternoon before I left, Larry Pace called. He was back for more treatment and asked if we could go for a drive.

"Larry, I'm leaving first thing in the morning."

"Oh. Okay."

"How are your counts?"

"They're still trying to get the white count up."

"Hey, we've made it this far. No lymphoma! I'll be back in a couple of weeks; call you then."

He softly answered. "All right."

* * * * *

I landed in Warsaw and Basha's brother, Richard, met me at the airport. We drove to Lodtz and I was surprised at the size of the Opera House. It was huge and had over two thousand seats. Their budget was so small and they didn't have enough nails to construct the sets properly, but somehow they held together. Basha had been very resourceful and had cast members and stage workers bringing cloth from their homes. Opening night was a great success and rightfully so; Basha was pleased. She did a spectacular job and the director, producers, cast and musicians all congratulated her after the performance.

Basha had lost her parents in recent years, but an aunt, a professor of biochemistry, and two of her cousins drove from Warsaw and beamed with pride. At the reception I began to feel very tired, so I gave Basha a big hug and told her I was very proud of her. Then I excused myself to go to my hotel.

The next morning I woke up with a fever. I walked to the opera house and found Basha. She took me to Agata, the company masseuse, a lovely young woman who also had some nursing skills. When she handed me a rather large thermometer, I put it in my mouth and she gasped. Basha translated: the thermometer was supposed to be placed between my arm and chest. Then I remembered as a child in the early fifties, my grandmother had one like that. Over the next hour I checked my temperature three times and it had shot up to 103. Agata had the right connections at the hospital, so I was able to see an oncologist that morning.

Just like the thermometer, the hospital looked like something in a black and white film shot just after World War II. The oncologist was a woman and spoke very good English. We did blood work, but my liver function, the LDH, that had shot up when I relapsed in June of 1999, was normal. This doctor was very kind, and said she didn't think the cancer had returned. She gave me a prescription for antibiotics. This spike of fever was just like the one the year before, when it lasted seven weeks. I was afraid it wouldn't break and that I had relapsed, but I couldn't give into the fear if the damn disease was back. I would have to get to Houston as fast as possible and face it. As Cleavon would say, **"Herrera, it is what it is."**

After two days of pills, lots of liquids and sleep - no fever and I felt fine.

We had to cancel our trips to Krakow and Basha's hometown of Naymasuff. We were out of time, so we took a train back to Warsaw. Again, the train looked like something out of the forties with panels of oak lining the compartments. The countryside in this part of Poland is beautiful, and the Polish people I encountered traveling there were very considerate and polite. We went straight to the airport.

Basha flew to Paris to spend time with some old friends and I boarded a jet to New York. I had a message to call a Steve Stuck at MD Anderson. When I phoned his office I learned that he was their Vice President in charge of Public Relations. We scheduled a meeting for the following week, when I'd return to Houston. Dr. Wharton had set the right wheels in motion.

Evan Bergman left a message and invited me to a play he had directed, called **The Director**, which was enjoying good reviews. Though we'd been in touch by phone, I hadn't seen him since February of 1997.

I saw the play, thought the work was very good and had drinks with Evan and the cast. I learned about a friend of one of the actors who'd had two bone marrow transplants in Arkansas and owned a bar in my neighborhood. Two days later I found this fellow. I needed to talk about what I'd been though, what he'd been through, but he was abrupt and said, "Man I bitchin. I'm kicking ass. Doing great." All the while he was putting eye drops in his eyes because he still had Graft Versus Host disease. Maybe he was putting up a defense, but it wasn't the conversation that I needed to have.

I would find myself getting angry with people. I was invited to a lovely dinner party and felt hostile toward most of the guests because their concerns and conversations seemed meaningless. I didn't give a damn about their houses in the Hamptons or their last trips to Europe or who was divorcing whom. It was tough to remind myself that most people don't care about cancer until it hits home. Intellectually I knew I shouldn't be so touchy, but sometimes I was abrupt when I shouldn't have been. Then I thought, how did all those soldiers handle coming back from Vietnam? At least no one was jeering at me and calling me a pig.

* * * * *

It was May and Central Park was beautiful. I went for a walk around the reservoir and recognized a runner. It was Steve McGraw.

"You're back. You made it. Great."

"So far, so good."

We had met in a computer class early in the spring of 1998. He told me that he'd sold his interest in the Triad Theatre. He was writing and getting more involved in computers.

"Willie Nelson has given me an idea for my one-man show and the internet. I'll be back in June; let's get together."

"Call me, we'll investigate." And he took off on his run.

Tandy was in Chapel Hill, North Carolina to do the lead in **WIT**, a popular play about a literature professor dying of cancer. I called her and mentioned coming down to see her work. Tandy said she didn't think I needed to see this play at this time, and that I'd had enough cancer drama in real life. I took her word for it.

I went to Bobbie MacGuffie's and we had dinner. She told me about her last trip to Africa where she bought two bulls for a village in Kenya, and taught the women there how to plow and plant crops. She said the women thought this lady doctor in her seventies was crazy, then added "But now they can feed themselves." Later, I retired to the Unicorn room. I had slept many nights in this room and spent more Christmases in this house than any other in my life. I felt safe here. I could sleep.

* * * * *

I returned to Houston and met MD Anderson Public Relations' Steve Stuck and Julie Penny. They had an overview of how to build interest in my book. We would start with the Houston CBS affiliate, doing a two-part news special on my case and build from there. A news crew would follow me as I went through my next set of scans. The technicians would explain each procedure, interview both Dr. Medina and me as his patient, discuss the results and briefly describe how the stem cell was being used to fight cancer. It was another six weeks before my next scans were scheduled, so there was plenty of time to make all the arrangements. Things were finally going in the right direction, and I felt stronger and healthy.

* * * * *

I found PharmD Hicks in the bed unit, and told her about my adventures in Europe and the hospital in Poland. When I mentioned being pleased to find the oncologist there was fluent in English, she pointed out that most oncology text books and abstracts are written in English.

"But I didn't meet any beautiful drug dealers like you two."

Hicks laughed. "As Larry Pace said once, 'Better living through chemistry.' "

"I've got to call Larry."

Her face lost all of its cheer, and her voice was very calm.

"Larry didn't make it."

"What?"

"Last month. Larry's gone."

I went to the Rotary House and ordered lunch. I sat by the window with a view of the construction site. A new building was going up and they had made a lot of progress. The ironwork was complete and the first three floors were bricked. They were just breaking ground when I came here in March of 1999.

I kept thinking that all Larry wanted to do was go for a drive, and that I'd been too carried away with my progress and my trip to New York. I should have been more perceptive and less selfish. He had never asked for anything before. He had helped me with programs on my laptop and taught me little tricks to make them work faster. **Why didn't he tell me** *more?* It wasn't in his nature. He was painfully shy. I should have been smarter. My bed unit friend with the swollen ankles and the sweet smile was dead. Cancer killed him.

* * * * *

43

I would come back for scans in August. Before I left, Dr. Medina requested that I pose for a publicity photograph with him and Dr. Giralt for the MD Anderson Magazine. I had noticed Dr. Giralt at a distance in the halls but we had never met. He was very personable. I was in the company of two of the top stem cell transplant oncologists in the world. As we waited for the photographer, I put forth one of my thoughts, "I think that the term "mini-transplant" should be changed. 'Mini' sounds like a little fuzzy rabbit or something cute. There is nothing cute about CMV and a stroke."

Dr. Giralt commented, "Some institutions make it sound as if the patient can receive a 'drive-through' transplant. As you know Mr. Herrera, that's not the case."

The photographer was fast and professional. Dr. Medina thanked me and I thanked him for asking.

"Very nice meeting you, Dr. Giralt."

"Likewise, Mr. Herrera."

I was flattered that Dr. Medina had requested me, as the patient to be photographed with them.

* * * * *

Over the next two months the dread of facing the scans was lessened a bit because of several matter-of-fact phone conversations with Lynn Roder of Houston CBS affiliate, KHOU-TV about what should be covered when we taped at the hospital. One day I e-mailed Dr. Medina:

> *"Everyone who is seriously involved in the pursuit of science becomes convinced that a spirit is manifested in the laws of the universe - a spirit vastly superior to that of man . . . in the face of which we . . . must feel humble"*
>
> Albert Einstein

He replied the next day, "I liked the quote."

* * * * *

It was time to get on a jet and face the scans, I was feeling better, and confidant that there would be good news.

On Friday, August 11th Julie Penny and I met Lynn Roder and her cameraman in the lobby of MD Anderson. After some show biz small talk, we went to work. Luckily, on the way for my gallium injection, we met Terry Longworth. I asked her to join us and to fill-in any vital information I might leave out. One would have thought Terry had been giving interviews in front of a camera for years. I kidded her about being a talk show host. She was charming, and explained clearly and logically the objective, process and technology of the gallium scan.

Next, was the bone marrow aspiration. Minutes later I was facedown, pants mid-butt, on the table. Larry took them patiently through each step starting with the swabbing of the skin: "First comes a little sting," and he proceeded. Once he was inside the bone, I heard somebody shifting around and mumbling, then the curtain being pulled back and the door opening and closing.

"Larry, what happened?"

"The cameraman had to leave."

The reporter explained, "He was doing fine until he took his eye away from the lens. Then he got faint."

"Guess it would look like it was on TV through the lens. I've never seen this procedure performed on anyone else, even though I've been drilled at least six times."

As soon as we finished, Larry had another patient. We set 11:00 Tuesday morning to meet with Dr. Medina, and the CBS folks rushed to another shoot.

Julie Penny said, "I think we've gotten some very first-class footage. This is going to make a powerful story."

"Dr. Medina is okay about giving an interview?"

"Oh, yes. He's been very charming about all of this."

"It would be a hell of a twist if these tests show that I've relapsed."

"Don't even think that. Dr. Medina says you are in great shape."

After we finished and they left, Dr. Kornblau came down the hall. He looked thinner. When he saw me, he immediately put his hand in front of his face to keep from breathing on me.

"Dr. Kornblau, you've lost weight."

"I've had a flu bug for ten days. First day back at work."

"I'll stay over here."

"Mr. Herrera, you're looking good. How long has it been?"

"It's been a year with No Evidence of Disease."

"Let's hope for another. You can start to relax after two years."

"I get CT and Gallium results Tuesday."

"You look a lot better than you did when I was working on you. Good luck."

The next night I took PharmD Hicks and her husband Travis to dinner. We relived parts of the past year and a half, told stories and laughed a lot. She had been right there with her brains, dedication and humor for some of the most brutal times of the past year and a half. And now I was out of the hospital, in real clothes, being able to enjoy food, wine, laughter and these special friends – a perfect evening.

* * * * *

Monday I had the CAT scan and the Gallium scan. I didn't stay to talk to the radiologist about the results. That night, I had dinner alone and went to bed early. Even though I was nervous, I managed to get some sleep.

The next morning in the shower, I noticed the beginnings of a herpes outbreak and thought briefly, **"Bad things are still growing in my body."** I tried to concentrate on taping the news special with Dr. Medina. "The stem cells taken out of my brother and put into my body had killed the Mantle Cell Lymphoma in my blood. I am part of medical history." I washed my hair and shaved extra close.

I called Dr. Medina's office and Darnell answered.

"It's, Anthony Herrera. I can't help but be anxious."

His voice was as strong as ever and calm, "Let me call you back in five minutes."

It was nearly nine o'clock. Why did he have to call me back? Maybe he was busy with another patient.

I didn't wait for the shuttle. I started walking to the hospital; it was less than half a mile. Before I got to Holcombe Boulevard my cell-phone rang and as soon as I heard Dr.

Medina's voice rather than Darnell's, I felt sick in the pit of my stomach. I knew it was bad news.

"Mr. Herrera, did I wake you?"

"No, I'm walking to the hospital."

"We have bad news. There was a large amount of Gallium uptake in the chest area."

"I'll be there in five minutes."

"I'll be waiting for you."

Everything seemed to spin out of control. I tried to concentrate on the sunlight hitting the trees as I crossed through the little park. A blue jay and a mockingbird squabbled overhead in an oak tree, but my entire body, my senses, my muscles and my nervous system were not being receptive to stimuli. As if on autopilot, I reached the front doors, pushed them open, nodded to the guard and pressed 8 on the "UP" panel of the elevator. Andrea met me in the waiting area and took me directly into an examination room.

Darnell opened the door and stuck his head in, "Dr. Medina will be with you in a minute."

I told Andrea I had to call Basha, that she was waiting for me to call. What would I say? A sleepy Basha answered, "Hello."

"Basha. Basha. It's bad. The cancer is back."

"Ah. Anthonee. No."

I could hear her start to pull for breath as her voice cracked.

"Oh. Anthonee. No. What went wrong?"

"I don't know. I need you down here."

I felt numb all over. I handed the phone to Andrea. "Just get her down here."

I reached for my wallet and took out my credit card. Strangely enough, my hand wasn't shaking. Joyce Neumann came into the room, and I slowly leaned forward into her arms. She hugged me so hard; it was as if she wanted to give me some of her strength. Just feeling her pulling me as close to her as possible gave me a moment of relief.

"Joyce . . .?"

She squeezed my hand.

"I'll call you."

And she was gone. As Dr. Medina came in, Andrea told me that Basha's Continental flight would be landing at George Bush International at 4:50 that afternoon.

"I'll write it down for you."

"Will you stay?"

"Of course."

Dr. Medina proceeded to calmly repeat that there was a large uptake of Gallium in my chest area; the cancer was back. He said we would start with chemo, followed by another donor lymphocyte infusion. At that point, I stood up.

"Screw this crap. I've fought for three and a half years. I've had it. Fuck it!"

Dr. Medina went on, but I really didn't hear anything else he said. Then the next thing I realized, I was back in the patient waiting area and Andrea said to call her later. It wasn't even noon.

As I got to the elevator I heard, "Anthony." There was the couple from Waco. She had a full head of hair and bright cheeks, and he wore a smile as big as Texas.

"I made it. The experimental program worked. I have my health!"

"I'm so happy for you."

Then her husband gave me a hardy handshake.

"Thank you. You're looking good. You must be well."

I managed to mumble something vague and got on the elevator. I needed a drink. I jumped in a cab and went to Anthony's Restaurant. I ordered a double Jack Daniels and a very rare filet mignon.

I called Jay, an independent driver, originally from Thailand who had driven me several times. Fortunately he came right away. It was nearly an hour to the airport and he was very nervous for me. We stopped and I bought two chilled bottles of Veuve Cliquot champagne. He told me about how the Thai police beat him, and how he had also been jailed unjustly in the U.S. I guess he was trying to comfort me. Hearing about his struggles served as somewhat of a distraction.

As I climbed out of the back seat, he shook my hand. He offered to wait while I went in to collect Basha. She came off the plane emotionally solid. We had a hug. On the way back to Wellesley Inn, Jay continued to talk about Thailand.

The stresses of the relapse, starting chemo again, another donor lymphocyte infusion, the possibility of CMV, or dying all subsided slightly, or at least lost their edge. I was getting looped, floating along in the back of a Lincoln Town Car, drinking champagne and listening to Polish and Thai accents and great Mexican music on the radio.

When we got to the motel, I had a message from Dr. Medina saying the CAT scan showed there was less disease than he'd originally thought, and I wouldn't have to start the chemo right away. He'd meet with us at 10:00 the next morning.

I phoned Landy Teller in Vicksburg, "Landy, I might die soon and I think perhaps I should marry Basha. I don't want her to have any legal or tax problems with the trifling amount of money I have left."

He assured me that we could handle it any way I wanted.

Basha was curled-up on the bed with a glass of champagne, and listened kindly as I paced and pontificated about my life, our lives together, how we didn't make it, could have made it, but here we were. Then we were both hungry and went to Stables Steak house. The surly waitress rubbed me the wrong way and I was quick to call her a bitch. Basha and I were asked to leave. I had never been thrown out of a restaurant before. If I wasn't drunk, I was close. We went back to Anthony's Restaurant and had a good meal. I behaved. Basha didn't reproach me for my bad behavior. Somehow, this night, etiquette, manners and reputation didn't seem that important to either of us.

The next morning Dr. Medina showed us my CAT scan and explained why there was less disease than he had originally thought. There were three little tumors forming a triangle in the sternum area, and because they were close together, they glowed like one big tumor on the Gallium scan.

Andrea came in as Dr. Medina continued.

"We now have more time than I thought yesterday. I suggest high-dose Rituxan followed by a DLI."

"We tried Rituxan in '98 at Sloan-Kettering and it didn't do shit."

"High-dose can make a difference."

"Can ... or will?"

"There is no way of knowing if it will work for sure, but we can try. There is very little disease; you can wait a month to decide."

Andrea asked, "Would this be a possible cure for Mr. Herrera, or just buy him some more time?"

"There is no way of knowing."

I asked, "What happens if we do nothing?"

"You will die within a year."

I went to the bed unit to find PharmD Kristin. She was shocked. "Get in here." She took me into an examination room. I was about to crack and lose it as I handed her a bottle of champagne. My little attempt at humor:

"I heard you were upset I didn't invite you for dinner with Hicks. Here. Hopefully this will make up for it." Kristin took the bottle and stuck it in a cabinet.

"I can't believe it. What are you going to do?"

"Medina says we should try Rituxan and I've got a month to decide. Right now I just want to get the hell out of here."

"You call me anytime."

"Would you come meet Basha? She's standing in the pharmacy line."

I introduced them, and they chatted for a couple of minutes. Kristen gave me a hug, we left the hospital and went back to the motel to pack.

To write an e-mail to Dr. Medina was the only thing I could think to do to keep from cracking right down the middle.

Dr. Medina . . .

Thank you for your help and concern in the last two days.

I can tell you don't like it when I use curse words. They are by no means aimed at you, but at the disease.

I realize that this is not easy for you. I am proud of what we have accomplished and will take some time to think all of this through. As I said, I will e-mail you with questions.

*My case is a huge investment on your part and I
trust you without question. We have not necessarily
failed, we just may have more to learn.*
Sincerely, Anthony Herrera

As I sent the e-mail, I received one from PharmD
Kristin. A Dr. Braunschweig on the bone marrow transplant
team was leaving MD Anderson and moving back to New York
for family reasons. He might be perfect to administer the
Rituxan. She had mentioned my case to him, and I was to call
him in New York the following week. She included the
number. I replied and told her I would check with Dr. Medina
and see if he approved of that plan.

My response from Dr. Medina was disturbing. It was
very brief, just *that he approved if* -- *"You decide to go
forward with treatment."*

That was it. Nothing about my e-mail to him or any
good wishes or thoughts or "hang in there." Nothing. I
phoned Bobbie MacGuffie.

"I'll be here; come and stay anytime you want. Call me
at any hour if you need to talk."

* * * * *

44

I went to my apartment from the airport, and Basha to hers. The trip and the stress were wearing on both of us.

I knew that drinking too much would not make the lymphoma disappear. I also knew that if I drank to escape and sleep, I would feel awful physically, and depressed emotionally when I awoke. So, I tried the gym. It worked when I got there. I figured that if I didn't get any treatment, the disease wouldn't start crippling my organs for four to six months since the tumors were so small. I could, as they say, get my affairs in order, jump a ship and see the world.

I didn't want to face another stay in the hospital, but I knew there would be no comfort or escape because nothing was known about the next step of treatment. No one had ever been this far before on the path of an immune system versus Mantle Cell Lymphoma. What if another Donor Lymphocyte Infusion *would* work?

I kept looking for an e-mail from Dr. Medina. My gut told me that he was no longer there for me on the emotional level. Just like when one is involved in a passionate love affair, and something goes wrong, you just feel it.

One of the people from the bone marrow transplant team told me months before that Dr. Medina had "presented" my case. He was very proud of his work and felt we had proven that this was a viable way to fight this deadly cancer. I could feel that something was wrong.

Tuesday, one week after we got the bad news, I called a private office number he'd given me on my very first visit, but I'd rarely used. He answered and sounded very distant. I asked him why he didn't respond to my e-mail. He went off on a monologue about the fact that I had used the word *investment,* and that he was not at MD Anderson for money. He said he didn't work hard on my case for financial gain, and that he devoted himself equally to all twenty of his patients, gave each the same attention and was not interested in my case for fame or profit.

At first I was thrown. I couldn't remember exactly how I had used the word. It was not his usual manner to go over and over an issue, but he was very upset with me because of my use of one word.

The next morning I was in a dark cloud. It was right there in my e-mail.

"My case is a huge investment on your part and I trust you without question. We have not necessarily failed, we just may have more to learn."

Investment of mental energy, years of training and expertise and his dedication to fighting cancer was what I had meant.

Late that night I drove to Rockland County and spent the night in Bobbie MacGuffie's. When I joined Bobbie for breakfast and went over the *"investment"* misinterpretation problem I was having with Dr. Medina, Bobbie gave me her input.

"Here's what's happened. I'm not an oncologist, but I have practiced medicine for over fifty years. He's angry at the disease. He's angry at the system. He's angry with himself. "

"He was so sure I was still in remission. It must have been embarrassing for him to have to cancel our television interview celebrating my case."

I had fallen out of the saddle hard on this relapse; lost my temper, gotten drunk, and basically said the hell with it. I had felt this way before when I relapsed in November of '98 and they found the disease was back and the cause of the fever. But, slowly I came back, and slowly I regained the strength to continue the battle. Now because I felt removed from my doctor, I was sinking into despair. Basha came up and we drove over the Bear Mountain Bridge, across the river to Patomac Lake where her cousin Teresa had a lake house. The objective was to walk in the woods and relax. The woods were beautiful and Basha found lots of mushrooms.

I could not get out of my tense, desperate mood. "B" Spears called me from the road. He hadn't heard. I told him he didn't want to.

We had a long talk about the choices I was facing and those that he may have to face one day soon if his tests came back positive.

Basha was nervous, and said I needed to walk in the woods again to relax.

"The nature is good for your health."

This was humorous and irritating at the same time. It began to rain. The ladies started to prepare lunch. I felt isolated and frantic, so I left. I drove into Manhattan, and went to the reference section at the Barnes & Noble across from my gym on 86th Street.

I found the New Oxford Dictionary of the English Language and wrote down the exact definition of the contemporary use of the word *"investment."* *"The investment of money. (now also time and effort)."*

Then I bought the New American Dictionary of English Language and took it back to my apartment. Listed there was another up-to-date use of the word: *"a commitment as of time and or support."*

I composed a letter to Dr. Medina. My panic about having alienated him over the use of a word began to grow into a fury. Why was I running around the countryside trying to resolve the meaning of a word? I was the patient. I was the one who had cancer tumors in my chest that would grow and kill me unless I was willing to allow myself to have strange stuff dumped into my body, which may or may not kill this cancer. Barrels of chemicals, local and total body radiation and my brother's immune system had been put into me and the damn disease was back, and now I was in a panic because I upset *my Doctor?*

I couldn't shake the anxiety or the anger. At night I would toss about and stare into the darkness. Jack Daniels in moderation helped, but the second weekend I made the mistake of staying in my motor home alone and drinking during the day. I paid the price with a massive depression the following day, but forced myself to get back into Manhattan and to the gym - it helped.

I sent the letter overnight to Andrea and asked her to hand deliver it to Dr. Medina. Two days later I called Andrea.

"He read it and didn't make any comment. I told him that you were going berserk and that this situation had to be dealt with right away."

"Thank you, Andrea. I'm going to arrange a meeting with Dr. Medina."

Two days later I flew to Houston and arrived in time to make it to MD Anderson for our one o'clock meeting. A nurse I didn't know showed me into an examination room. I paced for the next eighteen minutes and went over and over in my mind how to try to be as clear and direct and calm as possible.

Dr. Medina came in with Andrea McMillian. Andrea sat to my right and Dr. Medina sat a few feet away, in front of me.

"Dr. Medina, I feel that the misunderstanding of the word 'investment' has damaged our ability to communicate and I have slipped into despair. I need to feel that I have your support in order to muster up the courage to go forward with treatment."

He leaned back a bit and then started twisting his wedding ring with his thumb and forefinger of his right hand. As he began to speak, he started pushing back the fingers of his left hand. It was the same mannerism I'd noticed when he told me about the possibility of Hepatitis in March of 1999. He did not want to be having this meeting. His first word was also a signal that this was going to be tough. He began by using the word, "We" as opposed to "I."

"We at MD Anderson have . . ." He went on with a stream of general terms about treatments, approaches for dealing with lymphoma and MD Anderson policies.

I interjected, "Dr. Medina, I am upset and I feel that you have pulled away, on an emotional level."

"If I felt that I had a problem treating you, I'd turn you over to Dr. Gajewski."

He kept pushing back his fingers and went back to "We" and more generalities about various treatments.

I interjected again, "Doctor, I am very upset . . ."

"Mr. Herrera, if I have said anything to upset you, I apologize."

And with that, he got up and left. Andrea looked at me.

"He just wanted out of here."

"I didn't know I was going to be called in here. I was eating lunch when he paged me to come up here. I'm sorry that this didn't turn out better for you. I'll be in my office."

Then it struck me that even though he was a much more educated and sophisticated man, Dr. Medina's behavior was very much like that of my father, the Spaniard's conquistador pride. He could not admit that he had done something that might possibly have been out of line – causing so much anxiety in a patient. It was the -- *I am never wrong* syndrome.

I was disappointed that he didn't have the interest to investigate why I was so upset. When the foot flop problem happened, Dr. Medina was on the phone to Dr. Rossi within minutes. This disturbance between us had gone on for weeks with e-mails, phone calls, letters and now a trip from New York to Houston, just to discuss it. It had never occurred to him to pick up the phone and call Dr. Valentine, who was on the floor every day making rounds, just like all the other doctors fighting cancer.

I felt we had not communicated at all. Despair consumed me. Slowly I left the room and started down the hall to the waiting area when I saw Andrea talking with Dr. Giralt. As I walked up to them, he put out his hand, "Mr. Herrera, I've heard that you relapsed. Now you stay here with us. We're going to, we're going to keep after this thing, we are going to find a way."

"Doctor, this is a war between the dark side of nature and you folks in medical science. My body is just the battle ground."

Dr. Giralt put his hand on my shoulder and looked right into my eyes. "No, Mr. Herrera . . . *You* are our warrior."

He walked away. Andrea followed me into the waiting area.

"Giralt just gave me what I needed."

"Yes, he did."

She gave me a hug, and as I got on the elevator I thought, what good medicine . . . just a few words . . . *"You are our warrior."*

Because of Dr. Giralt's words I was now filled with hope and energy. I said aloud,

"Do you want to quit, Ethan?"
"That'll be the day."

45

Dr. Ira Braunschweig had left MD Anderson only two weeks before and was setting up his office in Garden City. There is an odd phenomenon about living in Manhattan. I rarely leave the little island, and for me it seems easier to go to New Orleans or Houston than Garden City, Long Island. Fortunately, I had driven my 240 D back from Texas and it was not that hard to navigate the route to Garden City. In my first conversation with Dr. Braunschweig, I asked about doing a CAT scan before we started treatment. He pointed out that I had just had one done in August.

I explained that I wanted to monitor the amount of disease right before we started, and re-check it after the four rounds to see if high dose Rituxan would make a difference.

The radiologist was on the way to Dr. Braunschweig's office. I would have the scan done, wait for the film and bring it with me for our first meeting. This was all very different. Clinics were in different locations in small buildings, unlike Sloan-Kettering and MD Anderson's massive complexes. This clinic was in a modest three-story office building. However, the staff, technicians and doctors were state-of-the-art. The patients waiting for their scans had the same expressions, fighting to be pleasant and positive, but terrified inside.

I drank the goop. It was different goop. It was red and more like Kool Aid than chalk milk. The newer machines were a lot faster than the first one I had climbed onto, on January 10th 1999.

When they finished, I asked to see the radiologist after he'd had a chance to study the scan. They were very polite, "Of course."

"Mr. Herrera, there is very little disease here." For a split second I froze. "I haven't seen the scan from MD Anderson, but there is very little disease here."

It had crossed my mind only once when I wasn't having night sweats. *What if my new immune system was fighting the disease?* I didn't dare let myself hold onto that hope though, because of three relapses in less than two years.

It was about seven miles to Dr. Braunschweig's office. As I walked through the door, very excited, "We need to get MD Anderson on the phone and get my last CAT scan up here tomorrow. Hi. I'm Anthony Herrera."

A very young looking man in a blue suit and tie, stuck out his hand. "I'm Dr. Braunschweig."

"You look like a kid."

He smiled. "I get that all of the time."

"I didn't mean any disrespect. Doctor, here is the CT that I just had done. There is very little disease."

The next morning I was back at ten o'clock and the CAT scan of August 14th had arrived. Dr. Braunschweig compared the scans and talked me through them. There _**was less disease.**_

"Doctor, in the fall of 1998, in just six weeks, the tumor grew so fast that it sealed up my gut. Now in six weeks, the scans show there is **less** disease. There is only one thing that could have happened. My new immune system works. For some reason the cancer came back, but the new immune system caught it and is taking it out."

"That's the correct assumption. I have to question if we should go forward with the Rituxan. Let's get a Gallium scan."

It took forty-eight hours to get the result of the Gallium. There was much less uptake. Dr. Braunschweig said he had talked to Dr. Medina, who still thought I should have the Rituxan as originally planned. I had talked it over with Bobbie MacGuffie and her input was, "If there is a chance that it might help the immune system in its fight with the disease, hit it on the way down."

I remarked to Dr. Braunschweig that it would be interesting scientifically to see what my new immune system would continue to do without the Rituxan.

"Mr. Herrera, this is not the time to experiment."
When I arrived two days later for my first infusion, Dr. Braunschweig was assembling bookshelves in his office.

"This is great, a carpenter, and a brilliant oncologist."

He smiled, "We're just getting set up. You're my second patient."

Bernadette, his oncology nurse from MD Anderson, was in the process of relocating. The doctor showed me into a room with four big recliner chairs, much like the ones I'd sat in at Sloan-Kettering. I settled in one, he put a butterfly needle and a line into my left arm and proceeded to hook up fluids and a bag of Rituxan.

"Doctor, if it works this time, what does Rituxan do?"

"Rituxan is an antibody that . . ." As he explained, I couldn't grasp the terms. I asked him to simplify.

"We infuse these cells into your blood stream. They seek out the lymphoma cells and cling to them. In basic terms, they "choke" the cancer cells and prevent them from multiplying."

"If it works."

"Right, if it works."

"And Rituxan is not chemo, it is not a chemical."

"Correct. "It is a protein that was discovered in the ovary of a Chinese hamster, but now it is manufactured."

"I guess you can't make stuff like that up."

He looked at me, smiled and handed me a folded piece of printed material that came with the Rituxan.

He had to stay with me in case there was a reaction. There were no other patients that afternoon, so he explained more about my new immune system and brought in medical books to show me graphs on research. He made a sincere effort to help me understand what had happened with the Mantle Cell Lymphoma and the treatments I'd gone through.

I began to understand that there might be battles between the disease and the immune system in the future, but that it was a very positive sign that my new immune system had "caught" the bad guys and was *taking them out* before I started the Rituxan.

The next Thursday Basha came with me. Dr. Braunschweig came in from time to time to check on me, and we got into a discussion about "the cooking meat over coals" theory as a cause of cancer. I interjected, "Humans have been eating meat cooked over open fire for thousands of years." Both he and Basha answered in unison "And humans have been getting cancer for thousands of years."

For the next two Thursdays, I spent six hours in the recliner chair getting infused and talking with the good doctor. The CAT scan in early November was clear. Nothing. No Evidence of Disease.

Then the Gallium Scan also showed some slight activity in the chest area. This was a very positive sign.

"Doctor, why are we still seeing activity on the Gallium?"

He began to explain but again I could not follow . . . So . . .

"Doctor, is it like we've had a fire, the lymphoma, and as far as we can tell the fire is out but there are still some embers and smoke?"

Dr. Braunschweig smiled and nodded, "Yes, yes, that is an analogy that will work." However, you need to have another Gallium scan in a month. We can't take any chances."

On the morning of December 7th 2000, the drive from the Upper East Side of Manhattan to Garden City was one of the longest journeys I'd ever had to make. ***"What if the cancer was back? What if all of this has failed? What if . . ."***

By chance I found a jazz station with Ray Charles singing a very old version of **"It Had to Be You."** I had first seen Ray Charles perform at Ole Miss in the sixties. I saw him rehearse for over an hour at CBS in 1976 when I was on **The Young and The Restless**. The music lifted me out of the panic. Then I was back on the little table sliding back and forth through a big tube.

Marion, the technician for the Gallium scan was very kind and arranged for the radiologist to go over the scans with me. There was just the slightest uptake, like thin little vapor clouds.

Dr. Braunschweig said this was a very positive sign and he felt that we were winning, but we would have to do another Gallium scan to make doubly sure.

"Doctor, can we make it six weeks or even two months? I need a break."

Doctor Braunschweig has a great smile. "Okay, Mr. Herrera, early February."

* * * * *

I didn't spend much time with Basha over the holidays. She had a very bad flu and worried that she was contagious. I did have Christmas Eve dinner with Teresa, Basha's cousin, her daughter and her husband Roberto, the oncologist. He was very interested in my journey.

"Four or five years ago at oncology conferences, we would snicker at the reports given by our colleagues from MD Anderson. In the last four to five years though, we've all been trying to catch up. I'm very happy the mini-allo transplant worked for you."

* * * * *

When I was growing up in Wiggins, I just wanted to "fit in". Spanish was never spoken in the house except when my uncle Anthony would come up from New Orleans. Now I wish I even understood the words in Agustin Lara's songs. I wanted to be in a warm climate, to study Spanish and take tennis lessons. After two late nights on the Internet, I found a tennis camp owned by a German doctor in Majorca, an island off of the coast of Spain. Perfect.

I arrived in January and was the only guest. A very pleasant young German fellow, Gunter ran the little restaurant and tennis camp. At mid-day, some thirty German tourists would walk up the long hill for lunch. For the next two weeks in Majorca, I heard nothing but German and slept soundly at night after two tennis lessons per day. So much for learning Spanish, but I did improve my forehand.

In February the Gallium uptake was zero. Dr. Braunschweig and I both were very happy and relieved.

"Doctor, you have a quality, a special something that makes this patient feel that you want to treat and care about my whole person; the physical, the mental and the spiritual. That's very important in helping sick people get well."

"To have moments like this one is the reason I became a doctor"

"What can I do to help keep my new immune stay strong and healthy? Do you know of any herbs or tonics?"
He thought very carefully before he answered.

"Eat right, sleep right, exercise and everything else in moderation."

46

Out of nowhere I heard from my daughter. She had a boyfriend and arranged for the three of us to have dinner in the East Village. She had spotted my 240 D Mercedes. "That's your car right across the street with the Texas plates."

"Yes."

She seemed proud and nodded at her friend.

"See, I told you that was his. A very good car."

Her friend was smart and very pleasant. It turned out to be a fine evening. The next week we had dinner at Basha's apartment. Three weeks went by without a word. Then I got another call. She wanted to talk. We met and she looked strained. She was *"taking a break"* from her relationship. She said we never *"talked"* about what's important. I chose not to say that she never even called after Sloan-Kettering. That was over three years ago. "We can talk. First, I want to know, do you want to work toward you and I having a relationship?"

"Yes. I mean not right away. But in the future."

"Good. Okay. This is not going to be easy for you to hear." I started to tell her that her mother had set me up when she was conceived. She stopped me abruptly. "I don't want to talk about my mother or her morality."

"Perhaps we could work with a professional?"

"NO! I'm not ready for that. I just want to scream at you. That's what I want, is to scream at you."

"No one is going to scream at me."

She calmed down and then said she had an appointment. I walked with her a couple of blocks. I gave her a hug when we parted. She said she'd have to think about things and she'd call me soon. That was the last I heard from her.

* * * * *

In April I flew to San Francisco to visit Willie and the band. Mickey Raphael and I took long walks in the snow the three days we were in Tahoe. Over the years, I've been back stage easily fifty times and each time the music, the band and Mr. Nelson just get better and better.

Once, years ago in Atlantic City, I had seen a drunk jump on the stage and LG, Willie's body guard, just gently took him by the arm and waltzed him right off of the stage into the wings where the casino security took the drunk away.

The second night in Tahoe a lot of hangers-on were in the dressing rooms. They were making noise, drinking the sodas and eating the food. All of a sudden LG appeared and roared,

"Everybody get the hell out of here!" He started to lock all the doors. I had left my coat in the first room and as everyone was moving out fast, I went back and asked, "LG, can I get my coat out of here?"

He looked at me with a bit of surprise, "Not you, Anthony. You're one of us." It was a fleeting moment for LG. But his words reinforced for me, the feeling of family.

In the caravan of the three buses, we traveled to Anaheim, California for the next night's gig. Frank Sacks came for the concert, and after lots of hugs and *come be with us again.* I went back to Los Angeles with Frank. I spent three great days staying with him, his son, Spencer, and his wife, Paula. I was very impressed with Frank as a father. At dinner Spencer interrupted me as I was talking, not in a rude manner at all, but just the way ten year olds do.

Very calmly Frank said, "Spence, don't interrupt." When I finished, Frank said to his son, "Spence, what is it you wanted to say?" When we finished our meal, Frank calmly said, "Spence, say goodnight to Anthony and go get started on your homework. I'll be up to help you in a few minutes." The next afternoon when I came in, Spencer and Frank were giggling and wrestling on the floor like they were both ten years old. What a good father.

I drove to Santa Barbara to be with Sondra Baker. Sondra put me up in Thais' guesthouse on a magnificent six-acre estate. I was exhausted and just wanted to rest, but Sondra really wanted me to meet her friend Mary Ann. It was eight o'clock and I needed to eat, so I thought I'd join them just for an hour. As it turned out Mary Ann was a professor, taught film, and once spent five hours interviewing John

Wayne about **The Searchers**. Suddenly I had tons of energy, and we talked until one-thirty in the morning.

That night one of the family's dogs, George, was accidentally locked in the living room. He woke me up barking at 4;00 a.m. Though I was very tired, I got up and opened the door, but George, who was a big dog, wouldn't go outside. I gave up and went back to my room. He followed me, jumped up onto my bed, rolled over on his back and promptly went to sleep.

I think and feel about Thais as I would if she were my niece and was very happy to learn that she had stayed in remission after the ordeal of a stem cell transplant. She was in excellent health, and even more beautiful than before cancer.

I know next to nothing about the world of golf, so when I met Thais' husband, Fred Couples at a long lunch, I wasn't star struck by the fact that he was one of the greatest players of the game. I met a man who adored his wife and her two children from a previous marriage. To me, he was a super star because he had fallen in love with her one month before she was diagnosed with cancer and was with her through all of her treatment.

Sondra and I could talk with each other for years. We had lunch every day overlooking the Pacific Ocean and crammed as much as we could into the time that we had together.

When I left, George followed me to my car but didn't jump in as he'd done for the past three days when I went on errands. He watched as I loaded my bags in the trunk. He wasn't very animated as I petted him and told him how happy I was to have a new friend. I said goodbye and he just stood there watching as I drove away.

47

September 11, 2001   I was in the studio in Brooklyn rehearsing a scene with Michael Parks. One of the crew said something about a plane that had just hit the World Trade Center. I went into the head prop man's office behind the stage. Several of the crew were watching the newsbreak. There was speculation about the accident involving "a single engine plane." I went back on the set to check if they were ready for our scene. They weren't. I walked back in just as the second tower was hit. I felt sick. There was more confusion. Suddenly, we all realized that it was no accident. Our country had been attacked. I went into the control room and everyone was watching the monitors in disbelief. The producer shut down for the day so the people who lived in Long Island could get home. I ended up in one of the writers' offices watching in silence as the tragedy unfolded. We sat in shock as Tower One collapsed like a giant metal accordion. Then Tower Two.

One of the writers ran down the hall and shouted, "They just hit the Pentagon." I thought, ***"I've fought for four and a half years not to die, and now this."*** It was a selfish thought, I know, but it was my first reaction. I tried to call Basha but the phones were dead. My cell phone wouldn't work inside the studio, but someone said the pay phone on the second floor worked, so I was able to get through and told her to turn on the television. Our Executive Producer, Chris Goutman ordered food and drinking water to be delivered to the studio. One option I considered was to stay, sleep in my dressing room and see what was going to happen next. Then Michael, who lived in Rockland County not far from Dr. MacGuffie's, said he wanted to get back to his wife and children and offered me a ride. Everyone was still glued to the live coverage. Maura West also lived north of the city and we agreed to caravan with her. Once we got outside the studio, we could smell the smoke from the Towers. Michael became emotional. "Damn them. Smell that."

We stopped and filled both vehicles with fuel. We stayed tuned to the news. We knew all the bridges to Manhattan were closed. But how would we get out of Brooklyn and north to Rockland County? Not ten minutes into our journey Michael was very upset, "Look at all these people just walking around. All hell could break loose at any moment. Are you packing?"

"What?"

"Are you packing? Do you have your gun?"

"No, but I damn sure wish I did."

During the years I lived in South Africa, I carried a pistol. One actress in the studio knew, thought that was "cool." I told Michael I never carried a gun in New York City.

We were headed away from Manhattan, and so were thousands of others. We finally maneuvered our way to the Whitestone Bridge but it was closed. Then we made it to the Throg's Neck Bridge and had to wait two hours before we could get across. A huge flatbed truck loaded with coffins was in the lane right next to us. We both noticed it, but didn't comment.

Traffic stopped. After an hour, Michael leaned over and got a bottle of red wine off the back seat.

"I've been saving this for a special occasion. This wasn't exactly what I had in mind."

He looked in the glove compartment.

"I knew it. No cork screw."

"I'm not packing a pistol, but I am packing a Swiss Army knife."

I made cups by cutting the bottoms off two empty plastic bottles and we drank a toast to staying alive.

Traffic started moving, very slowly; we'd get a couple of hundred yards and then have to stop. This went on for the next three hours. The wine helped calm us down somewhat, but then Michael said, "I wish we could get away from that damn truck."

"Not a very good omen."

Five hours after we started out, we drove up the driveway to Bobbie's. Michael said, "Right. A small castle."

"What?"

"I heard you describe this once as a castle. Not a huge castle, but a small castle."

It had been a strenuous trip. Michael finally smiled as I shook his hand and thanked him. "At least we got away from the coffins."

"Good luck."

For the next two days I stayed in front of the television and on the phone to Basha. I asked her to take the train to Tarrytown and I would pick her up, but she didn't want to leave the city.

I felt as safe at Bobbie's as I would have anywhere. On Friday September 14th I decided to drive into New York City. The atmosphere in our country was very tense. Little was known as to how and why we were attacked. I drove down the Palisades Parkway and paid six dollars to go through the tollbooth. As I went down the ramp onto the George Washington Bridge, I saw a huge American flag hanging down from the top of the bridge. At least forty construction workers wearing yellow helmets and vests cheered and waved little American flags to welcome us back to Manhattan. When I drove onto this giant of a bridge and saw the skyline of my wounded city, my chest swelled and then something happened that had not happened to me through all the agony of fighting cancer, I wept.

* * * * *

Over the next few very tense and scary weeks, I began to hear phrases on the news and in the press about the attack on our country, that I hadn't heard since cancer had first attacked my body over four years ago.

"We don't know why . . ."
"Don't know the origin . . ."
"Be vigilant . . ."
"Did this really happen . . .?"
"Try to carry on with your life . . ."
"The future is uncertain . . ."
"They are afraid there might be more cells . . ."
"Will they come back . . .?
"Your life has changed forever . . .?

* * * * *

I was working two days a week. Chris Goutman told me that because of 9/11 they were going to "lighten up" the James and Barbara story. For weeks, army trucks were on the FDR drive; police cars and fire trucks with sirens blasting sped through the streets and military planes could be heard patrolling overhead.

One night Basha and I did some shopping on the Internet and ordered two of the best gas masks we could find. I was very tired, as we debated the pros and cons of different models. I started laughing. Suddenly I thought how absurd our lives had become, two people in their mid-fifties at eleven o'clock on a Tuesday night, flipping around on an electronic device, trying to buy gas masks. The reality of the danger and the terror seemed for the moment at least, absurd.

In October I flew to Memphis. As the plane lifted over Manhattan, it turned south and we saw the wound where the Twin Towers once stood. Some of the rubble was still smoking.. I turned away from the window and covered my eyes until Manhattan was out of sight.

Bobby Worsham, a Sigma Chi from Corinth, Mississippi picked me up at the airport. He had been keeping my motor home for me. Years ago, he lost his twenty-year-old daughter in a tragic traffic accident, and he had recently gone through a divorce. We had both learned to get the most out of the present. We told stories about other fraternity brothers that had happened over thirty years ago, and laughed a lot. I bought two new Smith & Wesson revolvers and drove my RV back to New York.

In November, Dee Lyons called to ask if I would appear on The Debra Duncan Show on ABC TV in Houston. They wanted me to discuss cancer and the stem cell transplant. My producers at CBS worked out my schedule so that I could make the trip.

Joyce Neumann invited me to join her and her guest for dinner in her back yard to celebrate her fifth birthday. At one table sat Dr. Giralt, Dr. Champlin, Dr. Scott and some other people I didn't know. What a collection of brains at one table. Dr. Giralt and I chatted about life in general. I thanked him for his "warrior" statement and he was gracious. Toward the end of the evening Dr. Scott, his wife and a nurse were still at the table. I went over and re-introduced myself.

"Oh yes, Mr. Herrera, I remember you."

"Dr. Braunschweig said to send you his best if I should see you, and that he misses working with you."

"I understand he's doing well."

We exchanged a few more pleasantries and then, "Doctor, I hope you don't hold any hard feelings about my asking for Dr. Kornblau the day you came into my room in June of '99 with some bad news. It was just that I knew him, and I didn't know you."

"You remember."

"Doctor, that's not the kind of day one forgets."

"I am pleased that you are in remission and enjoying good health."

"Thank you." We talked for nearly an hour. Dr. Braunschweig was right, he was a "great guy."

* * * * *

Monday morning, a camera crew from the Houston ABC affiliate came to the hospital and interviewed patients and some of the wonderful people who'd taken such good care of me. Dr. Gajewski was great on camera, and very articulate when he spoke on the stem cell transplant, his colleagues' dedication, and that there were discoveries being made every week, right there at MD Anderson.

The producers had done their homework about my case, and about my life. As soon as I sat next to Debra Duncan, they showed a picture of Cleavon Little and a handsome picture of Professor Evans Harrington on the monitors. It got to me and I almost choked up, but caught the emotion before my voice broke. Debra's questions were very well thought out and covered as much information about what it is like to deal with cancer, as time allowed.

Joyce Neumann was the featured guest. My nickname for her is Super Nurse, but not when the cameras are rolling. Joyce was very precise in her explanation of stem cell transplants, so everyone could understand. My brother John came on and did a good job explaining that it was not painful to donate stem cells.

According to reports from Debra Duncan's producers and from the e-mail I received, that hour of Southeast Texas television enhanced people's understanding, and gave strength to at least some people fighting cancer.

* * * * *

48

In late April I had a routine checkup and CAT scan in Rockland County. I waited in reception for Dr. Mackey to read it, and when he walked in, I could tell by his expression that something was wrong. It showed a growth in my right lung. I knew by now that I couldn't fall out of the saddle every time there is potential bad news. So instead of getting drunk, I drove around a bit and then had lunch at Bennigan's in New City, where Bobbie MacGuffie and I often ate. Then I figured there had been enough time.

"Hello, Dr. Braunschweig, please." He picked up immediately.

"Mr. Herrera, I've spoken with Dr. Mackey."

I wasn't devastated but I knew my thinking wasn't that clear.

"Doctor, on a scale of one to ten, how panicked are you?"

"Four to five. Let's see what the Gallium tells us."

"Doctor, do you think we need a Gallium scan?"

"Yes. You will also have to have a needle biopsy, and it may not be conclusive. The more information, the better."

I was injected, and forty-eight hours later had the first of two Gallium scans. The technician helped me as I climbed down off the sliding table. I suddenly felt **this is not lymphoma.** I couldn't reason why, but I felt it in my gut.

After seventy-two hours, Dr. Mackey read both the scans for me. No uptake. Nothing on the reading of either scan to indicate lymphoma. Then we went over the last two years of CAT scans. He pointed out that there were two little spots in my right lung two years ago, and eight months ago they were the same size, but one had more than quadrupled in size since then. He concluded,

"Anthony, I don't know what is growing in your lung but with your history, you have to find out."

"Do you think it is cancer?"

"That is not my expertise. Go back to your oncologists who know your history, and find out what is in there. Don't let this go. After all you have been through, why take the chance?"

* * * * *

I phoned Joyce Neumann told her about the lump in the lung and that I wanted to work with Dr. Giralt. The next afternoon Dr. Giralt's head nurse called and I set up a consultation with him for Monday May 6th. I called Dr. Braunschweig and told him I was set up at MD Anderson, he replied, "Good, they are the best."

There was no way to know what Dr. Giralt would determine once he had seen the scans. If they found cancer with the biopsy, I didn't know how long I would have to stay in Houston. So having my motor home there, as a place to live, possibly for months I thought, would be a good idea.

Steve McGraw helped me drive to Texas. We stopped in along the way to visit his brother, then my friend Mickey Easterling in New Orleans and enjoyed some crawfish and authentic Cajun music with Mark Savoy and other friends in Eunice, Louisiana. It was a good trip.

I had called Tex at Almost Heaven and asked for a site right on the lake.

"There's one that will be available and it's the best view we've got; and it's yours for as long as you need it."

* * * * *

Dr. Giralt sat with me for an hour, and we talked about my case from the very beginning right up to the present.

"I think it is good for us both to have an overview. I've looked at all your scans. Anthony, do you think you have lymphoma?"

"No, I *don't*."

"What do you fear?"

"That I *do* have lymphoma."

"I don't think you have lymphoma either. What I fear for you is that you have lung cancer."

My thinking had been so fixed on lymphoma that I hadn't even considered another kind of cancer.

"Doctor, do you think I have lung cancer?"

"I certainly hope not. But with your history, we can't take the chance. We have to find out what is in your lung, and if we can't find out with the needle, we'll have to go to the knife. In case the biopsy is not conclusive, I want you to meet with Dr. Walsh. He's one of our top thoracic surgeons. You take him your scans; it'll save time."

"Before the biopsy?"

"Yes, Anthony, I'm ninety percent sure . . . we're going to have to go in."

Dr. Walsh was all business as we looked at the critical CAT scan.

"I'll go in from the back. I'll have to open up your rib cage so
I can put my hand in, cut the lung and take out the lump. We'll do a biopsy right on the spot. If it is lung cancer, I'll take off the lower third of your right lung."

"Doctor, I'm having the biopsy tomorrow. If that doesn't give us the answer and you have to go in, can we schedule the operation for the week of the 20th?"

He checked his digital calendar, "Fine."

"I'm an actor and the show I've worked on for over twenty years, off and on, has invited me to go to the Emmy Awards on the 17th."

"What show is that?"

As The World Turns.

"Sounds like fun."

* * * * *

Within the hour I was back in a clinic with a butterfly needle in my arm, while drugs eased into my bloodstream and the "conscious sedation" put me in a dream state.

They went in through my rib cage for a fine needle aspiration. It takes two days to get the pathology results. The waiting doesn't get any easier, and the last few hours are the most tense. I stayed with Angela Pillsbury at her house. I needed the company and she had been right there for me since the summer of 1999.

The second afternoon we went to a mall, and I bought three pairs of summer pants, I don't like malls and I don't like shopping. I needed a distraction. Dr. Giralt called me on my cell phone.

"No cancer found, only dead tissue."

"Do you think we still have to go in?"

"Yes."

"At least we know it is not cancer at this stage of our investigation. I knew that the needle might not give us the answer."

"I hear you're going to New York for a quick trip. When do you leave?"

"Tuesday morning."

"Come and see me Monday."

"Thank you doctor."

"Have a good weekend Anthony."

It was very hot, so I stayed at Almost Heaven for the weekend. In the early morning the ducks on the still water of the lake moved so smoothly, like perfectly bowed ships, that they didn't even leave a wake. Saturday night I visited with Tex and Syd at the store, but once back in my RV, I couldn't sleep. I watched **Casablanca** with Humphery Bogart, but still tossed and turned, so I put on **The Searchers**. After John Wayne brought Natalie Wood home, I slept.

Monday morning Dr. Giralt gave me a prescription for a drug similar to Neupogen but instead of stimulating the bone marrow to over produce white cells this drug increased the number of red cells to strengthen my blood for surgery. He also arranged for me to give a unit of my blood so they would have it if needed during the operation. When I walked in the blood bank, my friend, Miss Polk greeted me with a hug.

"I'm sorry they are going to have to cut you. Let's hope for good news, and I promise Mr. Herrera, that I will personally know where your blood is at all times."

We smiled at one another.

* * * * *

I flew to New York, and on Tuesday night Basha and I went to a concert at Carnegie Hall. As far away as New York seems when I am in the world of my RV, the ducks and MD Anderson, the hospital seems just as distant when I am in the middle of life in Manhattan.

The Emmy Awards were held at Madison Square Garden. At the reception I said hello to colleagues from ABC, CBS, NBC and old friends from both coasts. **As The World**

Turns won Emmy Awards for best makeup, hair and writing. Basha joined me for the party, an upbeat action packed evening, a lot hoopla. It was a lot of fun.

Forty eight hours later, I was back in Dr. Walsh's office watching a video to educate patients for thoracic surgery. The scar shown ran from the middle of the back, around the patient's side and up to his chest.

I'd have a scar like that in a few hours, but it was a small price to pay. Next, I met with an anesthesiologist. "Doctor on a scale of one to ten, how close will I be taken to death?"

"Seven or eight."

"I don't want someone young. I want a veteran working on me."

"I'll write that down on your order."

Dr. Walsh was much more personal; he wanted to know about my trip and the Emmy Awards.

"No upper body exercise for eight weeks."

"Eight weeks without squash?"

He sat and looked me straight in the eye. Then he spread his fingers, slowly slid one hand into the other and clasped tight. "Give mother nature a chance to mend. I've had some patients go back to tennis after five or six weeks and they've **really** regretted it."

He made his point.

"See you in the morning."

"No, you won't see me, you'll be out, but I'll see you."

* * * * *

My last appointment that day was with Dr. Valentine. It was May of 2002, and this doctor had helped me through many tough moments since March of 1999. He thought I was in good psychological shape, considering I was facing major surgery.

"My main concern at this point doctor is to live through the operation."

"You're not going to die tomorrow."

"Then I don't have to sign the consent form?"

"Oh, now Mr. Herrera." We had a little chuckle.

I realized I should leave my car at Almost Heaven. Tex said he would drive me to the hospital in the morning. "No problem. Just meet me at the store at 6:00 a.m."

I had dinner with Joyce Neumann and two of her friends that night. She told me about her trip to Japan, where she'd lectured on new developments in stem cell transplantation.

"Basha's not going to be with you?"

"She was ready to come down if I needed her, but Basha doesn't drive. Well she does actually, but a bicycle, not a car, and I found out today from Dr. Walsh that I won't be able to drive while I'm on pain medication. He also told me that I'd be able to go back to New York sooner than I'd originally thought, so we decided she could take better care of me there, than here."

"Sounds reasonable."

"And how many patients get to have dinner with Super Nurse the night before they are cut? I feel very fortunate."

Joyce just smiled but the other nurse at the table raised her glass in a toast.

Joyce asked, "What time do you have to sign in?"

"6:30 a.m."

"I'll meet you in pre-op."

I couldn't eat or drink anything, not even water, after midnight. I sat on the steps of my RV and remembered the day when I first saw the lump on the side of my neck over five years ago. The night was very clear and the moonlight reflected on the lake. When I left Wiggins to go to Ole Miss in September of 1961, I wanted to get an education so that I could have a more interesting life. That, I have had.

The words of Nano's poem worked. They gave me the faith that there is a positive force in nature, and I hoped that in the morning, a tiny particle of that force would be with me. As I drifted off, I quietly quoted:

How calmly does the orange branch
Observe the sky began to blanch
Without a cry, without a prayer,
With no betrayal of despair.

Sometime while night obscures the tree
The Zenith of its life will be
Gone past forever, and from thence
A second history will commence.

A chronicle no longer gold,
A bargaining with mist and mold,
And finally the broken stem
The plummeting to earth; and then

An intercourse not well designed
For beings of a golden kind
Whose native green must arch above
The earth's obscene corrupting love.

But still the ripe fruit and the branch
Observe the sky begin to blanch
Without a cry, without a prayer
With no betrayal of despair.

O Courage, could you not as well
Select a second place to dwell,
Not only in that golden tree
But in the frightened heart of me?

* * * * *

At 5:50 a.m. Tex and I climbed into his new big Ford pickup. On the way to town, we talked about the truck, Syd and Megan, new sites for RV's; anything but surgery. Suddenly, I realized I had forgotten to go to Admissions the day before and the form they needed was on the front seat of my car. "I don't have the proper paper work; maybe I won't have to be cut today". I caught Joyce on her cell, and she said she'd call me right back.

"Anthony, I talked to the charge nurse and since you're already in the hospital's system, there won't be a problem. See you there."

Perhaps it was my southern roots. I was a bit rebellious about having to show my ID card at the studio and my gym, and resented having to pay union dues. But that was before cancer and 9/11. Now I want to show my ID everywhere I can. Without my unions, and SAG and AFTRA's medical insurance, there is no question that I would have died in 1997.

On the ninth floor I found the right place to sign-in for surgery. All the other patients had family with them, and the nurse checking me in asked, "Who is going to take care of your valuables?"

"I thought I could leave them with security."

"You can leave your laptop, but not your credit cards and your watch."

Then a very soft-spoken black man led us all into the pre-op room. I was put in a cubicle behind a curtain and told to get into the gown that was on the bed. They gave me a bag for my shoes and clothes. In the bag was a teddy bear. The nurse explained that I would need the bear to hold against my rib cage after surgery, and that the stuffing inside of him was designed to absorb the shock when I coughed. With pride, she told me that Dr. Walsh was responsible for the grant to provide the bears without any cost to the patients. I smiled, but thought it a bit silly: a teddy bear?

When I came out from my little curtained room, Christine Murasky was standing there.

"I appreciate you getting up so early and being here."

"Of course."

She made sure she had the name of the security officer who took the bag with my clothes and computer. Then Joyce arrived and took my watch and wallet. I felt so fortunate to have such care from these ladies. I was reassured by both of them that Dr. Walsh was "the best." Christine wished me luck and left. Joyce gave me a hug.

"I'll check on you in recovery."

"You are my Super Nurse."

The anesthesiologist showed me back inside my cubicle and took my vital signs. He got very concerned about my blood pressure and went on about the dangers of high blood pressure. Finally I interjected.

"Doctor, I just want to live through the surgery and I hope that pathology doesn't find any cancer."

They put a line into the vein in my left arm and started a drug to relax me. It did. The anesthesiologist explained that he would insert an epidural for the pain after surgery. It would be placed along my spine and would numb the nerves in my back and chest, so I would not be in pain when I regained consciousness.

"There is a chance that if insertion is not done properly, you could be paralyzed on the right side of your upper body."

"A chance? Has it ever happened to a patient of yours?"

"No."

"Also, there is the chance, if insertion is not done properly, that you could end up a paraplegic."

"It's for legal reasons, that you have to tell me this, right doctor?"

"Yes."

He held up the clipboard I signed the consent form and then I rested back on the bed. A nurse came in and added another drug to the drip going into my arm. I was drifting off. *What if this were it. The grand secret? I don't think so. I hope not.*

"How calmly does the orange branch
observe the sky . . .

* * * * *

From a very far place, I seemed to feel someone touching my face. I attempted to focus. I was fairly sure I saw Dr. Walsh's face. I couldn't quite come back. But I did hear.

"No cancer."

I think I nodded that I'd heard him, and was out like a light.

Joyce Neumann was the first face I could see clearly in my hospital room.

"You're doing fine."

I called Basha and asked her to call Steve McGraw with my good news. The pain drugs kept me groggy, and I had two drainage tubes for my lungs in the side of my chest just under my rib cage. However later that afternoon, they had me up and walking. They wanted me to cough as much as possible and my ribs really hurt when I tried. They even hurt when I just breathed normally. I realized after one cough, that the teddy bear was not in the least bit silly. Out of instinct I pulled him close to my ribs and held him there. I named him Leroy.

Rosalie came to see me when I was still groggy.

"Mr. Herrera, you have more lives than James Stenbeck!"

Another nurse came in, "Mr. Herrera, time to do some walking."

"I really don't want to get out of bed, but with Rosalie here, I have to be a good patient."

Rosalie walked once with me around the nurse's station, and then hurried back to the bed unit. For the next two days they had me up and walking three to four times a day. I held Leroy very close to my ribs. He was my new "best friend."

Dr. Walsh came in that Saturday afternoon, checked the drainage and determined the tubes were ready to come out, which meant I could leave the hospital.

"I hear it definitely hurts when you pull out the tubes?"

"You'll feel it."

I couldn't see what he was doing. I felt some pain and flinched.

"Was that it?"

"No. Just clipped the stitches."

I took a deep breath and clinched my jaw. Then I felt the slightest sensation. Dr. Walsh announced, "That's it."

"They're out?" That was it. The anticipation was a lot worse than the reality."

Angela came to pick me up and take me to the Wellesley Inn. As she came into my room, I was just about to take off my hospital gown. She started towards me with her arms outstretched to give me a hug, but I moved back quickly.

"No, no. Let me show you."

I dropped the right side of the robe, lifted my arm and Angela let out a slight scream.

"Oh my God! I thought it was just going to be two little holes like some laser or something."

"Please, it hurts when I laugh."

When I had a consultation with Dr. Giralt, he was very pleased that the final pathology showed no cancer. He said he wanted me to come back to MD Anderson and repeat the scans in three months.

Joyce invited me to her daughter's graduation and a reception afterwards. I enjoyed being with them, and the next day I flew to New York with Leroy tucked tightly against my ribs.

* * * * *

I stayed at Basha's apartment for the first few days, then went back to my own place. After three weeks Leroy retired, but I kept him on my couch just in case. Steve McGraw and I worked on www.PoetryTheatre.org and Tandy was the first actress we taped and put up on the web. She performed a poem about 9/11 written by her stepmother, Susan Cooper. Tandy asked her father, Hume Cronyn if he would do a poem for us too, and he agreed. Steve and I were thrilled, and two weeks later; there we were with one of the greatest American actors of all time. We recorded Hume Cronyn performing two A. E. Housman poems for our website. That was a big day for us.

* * * * *

Dr. Walsh strongly recommended that I walk as much as I could. Every day I did between two and four miles. Some days I was too tired. **As The World Turns** called, and had a few days here and there for James Stenbeck to make appearances. With work on the website and some social life, the weeks slipped by and it was August, time to schedule the scans. I arranged the dates so I would be sure to see Joyce after her vacation, and also be able to spend two days with Willie and the band on the road. Steve McGraw's wife, Nancy gave me a book, **Reading Lyrics**. I bought another copy, and presented it to Willie when I caught up with them in Philadelphia PA in late July. I had marked the page that had the words to "Stardust" and the name of the lyricist, Mitchell Parish. Willie studied the page for a second and said, "Well, now we know. He flipped through more pages and stopped, Noel Coward, oh yeah, he wrote some good words."

He signed a copy of his book **The Facts of Life and Other Dirty Jokes** for me. "Willie, your idea of putting poetry on the web is now a reality. It's up there, out there, www.poetrytheatre.org. I sure would appreciate it if you would do some of your lyrics as poems for us."

"Just tell me what you want me to do, and I'll do it"

* * * * *

Climbing onto the table for the CAT scan on August 16th 2002 wasn't too bad. The technician was upbeat, and I had a lot of visiting to do in the hospital that day. The Gallium scan the following Monday was different. I'd brought music to listen to, and as we started I asked, "How long will this take?"

"Only about thirty minutes, unless the radiologist needs a second picture."

I listened to a CD from Willie's early years, and the half-hour flew by. As I got my things together to leave, the technician came back in, "Mr. Herrera, we're going to have to get a second scan."

For the first few minutes I felt sick to my stomach. Then I thought "NO." Don't panic. Whatever it is, deal with it. For the next half hour I lay there as the table went back and forth, and tried to think through how I would handle the next few months if the lymphoma was back, and I had to stay in Houston for treatment. It seemed to take hours before we were through. I requested that the radiologist go over the results with me. He agreed, but I had to wait another twenty-five minutes for him to review them. I checked my messages and tried to read a magazine. Finally my name was called, and I went back to meet Dr. Delpassand. He was very kind and showed me every picture. No Gallium uptake. I was still in remission. It was now two years since that "small amount" of disease was found.

It was a big relief.

* * * * *

I called Basha, Steve and my brother John with the good news. Basha was very happy for me. When I phoned

Chris Goutman, he told me there was a good story line coming up in the fall for James and Barbara.

Dr. Giralt and I reviewed the blood work and the scans. He requested that I get blood work done with Dr. Braunschweig every six weeks, but said I didn't have to come back for scans for six months. This was a big step forward.

"Dr. Kornblau once told me that two years would be a good sign. Why?"

Dr. Giralt chose his words carefully. "The chance of relapse is greater in the first two years of remission, and decreases somewhat after that amount of time. However with lymphoma there is always the chance of relapse."

We chatted some about my work as an actor, and he said he thought www.poetrytheatre.org was an inspired project. I left Dr. Giralt feeling positive, but also aware of the reality that the cancer could come back one day.

That night I had dinner with Dr. Goy; by now we were friends. The focus of our conversation was the importance of the mental and spiritual condition of the patient. He told me that in his senior year of medical school in Paris, he suggested on rounds with the oncology team once, that a psychiatrist should make rounds with them. He said, "They looked at me as if I needed a psychiatrist."

* * * * *

Steve McGraw flew to Houston and took a taxi out to Almost Heaven. I wanted to thank Susan and Tex for all their support, so I cooked steaks and invited them and Angela and Super Nurse for dinner. Miss Syd came and ate early. She had school the next day.

Steve and Joyce had a long conversation about the Internet. We told jokes and some stories. We ate on the deck overlooking the lake and the ducks and geese made sure we knew they were around. It was hot, but nobody cared. It was a good evening.

The next day Steve and I drove the motor home to Bossier City, Louisiana where Willie and family were playing for two days.

We arrived in time to go backstage and see the show the first night. The next day it was very hot, but I had a long lunch with Sister Bobbie and visits with the crew and the band. Paul English's son RP, a working actor at the age of thirteen, came over from Fort Worth with his mother and did three poems for us: two by Ogden Nash and one by W. B. Yeats. He did a very good job.

Later we climbed on Willie's bus. He performed the lyrics of four of his songs as poems for our website. It was a great moment for us. They had to get on the road again; he followed me to the door of the bus.

"Willie, we didn't get our movie made, but we got this done. Thanks to my job on, **As The World Turns**, I can afford to produce this myself -- your contribution means a lot."

We shook hands. He smiled.

"See you down the highway."

* * * * *

The next stop was Brookhaven, Mississippi to spend a few hours with Braxter Irby, my Sigma Chi brother who was still a hard working, dedicated doctor. We took a long walk with his new dog, a big black lab.

"Jake died about the same time you relapsed in 2000. I didn't want to tell you. You had enough to deal with."

"I'm glad you didn't."

Next we drove to Vicksburg to visit Landy and Peggy Teller. Peggy'd had a prayer group at her church praying for me for the past five years. I told her that it had helped.

When I pledged Sigma Chi at Ole Miss in the early 60's, we didn't have hazing during our initiation. Instead we had a teacher for the intense week before being initiated into Sigma Chi. Landy was our teacher. He talked about commitment, loyalty to each other and loyalty to ourselves. Landy was indeed a brother.

Steve flew back to New York from Jackson, and I drove north on the Natchez Trace through the forest and into the night. There is no commercial traffic on the trace and all the road signs are made of wood; Mother Nature all around, for two hundred miles. Here once again, I was headed out of the South and back to New York.

I owe a great deal of thanks to Felicia Behr, Chris Goutman and Mickey-Dwyer Dobbin at Proctor & Gamble. They kept me acting as my strength would permit. Being able to work gave me a sense of purpose and helped me endure the past five years of treatment for cancer.

Dr. Chatham and Dr. Medina are knowledgeable oncologists and played a very big role in keeping me alive. For their hard work I am grateful. My conflicts with them were because of emotions. They could not deal with my emotions and I could not deal with theirs. I was the patient.

There are so many people to thank; the nurse who talked with me in the darkest nights at Sloan-Kettering, Dr. Giralt, Dr. Gabrilove, Dr. Goy, Dr. Braunschwieg, Dr. Korbling, Dr. Bobbie MacGuffie, Dr. Gajewsky, Dr. Kornblau, Dr. Courier, Dr. Mackey, Dr. Valentine, Nancy-Cody, Lorraine, Andrea, Christine, Rosalie, Super Nurse Joyce Neumann and also those whose names my memory has lost, but whose kindness remains in my heart.

Would I have preferred more of a Hollywood ending to this series of episodes in my life's journey? Holidays with my siblings, my mother taking care of me, my father growing emotionally, changing and becoming a father more like the Turkish man. Yes, I would have.

My parents live three and a half hours by car from MD Anderson. They never came to see me, sent a card or gave me a phone call. They live in San Antonio, Texas, in the same city where the Alamo still stands and where Colonel Travis drew the line in the sand with his sword.

As Cleavon would say, *"Herrera, it is what it is."*

Without my brother John's stem cells, I would not have survived. During treatment, he was always there when I needed him. As I got stronger, he seemed to distance himself from me. I asked him several times to bring his son to visit at Almost Heaven so we could feed the ducks and fish in the lake together, do brother and uncle things. Something always came up and they never made it -- John works very hard.

I wish we'd grown closer, hopefully in the future.

Work, in the past, was the most important part of my life. But now walking in the woods, listening to music, reading poetry and talking, crying and laughing with friends are all more precious to me than work.

My case has made cancer history by using the stem cell to put a deadly lymphoma into remission.

Will the cancer come back? No one knows. When I have to climb on the table for scans, I hope for good news and try to be prepared for bad news. I try to be positive and realistic. I recently learned that the word **enthusiasm** means the spirit or God within.

Stella Adler said, *"**Stay close to Nature.**"* She was right.

In the storytelling of John Ford, John Wayne's character Ethan finds goodness in his wounded soul, through the evil fighting within him, to uplift the human spirit.

In the poetry of Tennessee Williams, a force keeps arching over corruption and renewing life.

In the genius of Einstein, he finds in the universe; *"**A spirit vastly superior to that of man, before which we must feel humble.**"*

That spirit is found in Nature.

I am alive because of this spirit and those who find it within themselves. I am alive and have my health because of the friends that stuck with me in the darkest hours: Willie and Family, Patrick, Frank, Angela, Tandy, Bobbie, Steve and Basha. They are now my family. The workers who greeted me with smiles, the dedicated nurses and doctors – with *"**guts and vision**"* who *"**ride with the big boys**"* – Thank You.

* * * * *

When I was a little boy, in the field next to our barnyard there was a corner fence post that was a railroad crosstie. Often, I would climb up the barbwire, sit on this post and gaze out into the field and the woods beyond. I would imagine myself on a pony with all my belongings packed in my saddlebags, riding away. I didn't know where, just away.

Now some fifty years later, I have traveled on another mystical horse. Even though my journey is not over, I realize now what I have been searching for all of my life. If my health stays strong, I plan to have a big dog like George, a wife, love and a home.

Printed in the United States
17642LVS00002B/46-153